The Hybrid Warship

THE HYBRID WARSHIP

The Amalgamation of Big Guns and Aircraft

R D Layman

and

Stephen McLaughlin

CONWAY
MARITIME PRESS

For Marget and for my parents,
Carol and John McLaughlin

Frontispiece: An interpretation by Ross Watton of a British sketch design of July 1941, combining detail features from *Lion* class battleships and carriers of the *Illustrious* type.

© R D Layman & Stephen McLaughlin 1991

First published in Great Britain 1991 by
Conway Maritime Press Ltd,
24 Bride Lane, Fleet Street,
London EC4Y 8DR

British Library Cataloguing in Publication Data
Layman, R.D.
  The hybrid warship.
  1. Warships
  I. Title   II. McLaughlin, Stephen
  623.825
  ISBN 0 85177 555 1

Designed by Tony Garrett
Typeset by Witwell Ltd, Southport
Printed and Bound in Great Britain by
Butler & Tanner Ltd, Frome

Contents

PREFACE & ACKNOWLEDGEMENTS

Like many projects, this book grew beyond all expectations as the work progressed, and whereas we thought there might be thirty or so hybrid schemes to document, there turned out to be more than twice that number. Describing so many projects from so many different nations demanded a reliance on archival records and the original books and periodicals; unfortunately, some things remained outside our reach. A visit to Washington uncovered much unpublished material in the General Board files now held in the National Archives, but it was not possible to investigate the Preliminary Design files at Suitland, Maryland; fascinating material was obtained from British sources, but there is no doubt more there, and the French Naval Archives remained stubbornly beyond our grasp. At times we found tantalysing references to projects but were unable to track them to their source; there is no doubt that more hybrid schemes exist, and we would be very grateful for information about them.

*   *   *

The authors owe thanks to many individuals for help in making this book possible. First and foremost must be Charles Schedel, director of *Warship International*'s INFOSER feature. Knowing of the interest we share in *outré* and imaginary warships, he introduced us to each other by mail. He has, over the years, also provided a steady stream of notes and citations for items of interest to hybrid research. Many others have contributed their time and expertise and thereby greatly enriched this book; they are listed below in absolutely no order whatsoever.

Invaluable help in archival research was provided by Peter F G Wright and Theresa FitzGerald, who searched out documents at the Public Record Office; similar aid was given by D J Lyon, head of Inquiry Services, at the National Maritime Museum. Ian M Burns also helped with documentation. Richard L Boylan, assistant chief of the Military Reference Branch, Textual Reference Division, of the National Archives searched for material on flying-deck battlecruisers; that nothing turned up in no way reduces our appreciation of his efforts. Major Stellan Bojerud, Royal Swedish Army, provided much information on *Gotland*, as did Paul Adams. R H Nailer made available a treasure trove of information from his researches on HMS *Vindictive*. Also of great help was the office of the Italian naval attaché in Washington.

Other correspondents provided various types of support: D K Brown and Anthony Mammola provided valuable professional critiques of submarine carriers; David Dickens furnished a transcript of Minoru Genda's Naval War College lecture and shared information from his deep researches into Japanese naval tactics. Special thanks are due to William H Garzke Jr, who made available to the authors unpublished materials and plans of the Gibbs and Cox Soviet battleship design.

So much material from so many countries often called for translation. Assistance with French was given by Victoria Elliott and Marget Murray Layman; help with Italian came from Lieutenant Colonel Earl J Palmer Jr (US Army, ret) and Isabelle Tabacot. The authors were also fortunate to find Ray Casanas, whose fluid translations from Japanese greatly enriched the chapters dealing with that nation.

Photographs and illustrations presented a host of problems; here Rob Cabo was a great help, generously offering photographs from his extensive collection and putting us in contact with Leo van Ginderen, who also helped with photographs. Mr Cabo also provided articles from European magazines. Graham Mottram, curator, and the staff of the Fleet Air Arm Museum provided valuable assistance in photographic research, as did G Stuart Leslie. The US Naval Imaging Command, the National Archives, Ministry of Defence, British Aerospace and Hawker Siddeley also supplied needed photographs. John Charles Roach generously helped with his drawings of Cairl's Through-Deck Cruiser. John McLaughlin, whose usual artistic province is the animal kingdom, illustrated those dubious hybrids that could not be made into mechanical drawings. Unless otherwise credited, all other drawings are the work of Stephen McLaughlin.

We are fortunate in having several large research libraries in the vicinity, and extensive use was made of their resources: the various libraries of the University of California at

Berkeley, the collections held in the Hoover Institution on War, Revolution and Peace at Stanford, and most of all the San Francisco Public Library. A special debt is owed to many friends and colleagues at San Francisco; Jan Torbet, friend of many years and documents librarian *extraordinaire*, located vital material in the library's collection on the gun elevation controversy, and many other points besides; the Inter-Library Loan unit obtained many rare and obscure books and articles quickly and efficiently; and Joann Sutton graciously checked for a necessary book at San Jose State University Library. Many others have helped in a myriad of ways, not least by providing encouragement and expressing interest.

All quotations from archival sources are verbatim, and the original punctuation, terminology, spelling and emphasis have been retained.

Quotations from documents held by the Public Record Office are by permission of the Controller of Her Majesty's Stationery Office. Quotations from the *United States Naval Institute Proceedings* and *Scientific American* are by permission of those publications. Quotations from *Brassey's Naval and Shipping Annual* are by permission of Pergamon Press plc. All credited illustrations are reproduced by permission of their copyright holders.

INTRODUCTION

The *Oxford English Dictionary* defines 'hybrid' as 'anything derived from heterogeneous sources, or composed of different or incongruous elements', which seems clear enough, but defining just what constitutes a hybrid warship presents certain problems. Obviously, it must be a vessel that combines the characteristics of two types of warship, but which two types, and what degree of combination is required to make a ship a hybrid? For example, the *Panzerschiffe* of the *Deutschland* class were frequently referred to as 'hybrids' in the naval journals of the day, combining as they did the guns of a capital ship with the size of a cruiser. Yet the reader will find little about pocket battleships in this book. For our purposes, a hybrid warship is one that combines the characteristic features of one type of warship — most frequently, but not exclusively, heavy artillery — while also being designed or extensively modified to perform the functions of an aviation vessel.

Defining the required features, however, does not provide a definition of the hybrid warship. The degree of the combination must be settled. Many conventional warships carried unusually large numbers of aircraft; for example, the US *Brooklyn* class light cruisers were designed to carry up to eight aircraft (although they never carried that number in service), while the *Tirpitz* could carry six aircraft, and the *Yamato* as many as seven floatplanes. No one would consider these ships hybrids, however. They are merely conventional gunnery vessels with an abnormally large aircraft complement.

The other side of that coin is the aircraft carrier with an unusually strong gun battery, in terms either of calibre or number of barrels. The *Kaga* and *Akagi*, the *Lexington* class and the *Graf Zeppelin* all fit into this category, yet they have never been described as hybrids.

One feature of the majority of the hybrid designs described in this book is the sacrifice of a considerable fraction of potential as a gunnery or aviation vessel for the sake of the other form of 'weapons system'. Typically, the hybrid battleship or cruiser will have a weaker gun battery — measured either by number or calibre of the guns — than a pure gunnery vessel of similar displacement would have carried. Thus, the US Navy's flight-deck cruiser design of the early 1930s carried nine 6in guns on 10,000 tons, as opposed to the nine 8in guns typical of American treaty cruisers. The conversion of the *Ise* class battleships involved the removal of the after turrets to gain the space required for the aircraft; this reduced the gun battery by one-third. Recent proposals to turn the reactivated *Iowas* into vertical/short take-off and landing (V/STOL) carriers involve a similar reduction in the main battery. At the other end of the scale, an aircraft-carrier hybrid must sacrifice some of its capability as an aviation vessel to mount its gun battery: both the United States and Japan considered carrier designs in the early 1930s that would have involved a considerable reduction in the size of the flight deck and the hangar in order to mount 8in gun turrets.

This sacrifice of potential does not provide a complete definition, however; another criterion is required, especially as one moves into the modern age. It is relatively simple to bolt on canisters for surface-to-surface missiles (SSMs), but this process does not instantly convert a small 'Harrier carrier' into a hybrid. The intended role of the ship, and her surface warfare and aviation features, have also to be considered. Clearly, the addition of aircraft adds new capabilities to the ship beyond those of a simple gunnery or missile vessel. A modern V/STOL-carrying hybrid such as *Kiev* is expected to perform several tasks, from over-the-shore power projection to anti-submarine warfare (ASW) to missile strikes against a US carrier group, while a helicopter carrier such as *Vittorio Veneto* is primarily an ASW ship with some provision for anti-aircraft (AA) defence. *Vittorio Veneto* has many of the traditional features of the hybrid, but her role is in reality one-dimensional.

These two features of the hybrid — the sacrifice of some potential as a 'pure' warship, and the multiplication of roles she is expected to play — can be boiled down to questions of form and function. One or the other alone *may* make a ship a hybrid; the combination of the two surely does.

One thread links all hybrid designs, no matter what form they took or functions they were expected to fulfil: the conviction that the two-ships-in-one hull concept was feasible. Some of these designs do indeed seem feasible, at least for

the era in which they were drawn up; others, however, were creations hopelessly botched by designers obviously ignorant of some of the fundamental principles of aerodynamics. Vast experience in the art of naval architecture by no means guaranteed a workable hybrid design.

*   *   *

Having outlined some of the qualities of the hybrid, the next question to be answered is why anyone wanted to build one in the first place. Here the story is more complex. The hybrid designer has been motivated by national or international political considerations, budgetary restrictions caused by economic conditions, treaty limitations, rumour stemming from incorrect or wrongly interpreted diplomatic or intelligence reports, deliberate deception, promotion of naval architectural theory, wartime expediency, and just plain fantasy. The hybrid has been advocated by high-ranking naval officers, naval architects of international repute, heads of state, influential politicians, tactical or technological theorists, and crackpots.

The first hybrids were experiments; their designers were not looking for a particular 'mix' of aviation and gunnery features. With no models to work from, they were trying to determine just what a successful aviation ship had to look like. By 1918 many of the required features of a workable aviation ship had been determined; the aircraft carrier was gradually becoming less of an experiment. Yet even as the 'pure' aircraft carrier emerged after the First World War, a new breed of 'intentional' hybrid designs began to appear.

By this time shipboard aviation had divided into two distinct and continuing lines: aircraft operating from conventional warships, and aircraft operating from specialised vessels. This led to two specific types of shipboard aircraft: the seaplane, either floatplane or small flying boat, for conventional vessels, and the wheeled aircraft (hereafter referred to as the aeroplane) for the flight-deck carrier. Many interwar hybrid designs sought to overcome this dichotomy, to give the gunnery ship the scouting and offensive range of the aircraft without eliminating the short-range punch of the big gun.

There was another rationale. As late as 1939 there were still those who shared the pre-1914 view of the founding father of US naval aviation, Captain Washington I Chambers, that a fleet would best be served by dispersing its aircraft among a number of individual vessels instead of concentrating them in special ships.

These considerations led to many proposals for merging big guns and aircraft into one hull between the world wars, thereby creating a ship that could do more than either a pure gunnery ship or a pure aircraft carrier alone.

The hybrid's first heyday ended with the coming of the Second World War; for most of the navies caught up in fighting a real war at sea, there was little time to spare for experimentation, and construction efforts were concentrated on vessels of proven worth. There were notable exceptions, however, that emerged from the urgency or uncertainty of wartime. At least four nations studied hybrid designs during this greatest of naval wars, but of these four, only Japan actually created such vessels.

By the end of the 1940s the hybrid concept seemed almost dead, doomed by the advent of jet aircraft, which accelerated the constant trend of shipboard aeroplanes to grow ever heavier and faster. Flight-deck carriers in turn grew larger and more complex. Handling high-performance aircraft on the constricted flight decks allowed in hybrid design was obviously out of the question. Besides, flight-deck carriers had replaced the big-gun warship as the principal element of sea power — there were no real candidates for it to be combined with in a hybrid design.

The hybrid was not dead, however; it was merely hibernating. Like all branches of shipboard aviation, its development had always been governed by advances in aeronautical technology, and there were always new advances. Almost from the beginning of powered flight naval men had looked for a reliable aircraft that could take off and land vertically and operate from a small deck, requiring no space-consuming launch or recovery devices. After witnessing a flight by Orville Wright on 17 September 1908, US Navy Lieutenant George C Sweet recommended such an aircraft for shipboard use; a design for a helicopter-like aircraft was reviewed by a subcommittee of the British Board of Admiralty in 1915 but rejected as impractical. The American, Italian and Spanish navies, and possibly the Soviet Navy, operated Autogiros experimentally from shipboard in the 1930s but this type of aircraft could not lift a payload heavy enough to be truly useful. It was not until the development of the helicopter that a useful vertical take-off and landing (VTOL) type became available, and it soon replaced the seaplane on conventional warships. In the late 1950s and '60s, a new type of

warship appeared, the helicopter carrier; but these ships touch only the fringes of the hybrid realm, for the modest performance and endurance of the naval helicopter restricts it to a few tasks, and the shipboard weapons are often of a defensive nature. Although some helicopter carriers carry impressive missile batteries (the Soviet *Moskva*, for example), they are almost purely defensive, in many ways analogous to heavy AA guns rather than to the main battery guns of a battleship or cruiser.

The 1960s saw the appearance of something far more impressive than the helicopter: the V/STOL aircraft, soon followed by the 'ski-jump' flight deck. The latter is the first major change in carrier layout since the angled deck and is remarkable both for its simplicity and effectiveness. The combination of V/STOL aircraft and ski-jump flight deck makes possible once again the operation of aircraft with high performance and substantial weapons load from relatively small ships, and the 1970s saw a number of V/STOL carriers built or proposed. Operating from relatively small ships, the British Harrier fighter-bomber proved its worth in the Falklands conflict; and while the current generation of V/STOL aircraft remains somewhat handicapped in radius and payload, a quick glance back at the history of aeronautical progress leaves scant doubt that these drawbacks will be overcome in the near future.

Another promising development for the hybrid is British Aerospace's SkyHook, a device allowing V/STOL aircraft to be launched and recovered by a ship without their ever touching deck, mechanically different from but conceptually akin to one seriously considered by the French Navy in 1913 and tested by it in 1924, and by the Royal Navy in 1920. These early schemes, some of which were successfully tested on land, involved aircraft suspended from lines intended to be placed outboard on ships. The American aviation pioneer Glenn Curtiss also experimented with this idea. SkyHook replaces the wires with an articulated crane, but the idea is much the same.

These innovations restore the feasibility of the hybrid warship by endowing it with the ability to operate high-performance aircraft without sacrificing the space required for surface weapons. The big gun has largely, although not entirely, disappeared, but the shipboard anti-ship missile has become an integral element in naval power. The sinking of the Israeli destroyer *Elath* by three Soviet-built Styx missiles fired from Egyptian fast attack boats in 1967 showed the potential of these weapons, and similar missiles are now carried by virtually every surface combatant.

V/STOL aircraft, ski-jump ramps and SkyHook, plus the anti-ship missile, add up to a new generation of hybrid warship designs that are perhaps more potentially useful than any of the actual or speculative hybrid projects that have appeared in the past seven decades. Although some stigma still attaches to the word 'hybrid', there can be no doubt that the hybrid warship is alive and well — and even at sea in the Soviet *Kiev* class. Recent justifications of hybrid warships have a familiar ring, for these same arguments were used fifty or sixty years ago. Perhaps only now are we entering the era of the hybrid predicted by some of its advocates in the 1920s. *Plus ça change, plus c'est la même chose.*

TRYING ON WINGS

The concept of the hybrid emerged early in the history of shipboard aviation. In a certain sense the first warship designed specifically as an aviation vessel could be termed a hybrid. This scheme, drawn up in 1912 for the British Admiralty's Air Department by William Beardmore & Co, was for a ship intended to carry aeroplanes and seaplanes, and also to function as a destroyer tender (it is interesting to note that its hangar arrangement was nearly identical to that proposed in 1975 for a nuclear-powered missile cruiser, which is described in our final chapter). However, the Beardmore design was purely an auxiliary with only a limited defensive armament.

Instead, the two vessels that can be termed the first generation of hybrid warships were created by the Royal Navy during the First World War. They were expedients, born of wartime exigencies, and meant to counter an immediate and pressing problem confronting the Grand Fleet in its task of controlling the North Sea and bringing the German Navy to battle. This problem was the Zeppelin, the rigid airship that gave the High Seas Fleet an immeasurable advantage in aerial reconnaissance and was also employed in a long strategic bombing campaign against Britain.

Admiral Sir John Jellicoe, commander of the Grand Fleet, was continually distressed about airships and had come to appreciate (and indeed, exaggerate) their capabilities even before the war. He issued repeated pleas to the Admiralty for ships that could carry aircraft to combat the Zeppelins; the first such vessel to join the Grand Fleet was HMS *Campania*, an aging liner converted into a seaplane carrier in 1914-15. Other conversions followed, and Jellicoe's successor, Admiral Sir David Beatty, shared his apprehension regarding German airships and continued the pressure for aviation vessels.

Actually, much had been done during the immediate prewar years to create a British shipboard air arm. Aeroplanes had taken off from four British warships, sometimes more than once,

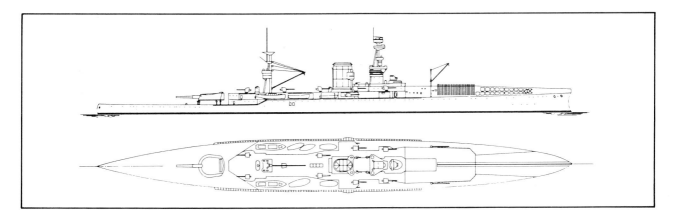

during 1912–13. Nor had the pleas of the Grand Fleet's commanders been ignored, as the growing number of seaplane carrier conversions testified. It was a continuation of this trend that brought into being the world's first true hybrid warship, HMS *Furious*.

Her genesis as such can be traced to Beatty's establishment in January 1917 of a Grand Fleet Aircraft Committee to study the fleet's aerial requirements. The committee concluded in a 5 February report that an aviation vessel was needed sooner than the ships begun or authorised in 1916 (including the flight-deck carrier *Argus*) could be completed. A ship larger and faster than any then in service was required, one that could operate high-performance aeroplanes against the enemy's airships. This need could be met, the committee recommended, by conversion of the light battlecruiser *Furious*, then nearing completion in the Newcastle-upon-Tyne yard of Armstrong Whitworth & Co.

Furious and her two near sisters, *Glorious* and *Courageous*, were a bit strange to start with. Creations of Admiral of the Fleet Lord Fisher during his 1914–15 tenure as First Sea Lord, they were designed for his pet project of an amphibious landing on Germany's Baltic coast. For this purpose, they were given large dimensions, light armour, shallow draught and powerful ordnance: four 15in guns in *Glorious* and *Courageous* and two single-mounted 18in in *Furious*. Early in the war the Cabinet had ruled that there would be no new capital ships (the war was expected to be too short for such ships to be completed in time to be useful) so Fisher obtained authorisation and financing for these freaks by the semantic trick of labelling them 'large light cruisers'. They were all laid down in mid-1915.

When *Glorious* and *Courageous* joined the fleet in early 1917, they soon became known as 'Spurious' and 'Outrageous' on the lower deck,

HMS *Furious* as completed, with aft 18in gun retained

Furious off the British coast on 3 September 1917, a few weeks before she was taken in hand for reconstruction that eliminated her hybrid features (*Graham Mottram collection*)

and, with Fisher out of office, they were held in no higher regard by the men at the Admiralty. Conversion of one or more of them to aeronautical purposes had been considered earlier, but nothing had come of it. Now, under the recommendation of the Fleet Aircraft Committee and with the concurrence of Beatty and the Board of Admiralty, such an alteration of *Furious* was approved in March of 1917.

Completed on 26 June 1917, she emerged as a hybrid rather than a pure aviation vessel due to Beatty's initial reluctance to have her stripped completely of main armament. Thus the aft 18in gun was retained but the forward mount was never installed; its place was taken by a 'flying-off' deck 228ft long by 50ft wide (at maximum) which sloped slightly toward the stem and enclosed beneath it an aircraft hangar. Derricks positioned on each side of the flight deck raised and lowered aircraft from the 64ft-long hangar through a large hatch whose cover when closed became a portion of the flight deck. Seaplanes could be launched from trolleys running down a slot in the flight deck's centreline.

Main particulars of *Furious* as completed were

Displacement:	19,100t normal, 22,405t full load
Dimensions:	786ft oa × 88ft (over bulges) × 21ft 6in mean, 25ft max
Machinery:	2 sets geared turbines, 18 boilers, 4 shafts, 90,000shp (90,825 on trials) = 31.5kts; 6000nm at 20kts, 11,000nm at 'economical speed'. Oil 3400t
Armament:	one 18in, eleven 5.5in (11 × 1), two 3in AA (2 × 1), four 3pdr (4 × 1), eighteen 21in TT (4 × 3, 2 × 2, and 2 × 1 submerged)
Armour:	belt 2-3in, deck 1-3in, barbettes 3-7in, turrets 5-9in, conning tower 10in
Complement:	880 incl 84 aviation personnel

The scale of protection was appallingly light for a ship of *Furious'* size, and no one, perhaps not even Fisher, was able to give an explanation for the exceedingly heavy torpedo battery.

Furious joined the Battle Fleet at Scapa Flow in July 1917 with an aerial complement of five Sopwith Pup single-seat fighters (or 'scouts' as they were then called) for anti-airship work and three Short 184 two-place floatplanes for reconnaissance. During the next four months she carried out experimental and operational cruises, on a few occasions skirmishing with German aircraft but never achieving her airmen's goal of downing a Zeppelin. Nor did she ever have an opportunity to fire her big gun in anger. This was probably just as well, for the retention of this weapon, intended for shore bombardment, was more and more regarded as a mistake. Its test firings shook and strained the ship severely, and the chances of hitting a moving target with single shots from such a ponderous piece of ordnance can best be described as remote.

A failure in the gunnery role, *Furious* was only partially successful as an aviation vessel, for although she embodied all that had been learned since 1912 of the art of launching aircraft from ships, she still lacked the ability to recover her Pups once they were airborne. Each flight had to end with touchdown at sea, where the aeroplane was supposed to be kept on the surface by floatation bags until it could be picked up. Even when this technique worked, the aircraft was inevitably damaged by the splashdown and often by the recovery. Because *Furious* dared not heave to in the submarine-infested North Sea, aircraft recovery was done by other, less valuable vessels — sometimes by a seaplane carrier sailing in company with *Furious* but more often by destroyers, which lacked adequate hoisting gear. And, of course, aviators coming down in this manner faced great danger to life and limb. With each Pup flight therefore a one-shot affair, a considerable — and understandable — reluctance to launch the fighters developed, and they were used only in the most pressing circumstances.

Early on, *Furious'* fliers began considering ways by which they might land on the ship. In August 1917, Squadron Commander E H Dunning accomplished this feat twice. Dunning's technique involved flying parallel to the ship as she steamed at high speed into the wind, then sideslipping close to the flight deck where his fellow officers seized rope toggles fitted to the Pup and wrestled it to a stop. On the third attempt the aeroplane went over the side and Dunning was killed. This disaster called a halt to any further experiments with a technique that required extreme skill and nerve on the part of a highly experienced pilot.

However, even before Dunning's death the Admiralty had considered the installation of a landing platform on *Furious'* afterdeck. The ship's pilots and officers believed this was impractical unless a more benign air flow were created by moving the superstructure and funnel to one side of the vessel, or eliminating them altogether, but they were not heeded. It would not be the last time that practical advice from the men doing the job afloat would be ignored by the boffins back at the draughting boards. Instead, in late November *Furious* was returned to her builders for remodelling that replaced the aft 18in gun and mainmast with a landing deck and another hangar.

Doubts about the feasibility of landing on this platform were soon proved correct. Even with a system of arresting lines installed and skids replacing wheels on the Pups' undercarriages, it was nearly impossible to alight on the afterdeck in the face of air turbulence created by the superstructure and hot gases streaming from the funnel. Of thirteen or fourteen attempts, only three were successful; in all the others the aircraft was lost or damaged. *Furious* did, however, prove the worth of the carrier concept when in July 1918 her aircraft destroyed two Zeppelins in their shed at the airship base in Tondern, near the mouth of the Elbe.

Thus, with the removal of her big gun, *Furious* steamed out of the pages of hybrid warship history and a new vessel hove into view: HMS *Vindictive*.

In August 1917 the Board of Admiralty reviewed the Grand Fleet aircraft situation and decided to convert another incomplete warship into a quasi-carrier. The configuration was the same as that soon to be given *Furious*: separate 'flying off' and 'flying on' decks fore and aft of a normal super-

HMS *Vindictive* in her original configuration, the hybrid version of her class and the first of it to be completed

structure (which seems to indicate that this would have applied to *Furious* originally had Beatty not objected to the elimination of both her big guns).

The vessel chosen for conversion was the large cruiser *Cavendish*, under construction by Harland & Wolff at Belfast as a unit of the five-ship Improved *Birmingham* class (also at times called the *Cavendish, Hawkins* or *Raleigh* class, or the 'Elizabethans').

These were the largest cruisers, other than battlecruisers, built by any navy since the heyday of the armoured cruiser. They were designed in 1915 for the express purpose of overwhelming any of the German armed merchant cruisers or light cruisers that had posed a threat to British commerce in the first years of the war. They were given a powerful battery of 7.5in guns, capable of crippling a fleeing auxiliary cruiser with a few hits at long range. Their trade protection duties required great endurance, which was provided by a combination of coal- and oil-fired boilers. These characteristics demanded large size, and the legend displacement for the class was almost 10,000 tons. These ships represented — unintentionally, of course — a transitional type between the typical light cruisers of 1914–18 and the larger vessels, eventually to be called heavy cruisers, defined by the Washington Treaty and built by all the major powers in the two decades between the world wars.

Cavendish was ordered in April 1916 and laid down in June of that year. Work on the entire class proceeded slowly — the German surface raiders had disappeared as a threat to the trade routes before the ships were even laid down — but work on *Cavendish* was accelerated after she was chosen for conversion, with the result that she was the only ship of the class to complete before the Armistice. She was launched in January 1918 and in June was renamed *Vindictive* in honour of the old cruiser that had performed so nobly during the Zeebrugge Raid. She was completed in October and joined the Grand Fleet at Rosyth that month.

A model of a proposed flight-deck configuration of *Vindictive* tested for air flow characteristics by the National Physical Laboratory in 1918 (*National Maritime Institute Ltd via D K Brown*)

Vindictive as completed was essentially a scaled-down, two-funnel version of *Furious*. Her main particulars were

Displacement:	9344t light, 9750t standard, 12,100t normal, 12,400t full load
Dimensions:	605ft oa × 65ft 2in × 17ft 6in (mean), 20ft 6in (max)
Machinery:	4 sets geared turbines, 12 boilers, 4 shafts, 60,000 shp = 29.75–28kts (63,600 = 29.12kts on trials). 3000nm at 23–24kts, 5400nm at 14kts. Oil 1480t; coal 860t
Armament:	four 7.5in (4 × 1), four 3in AA (4 × 1), four 3in QFG, six 21in TT (6 × 1)
Armour:	belt 1.5–3in; deck 1.5in, conning tower 3in, gun shields 1in
Complement:	648 incl initially 71 aviation personnel

Two of the torpedo tubes were to be submerged, but some sources indicate that they were not installed.

The ship's distinctive feature was her 193ft by 57ft aft landing deck, which terminated well short of the stern, thus giving a clear field of fire to the after 7.5in gun. Supported by tall stanchions, this deck had low bulwarks extending nearly its full length on each side. At its fore end and just aft of the pole mainmast was an aircraft barrier of the type provided for *Furious* after her remodelling —

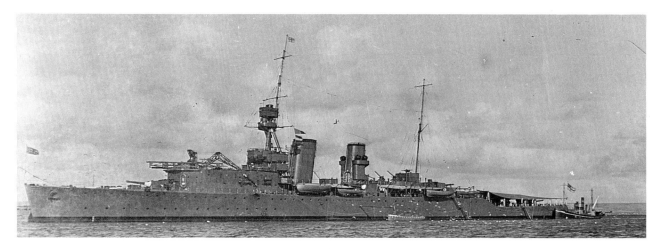

Vindictive after her reconstruction to more normal cruiser configuration during 1923–25. The only remaining vestige of her hybrid origin is the forward hangar, now topped with a catapult (*R D Layman collection*)

Vindictive running at speed, showing the distinctive silhouette presented by her aircraft platforms (*J M Bruce/G S Leslie collection*)

a gallows from which lines were suspended to the deck. The mainmast itself was offset to the starboard edge of the landing deck.

The forward platform was 106ft long by 49ft wide at maximum, enclosing beneath it a 78ft long hangar. The platform narrowed sharply to an unsupported projection that stopped considerably short of the bow but overhung the forward 7.5in gun. Although *Furious* had been given hydraulically powered lifts to her hangar decks in her 1917–18 reconstruction, *Vindictive* lacked this refinement; her aircraft were handled through a flight-deck hatch by derricks to port and starboard. A feature borrowed from *Furious* was the fore and aft aviation decks connected by gangways around the central superstructure, permitting aircraft to be transferred between them.

Vindictive retained her near-sisters' protection and machinery but mounted three fewer main battery guns. Her more orthodox armament, however, made her a more viable gunnery vessel than *Furious* could ever have been. The 7.5in gun was not a particularly successful weapon — its 200lb

shell was extremely large for hand loading — and the three-gun broadside of *Vindictive* was far from ideal for the sort of long-range work originally intended. Nevertheless, she could outrange and outpunch any German light cruiser she might have encountered.

On the aviation side, alas, *Vindictive* proved a nearly complete failure. The experiments aboard *Furious* showed that an attempt to land on a moving ship with centreline superstructure and funnel was tantamount to disaster. The danger was verified in wind tunnel air flow tests carried out on a model of *Vindictive* at the National Physical Laboratory in July 1918. Interestingly, similar tests were made of a highly modified *Vindictive*: although retaining the heavy armament and possibly even adding a fifth 7.5in gun, this model nevertheless represented a true flight-deck carrier with a starboard island incorporating the funnels and with fore and aft aircraft decks connected not by narrow catwalks but by a nearly full-beam centre section, making one long flight deck. The air flow on this model was shown to be much safer and more practical for flight operations, although the island rather dangerously narrowed the flight deck.

Proof in both theory and practice of *Vindictive*'s perilous configuration came too late to permit her design to be altered; however the lesson had been well learned by the time she entered service, with the result that only one landing was attempted on her, on 1 November 1918 by W W Wakefield (later Lord Wakefield of

Kendal) flying the Grand Fleet's last operational Pup. Astonishingly, it was successful, but nobody ever tried again.

Although *Vindictive* was initially given a contingent of Sopwith 1½ Strutters, she served only as a seaplane carrier during her few weeks with the fleet before the Armistice. She was never employed operationally, and her crew's only glimpse of the enemy came on 21 November 1918 when the German High Seas fleet steamed to internment.

With the end of the war, a large question mark hung over the ship's future. Already there had been talk of turning *Furious* into a flight-deck vessel, but *Vindictive* was deemed too small for a similar reconstruction. Before her fate could be decided, however, *Vindictive* went to war.

War in this instance was the confused *mêlée* along the shores of the Baltic, where the newly hatched republics of Estonia, Latvia and Lithuania were struggling to retain their independence from the equally new Soviet state, a conflict complicated by the attitude of Finland, *de jure* neutral but profoundly anti-Bolshevik, and the presence of an obstreperous leftover German occupation army.

Great Britain had been persuaded to safeguard the existence of the new Baltic nations, and so had dispatched a naval force to that sea. On 2 July 1919 *Vindictive* sailed to join it as the squadron's aviation vessel. The Admiralty probably chose her for this service out of reluctance to risk the larger *Furious* or the experimentally valuable flush-decked *Argus* in the mine-infested Baltic.

Vindictive, carrying a mixed bag of twelve Royal Air Force (RAF) aircraft (Short 184 floatplanes and Sopwith 2F.1 Camel, Sopwith 1½ Strutter and Grain Griffin aeroplanes) made an inauspicious Baltic début on 6 July by grounding near Reval (the modern Tallinn) so thoroughly that it took eight days to refloat her. No great damage was done, however, and she subsequently served almost continuously in the Baltic until late December, with only one brief return to home waters.

Vindictive flew her one and only 'carrier strike' on 30 July, when all twelve of her aircraft attacked the Bolshevik naval base at Kronstadt. Launched in two waves, they dropped a total of nineteen bombs that started a few fires and damaged a tanker. To get the aeroplanes launched into a 25 knot wind required adding a wooden extension to her flying-off deck which lengthened it to 118ft, an indication that its original length was insufficient for take-off by two-place craft carrying normal

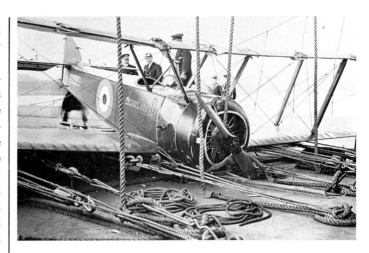

A Sopwith Pup caught in *Furious'* rope crash barrier after one of the unsuccessful landing attempts, an object lesson in the difficulty of landing an aeroplane on a ship with conventional superstructure (*J M Bruce/G S Leslie collection*)

service loads.

Thereafter RAF operations were carried out from land and harbour bases; the impossibility of landing on the ship made this arrangement a necessity. The aircraft flew extensive bombing, reconnaissance and fire-control missions. *Vindictive* operated a logistical ferry service for the RAF ashore, supplying aircraft, materiel and personnel, sometimes transshipped from *Argus* at Copenhagen. She also became a depot ship for the coastal motorboats (motor torpedo boats) that made the famous attack on Kronstadt harbour on 18 August 1919.

Leaving some of her aircraft behind for the fledgling Estonian Air Force, *Vindictive* departed the Baltic during the general British withdrawal from that sea at the end of 1919, having first endured a mutiny and attempted sabotage by disgruntled ratings.

Her brief war behind her, *Vindictive* again faced an uncertain future. She would soon become superfluous even as a limited aviation vessel, for the age of the flight-deck carrier was arriving with a vengeance in the Royal Navy. Within a few years *Eagle* and *Hermes* were afloat, and the conversion of *Furious* to a full carrier, mooted in 1919, began in 1922. *Glorious* and *Courageous* were shortly to be given the same treatment.

Her fate undecided, *Vindictive* served for a couple of years alternately in reserve and as a troop transport. Then, in 1923, she was taken in hand at the Portsmouth Naval Dockyard for conversion to a more normal cruiser configuration. This job, completed in April 1925, removed the aft aircraft deck, added two more 7.5in guns on the centreline, reduced and rearranged the AA armament, and made various and sundry internal modifications. A touch of the hybrid lingered, however, for the forward hangar was retained, its topside launching platform removed and replaced by a catapult, the first to be mounted on a conventional British warship. There was still no lift, but a large hydraulic crane, mounted to starboard, replaced the aircraft-handling derricks.

For the next five years *Vindictive* was in effect a catapult trials ship, developing techniques that were applied to other Royal Navy vessels in the 1930s. Nevertheless, she remained an active warship; during 1926–28 she served on the China Station, operating her aircraft for anti-piracy patrol and to help control civil disturbances. Normal aircraft complement was three machines, but up to six could be carried, which is more than could be crammed into any other cruiser in the world for several years. The aircraft were customarily Fairey IIID reconnaissance-spotter floatplanes, but occasionally they were replaced by the float version of the Fairey Flycatcher, a nimble little shipboard fighter.

In 1937 *Vindictive* was demilitarised under the terms of the London Naval Treaty and reconstructed yet again, this time as a cadet training ship, the hangar becoming a classroom. After the outbreak of war in 1939 she underwent her final transformation, emerging as a repair ship with the hangar removed. She served in home waters, off Norway and in the Mediterranean and South Atlantic until reduced to reserve in September 1945. She was sold for breaking up the next year.

Furious and *Vindictive* were not only expedients but experimental expedients, created at a time when the very concept of what an aviation vessel should be was still evolving. They were designed by men with little previous experience to draw upon in an era when knowledge of aerodynamics was imperfect at best. Their dual gunnery-aviation characteristics were not the product of theory; they were imposed by the practicalities of a period when aircraft were needed to combat the Zeppelin, yet it was reasonable to believe that they might have to take part in surface actions. This possibility was evidenced at Jutland, when Beatty's temporary turn to the north in the early stage of the engagement left his sole seaplane carrier, the weakest and slowest vessel in the fleet, as the ship nearest to the advancing German force. Luckily, she was never in any real danger,

but who could say that some such a situation might not recur, forcing an aviation vessel to battle the outriding destroyers and cruisers of an enemy fleet? On the other side of the North Sea the situation must have looked much the same, for the conversion of the German cruiser *Stuttgart* into a seaplane carrier left her with a relatively powerful gun battery, and so would the proposed conversion of the cruiser *Roon*. *Stuttgart*, however, saw only brief operational service, and *Roon*'s conversion never got beyond the stockpiling of some materiel.

The greatest spur to the creation of *Furious* and *Vindictive*, the rigid airship, was already fading from importance before the end of the war; it lingered for more than a decade afterwards, but its place was soon taken by the aeroplane. Aeroplanes greatly enhanced the range and speed of maritime scouting. Moreover, during the war they had demonstrated an increasing capacity for offensive action. Surface ships had to be defended against this growing menace, and this meant aviation vessels, yet something more than stopgap conversions would be required. At the same time, the notion that fleets could fight their battles entirely through their airborne proxies was a futuristic fantasy; the big gun was still needed. Thus the prospect of a ship more thoughtfully designed for combined gunnery-aviation purposes than the wartime expedients began to appear an inviting idea.

The wartime tocsin of expediency would be sounded again in hybrid history, but in the coming two decades of peace, treaties and financial uncertainty, the concept took deeper root than expediency alone ever could gain for it, and its small but devoted constituency among naval professionals, designers and interested amateurs ensured its repeated blossoming in the 1920s and '30s.

FLIGHTS OF FANCY

After the First World War, aircraft were objects of tremendous popular fascination. In military circles, the prophets of 'air power' preached the obsolescence of armies and navies in the face of this new and wonderful machine. And their predictions seemed to be coming true: in July 1921, Brigadier General William Mitchell's aviators sent a variety of ex-German warships to the bottom off the Virginia Capes, among them the dreadnought *Ostfriesland*. To many, this proved the vulnerability of surface warships, even battleships, to aircraft; few noted that the ships had been stationary, or that Mitchell's fliers had dropped their bombs from unrealistically low altitudes without having to cope with AA fire, or that the *Ostfriesland* as a design was already far out of date, or that there had been no damage control parties aboard the ships. The simple fact that a battleship had been sunk by aircraft seemed to verify the claims of the air power supporters, and statements in the press from such respected naval elder statesmen as Lord Fisher, Sir Percy Scott and Admiral William Sims buttressed these claims.

The reality, of course, was more complex. Throughout the 1920s, aircraft were not capable of sinking a battleship under realistic conditions, and this fact would remain largely unchanged until the late 1930s, when new, fast monoplanes capable of carrying large armour-piercing bombs or torpedoes with substantial warheads appeared. In the 1920s, with the prestige of the battleship taken down several notches by its undramatic performance in the First World War, the aeroplane seemed a fearsome weapon capable of dealing with any target.

In spite of the conventional image of conservative 'battleship' admirals fighting off aviation tooth and nail, the major navies were not slow to adopt aircraft. There were major problems to be solved, however, and chief among these was how to get the aeroplane to sea. Mitchell solved this problem for many air power enthusiasts by claim-ing that aircraft did not have to go to sea at all; what hostile warship would dare approach America's shores if it were certain to be met by an armada of long-range, shore-based, high-level bombers? Mitchell himself would later recant, and develop his own aircraft carrier scheme, with the ships being controlled by his independent air force. Others, however, had to work out schemes of national defence based on the available technology rather than on Mitchell's promises.

Mitchell represents an extreme, of course, but the fact remains that aviation was new and exciting in the 1920s, and novel schemes for the employment of aircraft were popping up everywhere. Even those who still held that the battleship was the 'ultimate basis of sea power' wanted to add the new aerial weapon to the naval armoury. This led to proposals for a number of hybrid warships that appeared in the publications of the 1920s.

One of the first of these attempts to combine big guns with aviation appeared in the *US Naval Institute Proceedings* of March 1923. The drawing, signed by T G A Strother, is actually dated 1921, and the vessel illustrated was clearly a product of the pre-Washington Treaty days, given its size. Although no actual dimensions are provided, the artist clearly anticipated a very large ship. He also very clearly used the recently completed *Hood* as his model for the hull shape and superstructure — certainly a reasonable paradigm, as *Hood* was the largest warship in the world and represented the latest word in naval design, as far as laymen were concerned. One also imagines that the original configuration of *Furious* served as another inspiration for the artist, although he moved the aviation facilities aft. The only other aircraft carriers which he could have used as guides were the flush-decked *Argus* and the recently completed *Eagle* with her large island-type superstructure.

This 'battleship of the future' has all its armament forward, eight 'super-calibre' guns, presumably 16in or 18in, in two triple turrets and one twin. This triple-tiered arrangement looks a bit top-heavy to the eye, although the Germans had considered a similar triple superimposition for some battleship designs during the First World War. Mounting the three turrets forward left the after portion of the ship free for a flying-on deck and flying-off deck, one above the other, similar to the arrangement that later appeared in *Furious'*

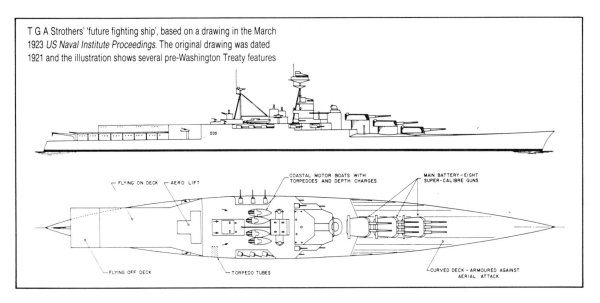

T G A Strothers' 'future fighting ship', based on a drawing in the March 1923 *US Naval Institute Proceedings*. The original drawing was dated 1921 and the illustration shows several pre-Washington Treaty features

final reconstruction, and later still in the *Glorious, Courageous, Kaga* and *Akagi* — our artist was ahead of things in this regard. The adventure of taking off over the stern (with a *negative* wind over deck) in a ship with no catapults is left to the reader's imagination.

This illustration shows several other features seen in the unofficial designs of the day. The curved or turtle-backed deck forward to deflect bombs would appear again in popular press battleship designs of the 1930s and '40s, when streamlining was all the rage. Also, there are no indications of funnels, smoke pipes or any other means of venting the exhaust gases; perhaps some form of discharge using sea water to cool the gases was intended by the artist. Such schemes were often discussed in the 1920s, and the technique would be experimented with or utilised on British, American and French carriers in the coming decade. Even without the turbulence caused by hot funnel gases, landing on such a ship would have been tricky at best; there is no attempt to streamline the superstructures, and the air currents over the stern would have been complicated by the multilevel decks. One unusual touch is the 'coastal motor boats with torpedoes and depth charges', an idea that harks back to the *Jeune Ecole*, perhaps, and would not reappear until the 'B.A.C. Ship' of 1942 (see Chapter 11).

The artist who designed this ship was obviously no naval architect, but professional training and experience in warship design were no guarantee against the sort of mistakes that were to mark so many interwar hybrid schemes. A case in point is that of Sir George Thurston.

★   ★   ★

Thomas George Owens (who changed his name to Thomas George Owens Thurston in 1915) had learned warship design under Sir Philip Watts at the Elswick shipyard of Armstrong, Whitworth and Company. He spent ten years with Armstrong, working on warship designs for both the Royal Navy and foreign navies. In 1898, he left Armstrong for Vickers, which had just obtained its own shipyard at Barrow. Before long, Thurston was the firm's chief naval architect, a post he held until retiring in 1929. Thurston was responsible for the design of a great many warships both before and during the war, including such famous vessels as the battleship *Mikasa* and the battlecruiser *Kongo* for Japan and the dreadnought *Reshadieh* for Turkey (which was still fitting out when the war broke out and was taken into the Royal Navy as HMS *Erin*, seeing extensive service with the Grand Fleet). He also designed ships for Russia, Peru, China and Mexico, and he was knighted (KBE) in 1920 for his work in ship design and construction during the war. He was by no means an amateur at the business of warship design.

Like many others in the 1920s, however, he *was* an amateur at designing aviation ships. A regular contributor to *Brassey's Naval and Shipping Annual* between the world wars, Sir George published several hybrid battleship schemes in that yearbook. His excursions into the realm of conjectural warship design began conventionally enough with a detailed analysis of the size and characteristics of battleships in the 1914 *Transactions* of the Institute of Naval Architects, a prestigious professional publication. This article, published under his original name of T G Owens,

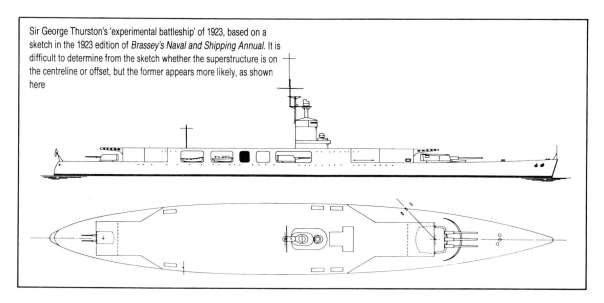

Sir George Thurston's 'experimental battleship' of 1923, based on a sketch in the 1923 edition of *Brassey's Naval and Shipping Annual*. It is difficult to determine from the sketch whether the superstructure is on the centreline or offset, but the former appears more likely, as shown here

proposed two 14in gunned battleship designs, and postulated the '60 per cent rule', the hypothesis that a battleship's armament, protection and machinery should total about 60 per cent of her design displacement, a yardstick recently revived by the well-known naval writer Norman Friedman. Thurston published an article on 'The Capital Ship of the Future' in the 1920–21 edition of *Brassey's*, describing a ship armed with 18in guns and displacing 57,000 tons (legend). This is about the size one would expect the *Hood*-type hybrid discussed above to have been, given its various features.

The Washington Treaty for the Limitation of Naval Armament, however, banished such giants from the drawing boards of the world's navies. The Washington Treaty has been described in detail in any number of publications, but at this stage it is necessary to examine its effects on hybrid warship schemes. Signed by Britain, France, Italy, Japan and the United States on 6 February 1922, the treaty restricted both the total tonnage of capital ships the various powers could have and their individual characteristics. For battleships, the individual limits were 16in guns and a 'treaty' or 'standard' displacement of 35,000 tons. Standard displacement was based on the ship being fully ready for sea, with all stores and ammunition aboard, but without fuel or reserve feed water; clearly, this was a fictitious condition, but it did create a standard for comparison between the world's navies, which had hitherto used a variety of 'normal', 'legend', 'design' or 'construction' displacements to describe their warships.

These qualitative limitations would prove a great challenge to naval architects for a decade and a half; previously, the only limitations on ship size had been political or economic. Remarkable efforts would be made to pack as much fighting power into the treaty ships as possible. One means of doing this seemed to be to combine gunnery and aviation into one hull, creating a hybrid ship that would not only be more useful than a conventional ship but that would also allow a more economical utilisation of the treaty-limited tonnage available. So went the argument, at any rate.

The Washington Treaty contained language that would suggest an attempt to prevent just such a merger of warship types. It specifically defined a capital ship as 'not an aircraft carrier', and defined the latter as a vessel of 10,000 tons or more 'designed for the specific and exclusive purpose of carrying aircraft' that 'must be so constructed that aircraft can be launched therefrom and landed thereon'.

Other portions of the pact's rather odd semantics permitted the hybrid to slip easily through its clauses. Under various provisions, an aircraft carrier could turn magically into a capital ship if armed with guns larger than 8in or disappear completely if displacing less than 10,000 tons, since these smaller 'auxiliary' warships were not limited in numbers at all. The treaty's definition of a carrier failed to encompass the seaplane carrier, and the dividing line between a carrier and a cruiser was blurred by a provision allowing the former to be armed with up to ten 8in guns.

Thus there was nothing to prevent any navy from building a battleship-carrier hybrid as long as it was willing to have this vessel included in its capital ship tonnage; similarly, cruiser-carriers were permitted as long as they did not exceed 10,000 tons or carry guns larger than 8in.

Into this confusing muddle Sir George boldly stepped. In the 1923 edition of *Brassey's*, he published an article on 'The Influence of the Washington Conference on Naval Design'. In this, he outlined and illustrated three 'Washington Conference capital ships'. All of these designs were clearly modelled on the design of *Nelson* and *Rodney*, only recently finalised and considered highly secret by the Admiralty; one wonders at the reactions of their Lordships when they saw their new battleship so accurately described in a popular yearbook. The first was a traditional slow (23 knot) battleship 'where gun power predominates'. Armed with nine 16in guns, it was in almost every detail cribbed from *Nelson*. The second was a battlecruiser 'where speed predominates', armed with six 16in guns — *Nelson* with one turret traded for more powerful machinery. The third was an 'experimental battleship' that was, in fact, a hybrid battleship-carrier, and a far more original design than its cousins. A sketch of this 'experimental battleship' was given in the article, as well as a few particulars. She was to be armed with three 16in guns in a single triple turret forward, the flight deck to extend partly over it; six 7.5in or 8in guns would be mounted in twin turrets, one on each beam in recesses in the hull and a turret right aft, again overhung by the flight deck. There were to be an unspecified number of 4.7in or 6in AA guns on 'disappearing' mounts, presumably somewhere on the flight deck. To further reduce interference with flying operations, there were to be no funnels; hot gases from the engineering plant would be vented through side ducts after being dampened and cooled by water.

The only superstructure on the 'experimental battleship' was to be a tall conning tower/tower mast affair, with some attempt made at streamlining. It is, however, unclear both from Thurston's article and the accompanying sketch whether this structure was to be on the centreline or offset as an island. Centreline placement is hinted at in the statement that the flight deck would provide 300ft of landing space 'abaft the mast' and a take-off run of about 120ft forward of it; however, some other British writers of the period divided the continuous decks of carriers into take-off and landing areas, delineating the two with a line as imaginary as the equator. Thurston may therefore have intended a continuous deck with an island superstructure offset to one side or another.

Given the lengths of the landing and take-off decks, the length of the ship works out to something very close to that which Sir George gave for his 'capital ship where speed predominates', about 730ft between perpendiculars (in British usage, from the rudder post to the point where the stempost intersects the design waterline; the waterline length would be some 40ft to 45ft longer). This would certainly be reasonable, as the ship is to have a speed 'exceeding 30 knots', implying a powerplant and length-to-beam ratio similar to his battlecruiser. The form and location of the 'disappearing' AA gun mounts can only be surmised.

Sir George averred that such a ship could have 'maximum' armour protection, both horizontally and vertically; by this he probably meant for the armour thicknesses to match those of his battleship and battlecruiser designs, a belt over the magazines 13in to 15in, decks 5in to 7in, with the armour somewhat thinner over the machinery compartments, as in *Nelson*. In addition, the 'fullest' underwater protection would be provided. All this could be achieved on a displacement within the 35,000 ton treaty limit. He did not specify the number or type of aircraft the vessel would carry beyond the statement that they would be capable of scouting, and bomb or torpedo attack. The ship would have several roles: it could take its place in the line of battle, 'joining in a naval action where the issue hangs in the balance' where its appearance 'might prove the determining factor'; or, acting as a 'solitary and powerful unit', it could deal easily with any cruiser or squadron of cruisers. Sir George concluded that such a ship 'would necessarily mean the acceptance of a considerably reduced offensive power, and could only be justified if forming a connecting link in strategical or tactical requirements'.

There he hit upon the major stumbling block to his 'experimental battleship'. With battleship tonnage limited to such a degree by the Washington Treaty, none of the major powers could afford to risk tonnage on an unproven experiment that might not work. The 'reduced offensive power', the limited number of main battery guns, would be too high a price to pay for a ship of uncertain qualities.

The article was widely reproduced, however, and was to have far-reaching effects in the years ahead. It was summarised in *Scientific American*, the *US Naval Institute Proceedings*, and *Literary Digest*, assuring its wide circulation among American readers, both professional navy men and anyone with an interest in science.

In 1924, Vice Admiral Amet of the French Navy presented a paper to the *Association Technique Maritime et Aéronautique* in which he praised Sir George's 'experimental battleship' and suggested that it would be an excellent type of vessel for the French service in the Mediterranean. This praise apparently convinced Thurston that 'the proposed combination of battleship and aircraft carrier was not illusory but a practical idea of great significance', and so he set about designing more hybrid warships. He presented his designs in the 1926 edition of *Brassey's* in an article entitled 'Battleship or Aircraft Carrier?' His ideas had developed greatly since his 'experimental battleship', and his new proposal was quite detailed.

It also aimed to appeal to a specific audience. Thurston considered that

> . . . the Government of any of the maritime nations not embraced in the Washington pact, having decided upon a scheme of naval construction, may wish, if possible, to keep within the Washington limits if by so doing their defense is not jeopardized. So, having a given sum allocated to such purpose, it would endeavour to ascertain if it were possible to devise an entirely new type of capital ship which, whilst not specifically designed to take part in a line action with fleets of any of the contracting parties, would possess powerful offensive, defensive and commerce-destroying qualities, having as one of the main features a powerful equipment of planes.

Sir George had realised that the treaty powers could not afford a radically new type of warship, for they would have to oppose those (presumably) conventional ships of the other contracting powers with ships of equal fighting power, 'so that, strangely enough, it is countries outside the Conference that will probably lead the way in new types'. Having stated that a naval power outside the conference was most likely to go looking for these new types of ship, Sir George went on to discuss his hybrid designs in the context of a South American republic, using as his yardstick in the design the existing Latin American battleships. In this he may well have been trying to drum up business for Vickers, where things were fairly slack in the postwar climate of tight budgets and arms control treaties. The South American republics had engaged in a heated naval rivalry before the First World War, and a return to that miniature arms race would have brought in con-

tracts. Unfortunately for Sir George, most of the South American nations were virtually bankrupt in the 1920s, so the hybrid ships he offered in his article were never taken up by the intended audience.

They were interesting ships for all that. He provided outline characteristics and sketches of two very similar ships. Sir George never gave them any designations, but for the sake of simplicity, they will be referred to as Designs A and B. Their main particulars were

	DESIGN A	DESIGN B
Displacement:	28,000t	26,850t
Dimensions:	70ft (pp) × 88ft × 23ft 3in	750ft (pp) × ?ft × ?ft
Machinery:	both ships: ?shp; 26.5kts (capable of 28kts during aircraft operations)	
Armament:	six 16in guns (2 × 3)	nine 12in (3 × 3)
	ten 4.7in DP guns (10 × 1)	ten 4.7in DP guns (10 × 1)
Protection:	10in main belt, 12in barbettes; 3in deck	9in main belt; 9in barbettes; 3in deck
Aircraft:	30	30

The ships were very similar, differing primarily in the arrangement and calibre of the main battery. In both, the flight deck extended somewhat more than half the ship's length, with the main battery turrets mounted below and forward of it. Design A had its second 16in turret superimposed above and abaft the forward turret; in Design B, a pyramidal arrangement similar to that of *Nelson* was used, with the second turret superimposed between the first and third. There was no ambiguity about the placement of the superstructure in these designs; a starboard island located about amidships left the flight deck unobstructed. The island included a rangefinder for the main battery and a seaplane handling crane. The placement of the island dictated an asymmetrical arrangement of the 4.7in guns — four to starboard and six to port — with no guns capable of bearing on the starboard bow. The 4.7in guns were ranged alongside and slightly below the flight deck. Water-dampened smoke was to be discharged downward through hullside ducts, four on each beam amidships; alternatively, Sir George mentioned in the article that funnels could be brought up through the island superstructure, although this arrangement would 'have the defects of the smoke and the vibration of heat exhalation interfering with the sighting of the guns'.

The flight deck was relatively broad, with a rounddown slightly overhanging the stern. A single lift located just aft of amidships served the hangar deck. Sir George had learned a lot since his 'experimental battleship' of 1923, but his new designs still were fatally flawed. The forward edge of the flight deck ended just abaft the main battery turrets; with the ship steaming at 28 knots into the wind, these massive structures and their thickets of barrels would have created powerful air turbulence at the delicate point at which an aircraft taking off is just becoming airborne. Taking off through such turbulence would not have been impossible, but would have been dangerous enough to make routine flight operations quite impracticable. This was a fault that a great many hybrid designs would suffer from, and was one of the great problems in hybrid design.

There was another problem with the designs. In order to secure reasonable arcs of fire for the main battery guns, Sir George had cut away the forward corners of the flight deck so that, instead of maintaining its full width for its entire length, it narrowed forward, with the apex of the triangular plan just behind the after main battery turret. This was a dangerous feature, for a very simple reason: to get a good take-off run, a heavily loaded aircraft such as a torpedo bomber would have to taxi down the exact centre of the deck without deviation. Yet the normal roll of the ship could easily cause deviations from such an exacting run, which would send the aircraft off the side of the deck before it had built up enough speed to get airborne. The dangers of this configuration had been demonstrated as early as 1915 in launching experiments on HMS *Campania*, and although early British carriers had such 'pointed' decks the feature was dropped in all subsequent carrier designs everywhere.

There were other flaws in the design, less serious but certainly inconvenient. One was the provision of only one lift; its position amidships was also problematical. This placement left insufficient space forward of the lift for take-off by loaded aircraft; all the aeroplanes required for a mission would have to be brought up from the hangar, then wheeled aft, thus slowing down flight operations. Moreover, the lift would have had to remain up during take-offs, slowing things even more.

Like his earlier article, Sir George's 1926 article was noted by the US Naval Institute's *Proceedings*. In the 'Professional Notes' of the October 1926 issue, Lieutenant Commander W G Greenman, the editor of this feature, briefly mentioned Sir George's new hybrids, then went on to discuss a similar design he had discussed with a 'student of naval design'. This anonymous student was apparently inspired by the work of Sir George, although he added a few features of his own. This design must now be utterly lost, and no sketch was published, so all we have is a written description, which is offered here in its entirety.

He [the 'student of naval design'] preferred a shorter, slower, and more heavily-armored type of ship, with a small displacement. His design, while it had the six 16-inch guns of the Thurston design, provided for the launching of planes by means of a catapult, and, moreover, carried only twenty aircraft. This ship was to displace 27,000 tons, and was to be armed with six 16-inch, eight 6-inch, and eleven 4.7-[inch] anti-aircraft guns, was to be armored with an 11-inch belt over the boiler-rooms and magazines, and was to have two funnels abreast at the extreme sides of the ship amidships. The bridge and tower-mast formed a 'marble arch', as my friend termed it, through which planes could be run on to the catapult which was placed between the bridge and the second turret. The secondary guns were to be placed amidships, and the anti-aircraft battery on the foc'sle and in various other positions forward and amidships. Two guns were arranged so as to command the flight deck, the reasons given being that an armored enemy aircraft might land on the aft end of the flight deck under the cover of dusk or a smoke screen and make the flight deck untenable by means of machine-gun fire. The flight deck would then be damaged by small bombs. To provide against the possibility of such a forlorn hope on the part of the enemy — for the attacking plane would certainly never get away again — two high-angle guns in stout shield [sic] with covered access provided, were fitted to command the deck abaft the funnels.

The tendency towards the incorporation of the features of the aircraft carrier would certainly not stop at the battleship. Large cruisers would appear, with their after-part devoted to aircraft and carrying a battery of 8-inch guns forward. To counter these, light battle cruisers of about 20,000 tons, with 12-inch guns and a more numerous complement of aircraft would probably be constructed.

The aircraft carrier, as we know her to-day, will not, I think, survive as a type. There are so many reasons why she would be better combined with the older types that there seems to be no reason for continuing her as a separate type.

There were, of course, many good reasons for continuing the aircraft carrier as a separate type, although Greenman had foreseen the flight-deck cruiser (to be described in subsequent chapters), and the way in which the 8in gun cruiser would give birth to larger 'light battle cruisers' once the treaties had lapsed. As for the hybrid design discussed, the twin islands connected by a 'marble arch' bridge had been contemplated as early as the Beardmore design of 1912, and in several other

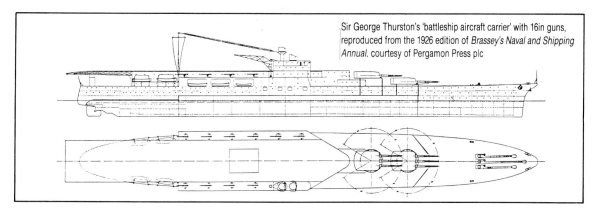

Sir George Thurston's 'battleship aircraft carrier' with 16in guns, reproduced from the 1926 edition of *Brassey's Naval and Shipping Annual*, courtesy of Pergamon Press plc

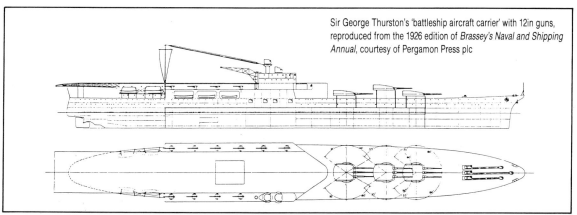

Sir George Thurston's 'battleship aircraft carrier' with 12in guns, reproduced from the 1926 edition of *Brassey's Naval and Shipping Annual*, courtesy of Pergamon Press plc

A conceptualisation of the hybrid warship proposed by 'a student of naval design' and discussed in the October 1926 *US Naval Institute Proceedings*. The design is entirely conjectural but incorporates the features of the vessel as described (*drawing by John P McLaughlin*)

carrier schemes since, always to be rejected because of the dangers it posed to aircraft operations. The idea of a 'forlorn' attack as described in the article seems absurd today, but no more absurd than the idea of the *kamikaze* would have seemed to the writer of 1926. Catapult launching of aircraft had both advantages and disadvantages: it would have made take-off easier, given the air turbulence created by the turrets in the forward part of the ship, but the launching cycle of a catapult was far slower than that of rolling take-offs, and it would not become standard practice for carriers until the short flight decks of the escort carriers made it mandatory. All in all, this design shared the flaws of Sir George's hybrids while adding a few of its own. One has to wonder at the identity of that 'student of naval design', and also wonder how many strange and fascinating hybrid designs are lost in somebody's attic, or have been weeded from archives, disappearing without trace.

Sir George and the unknown student should not be judged too harshly because of their flawed designs. Many of the worst features were to reappear time and again, even after the navies of the world had gained far more experience in aerial operation. They were in some cases the result of the basic conflict between heavy guns and aeronautical equipment, although some later designs would show that these conflicts could be resolved through careful design compromises. The flaws of Sir George's hybrids were perpetuated because so many of the designs were drawn up by naval architects who, despite broad experience and expertise in their own profession, were largely ignorant of aerodynamics and the practical aspects of aeroplane operation.

Despite the interest shown in periodicals of the day, Sir George Thurston's hybrid designs had little impact on warship construction, but they did exercise an altogether disproportionate influence in other areas, specifically in the American press and the US Navy, where the hybrid seeds Sir George had planted were to bear strange fruit indeed.

'THIS IDIOTIC CANARD'

Not since *Gloire* had a warship caused so much of a stir before she was even launched. The two ships under construction had the US Navy's Bureau of Construction and Repair hopelessly confused; they were the subject of a resolution proposed to (but never passed by) the Senate. According to *Popular Mechanics*, they threatened to 'revolutionize the art of battleship designing'. And the *New York American* reported that they would be 'the most powerful and destructive weapons of warfare ever constructed by any nation' for they were to be 'combined floating fortresses and aerodromes'.

They were *Nelson* and *Rodney*, and for two and a half years they generated a remarkable amount of controversy and anxiety, both in the American press and in the US Navy.

The origins of all this fuss and bother are now obscure, as indeed they were at the time. No one source for the mixture of fact, misinterpretation and rumour can be credited (or blamed) for the strange stories that grew up around the world's first 'treaty battleships', but the hybrid stories started early and continued until the ships had been launched, when their true form at last became apparent.

To make any sense of it all, one has to start with *Nelson* and *Rodney*. And to discuss *Nelson* and *Rodney*, one has to start with the G3 battlecruiser design of 1921.

The G3 was one of the most brilliant capital ship designs ever conceived. It had behind it all the experience which the Royal Navy had gained in the First World War, its protection was far in advance of anything under consideration anywhere else in the world, it would have mounted an armament equal to any other capital ship, and it would have had a speed of 31 to 32 knots. These characteristics demanded a very large ship of 48,400 tons legend displacement. The design would have been larger still if it had not been for a then-unorthodox arrangement of the main battery. The three triple 16in turrets were all forward of the machine spaces, two super-imposed forward of the tower mast and one immediately aft of the tower. The funnels, boat deck and half the secondary armament of eight twin 6in turrets were aft of 'X' turret, which meant that there was a 40 degree arc across the stern where no main battery gun could bear. This blind arc was accepted by the Naval Staff because mounting 'X' turret amidships allowed its magazine to be placed in the widest part of the hull, where it could have the maximum torpedo protection. Had the third turret been mounted aft of the machinery, it would have been in a narrower section of the hull; not only would its underwater protection have been less deep, but the magazines would have had to be longer, thus increasing the length (and weight) of the armoured citadel.

The Washington Treaty made the construction of such large ships impossible, so the superlative G3 design remains only a might-have-been. However, many of its features were incorporated in the first post-treaty battleships, the two ships of the *Nelson* class. The speed was cut to 23 knots, the scale of protection was somewhat reduced, but the main battery was unchanged: nine 16in guns in three triple turrets. In *Nelson*, all three turrets were sited forward of the tower mast, but the logic was the same: to place all the magazines in the widest portion of the hull, thereby shortening the citadel and allowing the heaviest armour and deepest underwater protection. In order to reduce the weight of the machinery, the ships were made relatively long for their modest speed.

The secrecy surrounding *Nelson*'s novel design was unusually great; the only data officially released were the dimensions of the ship. The 1924 edition of *Jane's Fighting Ships* reported that 'Plans and other details of these ships have been withheld by Admiralty request', and as late as 1925 the authoritative British publication *The Engineer* based its description of the ships on the testimony of an American naval officer before a Congressional subcommittee. Such secrecy was bound to generate interest above and beyond that which the first 'treaty' battleships would naturally excite, and any scrap of data was mulled and mooted by the naval writers of the day. This process seems to have been the germ of the rumours that appeared soon after the *Nelson* design had been finalised.

And soon it was. The design was approved on 16 October 1922, invitations to tender went out that same day, and on 11 November the bids of Cammell Laird and Armstrong were accepted.

The keels of both *Nelson* and *Rodney* were laid on 28 December 1922, and on 8 January 1923, an article appeared in the *New York Times* suggesting that these new battleships would be hybrids.

The article stated that the 'warship of the future' would be a 'contest of wits', since the Washington Treaty limited size and armament. *Nelson* and *Rodney* would be the first of this new breed. While there had 'been no official disclosure of the plans for the two new British ships', the *Times* reported that

> Frequent items recently in the British press . . . have given what appears to be a clear, general picture of the ships, which presents vessels so strikingly superior to anything now afloat that they will be queens of the seas. . . .

There was more to it than that, however. The reports and rumours were already flying, for the article went on,

> With the main battery consolidated thus in three turrets, it is indicated that the British designers are preparing to use the huge deck sweep for airplane take-off, landing and storage. There has been some hint that all three turrets would be on the forward deck, giving up the entire after deck to aircraft and making each battleship a potential airplane carrier as well. There is no official confirmation of this point.

This article was calm in tone, looking upon the potential hybrid nature of these ships as an interesting technical feature, and the article itself was consigned to page 21 of the paper. Soon, however, these fearsome engines of war would be front page news.

It should be noted that the *Times* had felt justified in printing these reports less than two weeks after the ships had been laid down. The 'hints' and 'indications' must have been in wide circulation already. The very next day the *Times* had more to say on these new ships: 'Speculation in Washington about the construction of the two new battleships . . . has given rise to an uneasy feeling that they will be superior to our 16-inch gun battleship *Maryland* and her two sister ships . . .'. Furthermore,

> In designing the new battleships the British are using their wits as usual . . . it may be supposed that the new vessels will be the last word in theoretical effectiveness . . . [they] are to have a length of 680 feet and a width of 106. . . Nine 16-inch guns arranged in three turrets will be carried. There is a report that these turrets will be placed well forward, allowing deck space for the landing and dispatch of airplanes . . .

After reassuring the reader that there was probably no reason for concern regarding the relative strengths of the US and British navies, the article ended with a look forward to 1931, when battleship building would begin in earnest. The anonymous author asked, 'who knows what the value of the capital ship as compared with the fighting airplane will be by that time?'

Some of this speculation was certainly fuelled by Sir George Thurston's 'experimental battleship', which appeared in *Brassey's* at about this time. His ship, with its combination of battleship and aircraft, must have seemed reasonable to American observers, especially coming from so eminent a naval architect. They may have assumed that Sir George had a pipeline to the Admiralty, and that he knew what the new British battleships would be like.

Yet in spite of Sir George's article in the 1923 *Brassey's*, American concern over the characteristics of the new ships seems to have died down at this time. They were not in the news again until December 1924. By then, the 'uneasy feeling' about them would have grown to anger and fear.

By that time, Anglo-American relations had cooled considerably, especially in naval circles. In Britain, there was resentment over the treaty-enforced equality granted to the US Navy — the Americans did not have overseas commitments on the scale of the British Empire, so why did they require an equal navy? In the United States there was a strong feeling that America had been denied its rightful place as the world's no. 1 seapower by a British diplomatic trick. In such an atmosphere, any action by any power could be interpreted as a deliberate threat, and both Britain and the United States were quick to see dangers in the policies of the other. It took nothing more than a plan to increase the elevation of battleship guns to set off a wave of recriminations and ill feeling.

The US Naval War College had demonstrated in its war games that the American battle line would suffer a tremendous disadvantage in an engagement with the Royal Navy because of the greater range of the British guns. To counter this, it was proposed to increase the elevation of the guns in US battleships to 30 degrees; a request for the money to do this was put before the House of Representatives in January 1923.

In part, the arguments in support of this measure were based on statements from the Secretary of State and the Secretary of the Navy to the effect that Britain was already engaged in increasing the elevation of the Royal Navy's battleship guns. These reports were incorrect, and in March 1923, the British Ambassador presented a memorandum to the Secretary of State requesting that these statements be publicly corrected in order to allay 'those sentiments of mistrust which it was one of the primary objects of the Washington Conference to dispel'. Both the navy and the State Department published these corrections; however, the American proposal to increase the range of its own battleships' guns had been approved by Congress in the meantime. With the British gun elevation matter cleared up, the approval went into limbo, but it was never retracted and the matter came up frequently in both houses of Congress. The American battleships were still outranged by the British battle line, so the modification was still desired by the navy, and in his annual report for 1923, published in early 1924, the Secretary of the Navy again advanced this proposal.

This drew a 'remonstrance' from the British Chargé on 14 February 1924. Chapter II, Part 3, Section 1(d) of the Washington Treaty stated that, 'No alterations in the side armour, in calibre, number or general type of mounting of main armament shall be permitted', and the British felt that an increase in the elevation of the guns would be a change in the 'general type of mounting'. On the other hand, the State Department saw no impediment in the treaty to increasing the gun elevations, a judgement based on information from the Navy Department which indicated that the required modifications would be relatively minor. Notes were exchanged between the British Embassy and the State Department throughout 1924, and the disagreement was to continue until 1927, when it seems to have died a natural death. The protest caused a considerable stir in the Congress, where both houses repeatedly asked the Secretary of State for information about who was protesting, and on what grounds the protest had been lodged. This Congressional questioning and the general Anglo-American naval antagonism may have led to the revival of the reports of *Nelson* as a hybrid, and their increased tone of bitterness and suspicion. These reports would continue, on and off, until *Nelson* was launched in September 1925.

The new flurry actually began calmly enough with the testimony of Captain Henry H Hough, Director of Naval Intelligence, before the House Subcommittee on Navy Department Appropriations on 18 November 1924. The captain provided a largely accurate description of the new British warships, making no mention of any aircraft facilities; nor did any of the subcommittee's members raise that issue in their questions. The captain's description of the ships was considered important enough to be reported in the *New York Times* on 15 December 1924.

The most active period of speculation about the new British ships now began. On 11 January 1925, the *Chicago Tribune* reported, 'New British Sea Giants Make Old Navies Obsolete — Link Plane Carriers with 16-inch Guns'. This dramatic headline led the reader into a detailed description of these fantastic vessels, which were to be

craft unlike anything that naval science has ever seen or heard of before. The design of the . . . Nelson and Rodney . . . will put all existing warships back in the Victorian era.

These fighting ships, which are already near completion, will have an appearance as strange as anything H. G. Wells ever imagined in his visionary novels on warfare of the future.

Without a funnel showing and scarcely any superstructure they are designed to serve a double purpose. A clear deck space gives a long broad sweep for the launching of airplanes, thus increasing the vessel's battle radius by hundreds of miles. . . .

The arrangement of the big guns will also be new, being concentrated forward. They will consist of nine sixteen inch guns in three turrets. . . .

Heavily armored decks will be laid as a protection from attack from the air. The magazines are being grouped forward under superarmored decks. . . .

The absence of funnels provides unobstructed space for planes. The smoke fumes from the engines will be carried off via tubes stretching alongside, which will also aid in throwing up smoke screens.

Bombing tests and aerial tactics for the new style of sea fighting have already begun. . . .

It is declared . . . that the Nelson and the Rodney mark the beginning of a new British navy.

Under its owner, the Anglophobe Colonel Robert McCormick, the *Chicago Tribune* 'steadily and vehemently maintained an extreme right-wing position on various issues — it condemned labor unions and attacked the participation of the United States in world affairs', so it is easy to imagine such a paper printing as Gospel reports of these strange new, and alarming, battleships under construction in Britain. The alarm was not confined to the *Tribune*; the *New York Times*, considered the bastion of American journalistic integrity, picked up the *Tribune*'s report, while the *Washington Post* reported on 15 January 1925 that

It is now revealed that the ships will be far in advance of anything now in existence so far as fighting

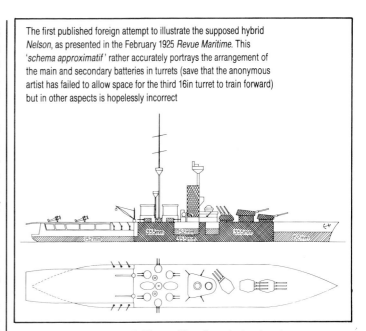

The first published foreign attempt to illustrate the supposed hybrid *Nelson*, as presented in the February 1925 *Revue Maritime*. This '*schema approximatif*' rather accurately portrays the arrangement of the main and secondary batteries in turrets (save that the anonymous artist has failed to allow space for the third 16in turret to train forward) but in other aspects is hopelessly incorrect

efficiency is concerned. They will make existing battleships obsolete by bringing to bear an overwhelming gun power, concentrated in forward turrets. . . .

The article went on to quote verbatim the aviation facilities of these ships as reported in the *Tribune*. It concluded that

Thus it will be seen that capital ships are undergoing complete evolution as a result of developments in air warfare. The capital ship of the early future will not only be protected as much as possible against air attack, but it will be equipped with airplanes and means of launching and receiving airplanes at sea. . . .

Who can figure out the proportionate fighting strength of such a capital ship, as compared with existing battleships? . . . As aircraft develops [sic], it is certain that battleships not equipped or accompanied by airplanes will not be able to hold their own against ships like the Rodney and Nelson. Speed will not save a ship pursued by bombing planes, and big guns are useless against planes.

The World of New York told its readers that 'the two American scout cruisers [*Lexington* and *Saratoga*] which are being converted into airplane carriers will carry about 150 planes, or little less than twice the number of two British battleships are credited with being able to carry'. That would put some eighty aircraft aboard each of the hybrids, a remarkable accomplishment for a 35,000 ton vessel also burdened with the heaviest shipboard artillery in the world.

The hyperbole reached its peak in the *New York American*, which informed its subscribers that 'cable despatches from London describe them as being the most powerful and destructive weapons

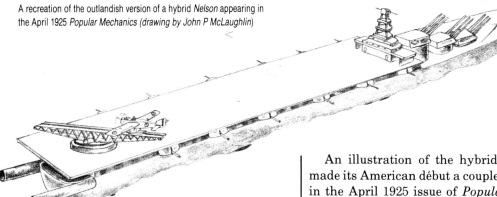

A recreation of the outlandish version of a hybrid *Nelson* appearing in the April 1925 *Popular Mechanics* (drawing by John P McLaughlin)

of warfare ever constructed by any nation, and as combined floating fortresses and aerodromes'.

Oddly enough, all this frenetic press activity did not immediately inspire any sketches of these new British wonder ships in the American press; the first such attempt appeared instead in France. The ideas of Sir George Thurston had been covered by the professional naval journal *Revue Maritime*, as had the building of the new British battleships and the foreign press reports about them. All the elements were therefore available for a French version of the *Nelson*-as-hybrid, and in the February 1925 issue the editors of the '*Chronique des marines françaises et étrangères*' column treated their readers to just such a vessel. Drawing heavily on the testimony of Captain Hough as quoted in *The Engineer*'s 9 January 1925 issue and 'reports in the British, American and Italian press' — with a liberal dose of Sir George's 1923 battleships thrown in — the resulting '*Schéma approximatif*' of *Les bâtiments «Hush, Hush»* was as unlikely a beast as one could imagine; about all that can be said in favour of it is that the turrets are shown in more or less the proper arrangement — although the draughtsman has left insufficient room for the third turret to train fore and aft — and the 6in guns are placed correctly in turrets. Everything else about the sketch is either wildly improbable or completely bizarre. The hull is more French than British, with a clipper bow and a complete waterline belt 6in thick at the ends; the tower superstructure and masting are lifted directly from Sir George's battleship designs, while the two enormous squat funnels are excessively large for a vessel known to be of moderate speed. And, of course, there is a 'landing deck for aircraft' aft, complete with aeroplanes but no apparent means of launching them. There are no catapults, and rolling take-offs would be impossible with those funnels, masts and superstructure forward.

An illustration of the hybrid *Nelson* finally made its American début a couple of months later in the April 1925 issue of *Popular Mechanics*, a magazine with a wide circulation in the United States; it was, perhaps, even more improbable than the French drawing. The drawing was obviously based on the description in the *Chicago Tribune*, and was clearly executed by someone with little knowledge of naval design or aeronautical operations. It has a puny superstructure with disproportionately small 16in turrets triple-tiered forward. Aft is that 'long sweep' of deck for aircraft, but the artist has completely spoilt the arrangements by sticking a huge catapult right aft. This would obviously make the landing-on of aeroplanes impossible, so the artist shows a line of seaplanes on the deck — at least, they seem to be seaplanes; certainly the aircraft flying over the ship have floats. The catapult is huge, well over 100ft long, and stands some distance above the deck, judging by the height of the human figures near it. Yet there is no crane either for hoisting the aircraft onto the catapult, or for lifting them out of the water. The funnels are horizontal tubes extending aft for a considerable distance, and the secondary guns are shown in casemates. The artist clearly had not read Captain Hough's description of the ship, which mentioned the fact that the 6in guns would be carried in 'light, closed turrets'.

This fanciful ship was 'Built to Fight But Not Run Away', but one wonders how well it could fight, cluttered with those impossible aviation arrangements and little in the way of visible fire control. The illustration would have been a little more rational if the artist had removed that enormous catapult from the after end of the flight deck and sponsored a pair of more reasonably sized catapults forward near the superstructure. Then the vessel could have launched aircraft — this time aeroplanes — and recovered them. Trying to make a workable ship out of this ill-informed medley is not really worth the effort; it is absurd, from its undersized gun turrets forward to its horizontal chimneys aft — which would have

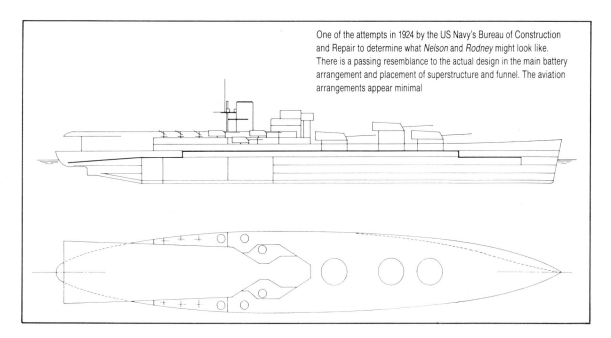

One of the attempts in 1924 by the US Navy's Bureau of Construction and Repair to determine what *Nelson* and *Rodney* might look like. There is a passing resemblance to the actual design in the main battery arrangement and placement of superstructure and funnel. The aviation arrangements appear minimal

thrown smoke and turbulence up in the face of any aeroplane attempting to land on this unwieldy vessel that threatened 'to revolutionize the art of battleship designing'.

The excitement stirred up by rumours of British hybrid battleships was not confined to the popular press; it reached into the highest councils in the land. On 16 January 1925, during a debate on the Navy Department's appropriation, the Washington Treaty, American battleship gun elevations and *Nelson*'s alleged hybrid characteristics all came up for discussion. Senator Peter Gerry of Rhode Island informed his colleagues that the new British vessels

> are supposed to be the latest things in battleships. They will carry nine 16-inch guns, and the newspaper reports assert that these guns will be placed forward, and that the afterdeck will be used for an airplane platform . . . and that there will be no stacks in order to allow the airplanes to land on the battleships.

The senator displayed a fair knowledge about the problems of aviation at sea when he further informed his colleagues that

> If you place stacks on an airplane carrier, the British have found in their experiments that it makes a difference in the air currents and you have difficulty with your airplanes landing on the deck.

Senator Kenneth D McKellar, a Democrat from Tennessee, seized upon this information. He was clearly nettled by the British protest over the elevation of US battleship guns, and on 21 Janu-ary, he put forward a resolution that began, 'Whereas it has been stated on the floor of the Senate, by the chairman of the Committee on Naval Affairs, that "a protest has been made by another power to this country against elevating the guns of our battleships . . ." '. The resolution concluded that the President of the United States be

> respectfully requested to obtain the information from Great Britain . . . and to inform the Senate, if not incompatible with the public interest, whether . . . *Nelson* and *Rodney* . . . conform to the provisions of said [Washington] treaty; whether the same are battleships or aircraft carriers; if combined battleships and aircraft carriers, whether or not such ships, as aircraft carriers, do not violate Article X of the treaty by carrying guns in excess of the caliber therein permitted; whether the said ships as aircraft carriers do not violate Section IX of the treaty in reference to tonnage and in reference to the number of guns carried.

Similar resolutions had been proposed in both the Senate and House before regarding the protest and its legal basis, but only McKellar's resolution brought up the hybrid rumours; perhaps he thought he could catch the British out on the battleship/aircraft carrier clause of the treaty and thereby get them to withdraw their diplomatic protest over battleship gun elevation. If so, he was to be disappointed on all counts; Senate Resolution 310 never got beyond the committee assigned to study it. It did, however, make the front page of the *New York Times*, demonstrating that this paper judged the public interest in this issue to be considerable.

Even after *Nelson* was launched and accurate

descriptions of her had been published in the press, at least one American newspaper still worried about the possibility that she and her sister were hybrids far outclassing anything in the US Navy. In an editorial entitled 'A Mystery Ship' that appeared in the 13 October 1925 *New York Times*, the battleship-carrier issue was brought up again. After reviewing the known facts about the new ship, the editorialist said that

> Archibald Hurd, the British naval specialist, says that the Nelson 'is certainly a mystery ship.' It is curious that he traces to American sources the story that she will carry a large number of airplanes and will be half battleship and half carrier. It is as if Mr. Hurd believed the report himself, but did not want to publish the facts as coming from him.

This attempt to give the rumours some life was to be the last gasp of the *Nelson*-as-hybrid theory in the popular press. Subsequent articles in the *New York Times* described the ship with increasing accuracy, and no more mention was made of her carrying large numbers of aircraft.

The parting shot in all this absurdity was fired, appropriately enough, by Senator McKellar. On 8 December 1925, he submitted Senate Resolution 73, a word-for-word repetition of the resolution he had unsuccessfully sponsored back in January. The resolution was referred to the Committee on Naval Affairs, and was never heard from again.

The popular press and indignant politicians had not been the only ones to imagine the new British battleships as hybrids. That peculiar fixation had lodged just as firmly in the US Navy, and several attempts were made to determine what these ships would look like. To follow this parallel story, we have to retrace our steps.

The secrecy regarding *Nelson* and *Rodney* was even more frustrating for the US Navy than it was for the press, and with more reason: the navy was worried that the new British ships would outclass the American battle fleet, which was already outranged by the British battle line. The navy needed to know what these new ships would be

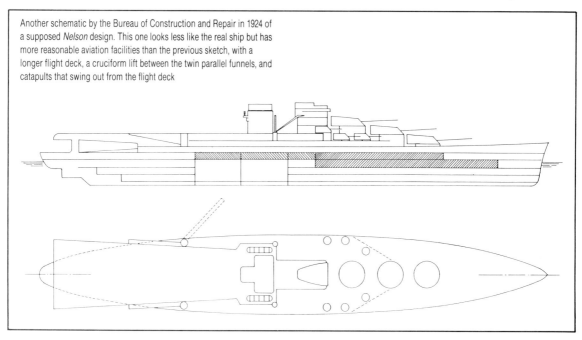

Another schematic by the Bureau of Construction and Repair in 1924 of a supposed *Nelson* design. This one looks less like the real ship but has more reasonable aviation facilities than the previous sketch, with a longer flight deck, a cruciform lift between the twin parallel funnels, and catapults that swing out from the flight deck

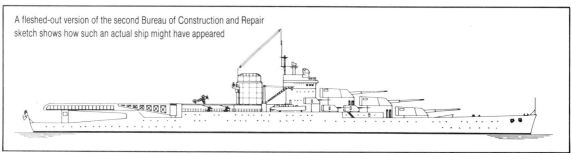

A fleshed-out version of the second Bureau of Construction and Repair sketch shows how such an actual ship might have appeared

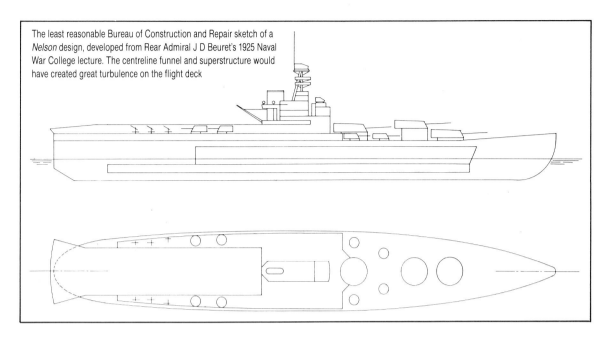

The least reasonable Bureau of Construction and Repair sketch of a *Nelson* design, developed from Rear Admiral J D Beuret's 1925 Naval War College lecture. The centreline funnel and superstructure would have created great turbulence on the flight deck

like, but it was not getting many hints from its erstwhile colleagues in the Admiralty; in spite of close co-operation during the First World War, the two English-speaking navies were not on good terms in the 1920s, and there were no bits of inside information from the British on their new ships. So the Office of Naval Intelligence had little more to go on than did the press. In October 1924, the Preliminary Design branch of the Bureau of Construction and Repair (the bureau responsible for ship design) set about trying to establish what sort of ships the British were building. They failed miserably.

The information they had to work with puzzled them. To start with, there was that business about all the guns being mounted forward; it was not officially verified, of course, but there were so many reports to that effect that it must have seemed a certainty.

Just as puzzling was the length of the ships, which *was* officially verified. *Nelson* and *Rodney* were 702ft on the waterline, considerably longer than an American battleship of comparable displacement would have been. The American designers did not understand this; their own practice was to armour a fixed percentage of the waterline, so the longer the ship, the more armour it would require. So, by American standards, *Nelson* would require a great weight of armour to protect the long waterline, despite the fact that her displacement was limited by the Washington Treaty. They did not realise that the Royal Navy had given up armouring a fixed fraction of the waterline, and had made the ship long to decrease

the power she needed to make her 23 knot speed, thereby saving on machinery weight. All the American assumptions from this point on were wildly incorrect.

If the *Nelson* was so long, her great length had to be for a definite purpose. What purpose? With all the guns forward, it would leave a long stretch aft without any clear reason. What good was a long, unobstructed length of deck? Why, for aircraft, of course.

The logic of it is very clear, and perfectly sound once one accepts the incorrect assumptions upon which it is based. And it had an American antecedent; in January 1918, inspired perhaps by *Furious*, the Bureau of Construction and Repair had conducted wind tunnel tests on a model of the dreadnought USS *Pennsylvania* to 'determine aerodynamical and structural conditions suitable for landing light airplanes upon the after-deck of the full-scale ship'. A number of light decks over the after main battery turrets were tried in the wind tunnel, and it was concluded that 'the ample beam of the vessel insures a uniform air stream broad enough to afford . . . a favorable directional flow for landing small craft upon the ship'. The fact that any of these decks would have required a series of supports that would have seriously interfered with the operation of the after turrets, and that the tests took no account of the air turbulence generated by the hot funnel gases, was not considered.

Whether these tests had any influence on the American designers attempting to deduce what the *Nelson* would look like is unknown, but it is

Nelson fitting out in September 1926. By now it was clear that reports
of her supposed hybrid design were false (Naval Historical Center)

certainly indicative of the failure of some naval
designers to appreciate all the factors in landing
an aircraft on a ship at sea, and so must have
made the hybrid Nelson seem a little more reasonable.

The result was a pair of sketches that attempted
to show what the British design might look like.
Both ships are fascinating more for what they
reveal about their American designers than for
what they reveal about Nelson. The length of hull
that needed to be armoured by American
standards ruled out a thick belt; but this was not so
serious, since it was known that the British ships
were to have internal, steeply sloped belts. A thin
belt, sufficiently sloped, could offer reasonable
protection at anticipated battle ranges, so these
putative 'British' designs were given 7in belts
sloped at 30 degrees. This would approximate the
resistance of a 12in belt at 16,000 yards.

The designs worked out by the Bureau of
Construction and Repair can be criticised on any
number of points. While one of the sketches shows
a ship relatively close to the Nelson in its main
battery arrangement and funnel location, the
other seems to have been more thoroughly
thought out in terms of aviation facilities. Both
have centreline superstructures and one also has a
centreline funnel; on either ship, these features
would have made for impossible turbulence over
the cramped flight decks. No indication of launching arrangements is given, although one sketch
shows a large, odd structure that swings out from
the side of the flight deck — perhaps a catapult
pivoted at its rear end. The same sketch also has
funnels split to each side of a cruciform lift; the hot
gases from these funnels would have been just as

dangerous as those from a centreline funnel.

These attempts at hybrid design did not dis-
courage the American naval architects and intelligence analysts. In 1925, an Office of Naval
Intelligence (ONI) memo reported that the design
of Nelson and Rodney had 'three triple 16 in.
turrets forward, with the after part of the ship
giving up a turret to mount a deck. Thus, for one-
fourth of a battleship you get one-half of a carrier',
and that 'this looks like a winning proposition'.

In May 1925, Rear Admiral J D Beuret, Chief of
the Bureau of Construction and Repair, gave a
lecture at the Naval War College on 'Naval Design
with Particular Reference to Underwater Protection'. Included with this lecture was yet another
sketch from Construction and Repair of the possible appearance of the Nelson, and again it was a
hybrid battleship-aircraft carrier. The surviving
drawing can be made out only partially, so the
intended appearance is at some points uncertain,
but the overall impression is unmistakable, and
unmistakably implausible. Again, there is the
centreline superstructure and funnel, the thin
(7.5in) belt, the short flight deck (about 300ft long).
The hangar allowed for fifteen aircraft — scarcely
the 'one-half of a carrier' that the ONI had
expected. The secondary armament consisted of
8in guns, an unwieldly calibre for anti-destroyer
work. The AA battery was to be twelve 4in guns.

The fact that Beuret chose to illustrate his
lecture with such a drawing indicates the degree of
interest in Nelson and Rodney, and the conviction
in some American naval circles that they would be
hybrids. Captain Hough had described the new
British ships to a Congressional subcommittee in
November 1924 (only a few months earlier) without mentioning anything about aircraft features.
Perhaps some officers in the ONI took the hybrid

theory with a pinch of salt, or perhaps the captain felt the reports of hybrid *Nelsons* were too uncertain to offer as an official opinion to the House of Representatives.

★ ★ ★

The *Nelson*-as-hybrid rumours had had a good, long life and had caused a considerable stir in their time, but by late 1925 the real form of the new ships was becoming apparent. In the October 1925 issue of *Scientific American*, the British naval writer Hector C Bywater accurately described the new 'treaty' battleships, and provided a relatively accurate illustration. In his article, Bywater was at some pains to deny the hybrid theory; he mentioned the Admiralty's policy of secrecy, and pointed out that

> It has given a handle to publicists and agitators who pander to anti-British sentiment, and these people have contrived to generate a suspicion in the United States that Great Britain is deliberately flouting the technical clauses of the Treaty by endowing her new battleships with unauthorized powers of offense. . . It has now become possible to furnish some information relating to the "Nelson" design which, although not official, may be accepted as reliable . . . these details completely refute charges preferred by American critics to the effect that the ships are camouflaged aircraft carriers.

But Bywater's refutation of the hybrid myth was restrained compared to that of the editor of *Scientific American*, who gave his opinion of the whole affair in a side-bar to Bywater's article. Entitled 'That Airplane-Carrier-Battleship Myth', it told in no uncertain terms what the editor thought of the hybrid theory.

> The man who set going the rumor that the new Treaty battleships, *Nelson* and *Rodney*, were to be camouflaged airplane carriers . . . was possessed at once of a perfervid imagination and a ludicrous ignorance of the simplest elements of warship construction.
>
> The genesis of this mare's nest is to be found, doubtless, in the widely published statement that the main battery of these ships would be grouped forward of the bridge. Here was a change, so completely without precedent as to be absolutely sinister in its implications! What new deviltry was here afoot!

The editor continued in a similarly cutting fashion to dismiss the line of reasoning that led to the hybrid theory.

Nelson in early 1927. Far from being a hybrid, she lacks aviation facilities entirely. A portside crane to handle a single seaplane was added during her 1937–38 refit. Sister *Rodney* had a catapult installed on her 'X' turret in 1936 and could accommodate two aircraft. Aircraft were removed from both vessels during the Second World War (*Naval Historical Center*)

For what other purpose could this have been done than to provide a flying deck for a fleet of airplanes. . . To render this precious charge of dishonesty plausible, the public was told that the boiler-room smoke was to be carried in horizontal ducts and discharged astern. . .

That the limits of absurdity were reached in this proposal is seen in the fact that airplanes at the end of their run, in taking off, would have to leap-frog over a huge conning tower at least 100 feet high.

Finally, he dismissed the whole thing with magnificent disdain.

Nevertheless, this idiotic canard received widespread publicity throughout the press of this country.

There is a double irony in all of this. The first is that, had any of these newspaper writers, intelligence officers, politicians, naval analysts or designers wanted to see what *Nelson* and *Rodney* were really going to look like, they had only to look at Sir George Thurston's 1923 *Brassey's* article. The design given top billing in this article was not the 'experimental battleship' that seems to have contributed to the fuss; it was his conventional battleship 'where gun-power predominates'. This design was *Nelson* in every particular; dimensions, main battery arrangement, secondary battery, armour thicknesses and disposition, tower mast — absolutely every feature of the design had been copied from *Nelson*. Anybody with 25 shillings could find out every detail of Britain's mystery ships only a few weeks after they were laid down; the catch was that you had to pick the right sketch of the three presented by Sir George. Although he was an able designer, Sir George's designs had often been modelled on other ships, and so it was with his 1923 battleship sketches. Only his hybrid designs were truly original.

The second irony is that the design of *Nelson* and *Rodney* made no provision whatsoever for aircraft, and the ships were not equipped to handle them until some years after their completion.

'AN EXCEEDINGLY USEFUL TYPE OF WARSHIP'

Fantasies and phantoms aside, there were a variety of official hybrid projects contemplated between the wars by the major naval powers. In almost every case, however, the vessel wedded to the aeroplane was the cruiser rather than the battleship. In considering such vessels, the question arises as to where the dividing line should be drawn: is there a point at which a carrier is so heavily armed and armoured that it can perform the functions of a cruiser as well as those of a pure aviation vessel?

The question is significant because during its first decade the carrier's role was in many ways so similar to a cruiser's that it was often seen as a new type of cruiser. For example, fleet scouting was one cruiser task that carrier aircraft virtually took over, as aircraft from a single carrier could, in good visibility, reconnoitre an area far more quickly than a whole squadron of cruisers. Carriers were also seen in such traditional cruiser duties as commerce protection (ie, locating and destroying surface raiders) and screening the main fleet against attacks by light forces. These cruiser-like roles were so distinct that some Royal Navy schemes after the First World War called for separate battle fleet carriers, slower ships carrying mostly spotter/reconnaissance aircraft.

The cruiser-like conception of the early carriers was evident in their armament. Many early carrier designs, both actual and theoretical, featured relatively heavy armament, and often armour. This was considered desirable on two grounds. First, there was the possibility that at night or in low visibility or as the result of mismanoeuvring, a carrier might have to defend itself from gunnery vessels; this danger was heightened by the fact that the manoeuvres of carriers, dictated by the wind, might take them away from support. Second, there was the belief that aircraft would be largely or entirely eliminated in fighting preliminary to a fleet action and that the carriers should then join in the gunnery engagement. For this, a cruiser's armament was

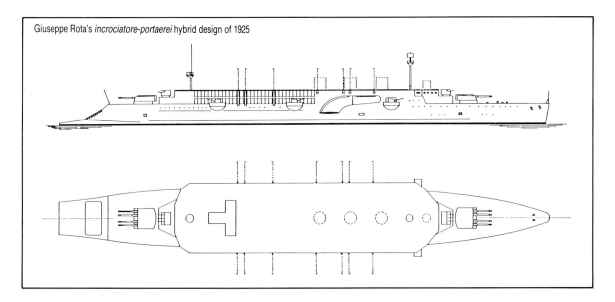

Giuseppe Rota's *incrociatore-portaerei* hybrid design of 1925

about the minimum useful battery.

Thus, although the three first-generation carriers, *Argus, Hosho* and *Langley*, sported only a few low-angle and small-calibre guns, batteries of light cruiser number and calibre were seen in the next generation of carriers. Even after her conversion to a full flight-deck carrier, *Furious* retained ten 5.5in guns; *Hermes* had six and *Eagle* nine 6-inchers, while France's *Béarn* of 1927 mounted eight 6.1in guns in armoured casemates.

It is therefore hardly surprising that the Washington Treaty also sanctioned large, heavily armed carriers, mainly at the urging of the American delegation. The individual carrier limit was fixed at 27,000 tons, and the guns restricted to 8in calibre. Even larger carriers were permitted under Article IX; it stated that any of the signatory powers could, 'provided that its total tonnage allowance of aircraft carriers is not thereby exceeded, build not more than two aircraft carriers, each of a tonnage not more than 33,000 tons standard displacement, and in order to effect economy any of the Contracting Powers may use for this purpose any two of their ships whether constructed or in course of construction, which would otherwise be scrapped. . .'. As is well known, it was this clause that allowed the American *Lexington* class and the Japanese *Kaga* and *Akagi* to be built.

The potential for large and heavily armed carriers implicit in the Washington Treaty would lead to several designs for powerfully gunned vessels between the wars. The treaty also provided another route to hybrid warships by failing to limit the number of 'auxiliary' vessels — cruisers and other combatants below 10,000 tons standard displacement — which the signatories could build. Thus, there was a constant temptation to design relatively small aviation ships of one sort or another, a process which could lead to combination cruiser/carriers.

Another attraction exercised by the hybrid during this period was its alleged economy. We have seen how Sir George Thurston had tried to sell his battleship-carriers as a sort of 'two for the price of one' bargain, and this appeal eventually drew a fair number of politicians, naval officers and designers into the grey realm of hybrid warships.

One or another of these factors — the carrier's cruiser-like roles, the increased scope of cruiser capabilities when aircraft were available, the artificial restrictions imposed on the whole issue by the treaty system, and the apparent economy of the hybrid — led three European nations to turn their attention to the hybrid during the 1920s.

In the early 1920s Italy's naval policy was being re-evaluated in the light of changed conditions brought about by the First World War and the nation's expanding colonial empire. Aviation vessels of various types were given consideration during this period; one remarkable proposal, put forward by Tenente di vascello (Lieutenant) Giuseppe Fioravanzo in 1921, called for an 11,000 ton *incrociatore antiaereo* armed with eighteen 4in AA guns and carrying sixteen pursuit aircraft. The idea was not taken up at the time, but it may have inspired the *incrociatore-portaerei* proposed in 1925 by Generale del Genio Navale Giuseppe Rota.

Rota's design is further proof that even the most skilled naval architects may err grievously when they enter the field of maritime aeronautics, for it is surely one of the most unworkable hybrids ever conceived. This despite the fact that he had a long and distinguished career, and was considered by the British journal *Engineering* to be 'Italy's premier naval architect' at the time of his death in 1953 at the age of ninety-three. Born before the unification of Italy, he entered that new nation's naval construction corps in 1883. In 1900 he was awarded the first gold medal of the Ministry of Marine for advances in the science of naval architecture, and in 1904 was appointed director of the Royal Shipyards at Castellamare di Stabia, where he presided over the construction of the cruisers *San Giorgio* and *San Marco* and the battleship *Napoli*. In 1911 he became director at La Spezia yards, supervising the building of the dreadnoughts *Dante Alighieri, Conte di Cavour* and *Andrea Doria*. For all Rota's experience in the construction of warships, however, only a few were built to his own designs: the two small colonial protected cruisers of the *Campania* class and the scout cruisers *Nino Bixio* and *Marsala*. In 1920 he was named Director General of Naval Construction and soon after became vice-president of the navy's Committee on Design. Rota retired in 1925, the same year in which he put forward his strange hybrid.

Few details remain of this 'Progetto Rota', as it was dubbed; we lack such vital information as dimensions, propulsion, protection, speed and aircraft complement. What remains is a portrait of a ship of 12,480 tons standard displacement, armed with eight 8in guns in quadruple turrets fore and aft of a flight deck extending about two-thirds of the vessel's length. AA armament was composed of six single 3.9in guns in sponsons plus twelve 40mm in sextuple mounts superimposed above the 8in turrets.

An unusual stern slopes down to the waterline, forming a ramp that leads to the large angled hatch of a seaplane hangar abaft the after turret. This manner of seaplane recovery or dockage was a recurrent theme in carrier design; it was broached as early as August 1915 in a British carrier scheme, was considered at length during design studies for HMS *Argus*, and apparently was proposed for the old Russian Black Sea cruiser *Komintern* when her remodelling into a seaplane carrier was either studied or undertaken in the 1930s. As late as the mid-1950s the idea was considered in an American proposal for conversion of *Commencement Bay* class escort carriers into tenders for the Martin P6M jet-powered flying boat.

The internal arrangements of Rota's creation have a Heath Robinson touch. Rota's observations of foreign aviation vessels apparently brought home to him that most vexing problem, the discharge of the boilers' hot gases; conventional funnels interfere with flight operations, while long horizontal ducts can overheat the ship's interior. His solution to this dilemma was a combination of both systems. Three retractable centreline funnels would be used during normal steaming; for flight operations they would be lowered flush with the flight deck and gases vented laterally, after dampening, through a downward-curving funnel extending along the starboard side. Forward of the funnels was a retractable navigation and ship-handling station; there were two masts, also retractable.

The machinery arrangements of this design can only be described as impractical. The combination of centreline and horizontal funnels must have added considerable weight to the design, complicated internal spaces and wasted a tremendous amount of space that could otherwise have been devoted to a larger hangar. As it stands, the area available for aircraft stowage is restricted to that portion of the superstructure abaft the retractable funnels. The only lift is at the after end of the flight deck.

What role this vessel was supposed to play in the Mediterranean remains unexplained. Perhaps it was simply intended to act as a scout for the fleet, using its aircraft to extend its range of observation, or perhaps the French North African convoys and other commerce were to be its prey. One thing is certain: despite its cruiser characteristics, its tonnage would have made it an aircraft carrier under the terms of the Washington Conference.

The design was considered at an 11 August 1925 meeting of the Committee of Admirals; Benito Mussolini himself was present, in his capacity as interim navy minister. The design was 'not considered suitable by its contruction as a cruiser of the classic type and not a good substitute for a true aircraft carrier'. It was also decided at this meeting that aircraft carriers were 'useful but not necessary for the Italian Navy'. This judgement cast a pall over all interwar Italian carrier schemes; none ever went further than the draughting board, for Mussolini, strongly under the spell of air power prophet Giulio Douhet and backed by

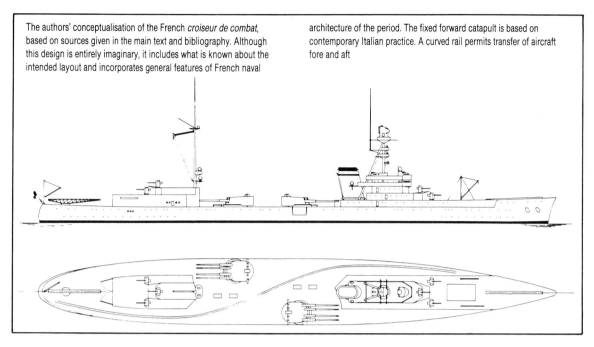

The authors' conceptualisation of the French *croiseur de combat*, based on sources given in the main text and bibliography. Although this design is entirely imaginary, it includes what is known about the intended layout and incorporates general features of French naval architecture of the period. The fixed forward catapult is based on contemporary Italian practice. A curved rail permits transfer of aircraft fore and aft

Panzerschiff Deutschland in 1939, in her original configuration and before being renamed *Lutzow*. She and her sisters were responsible for ending French interest in the *croiseur de combat* concept (*Naval Imaging Command*)

the hierarchy of the independent air force *Il Duce* himself had created, resolutely blocked construction of carriers until it was far too late to do the *Regia Marina* any good.

★　★　★

In 1922, following the Washington Conference, the French Navy drew up a plan for aviation that included the conversion of the battleship *Normandie*, renamed *Béarn*, into an aircraft carrier and recommended construction of two 30,000 ton *croiseurs porte-avion*. In the somewhat fluid terminology of the day, this may simply have referred to aircraft carriers of cruiser speed, as opposed to slow carriers. However, if the displacement given was the intended standard displacement, these ships would have fallen out-

side the treaty-defined carrier tonnage limits. The only tonnage available would have been from the capital ship category. Under the terms of the treaty France was permitted to build three new capital ships during the battleship building holiday, to be laid down in 1927, 1929 and 1931; moreover, France specifically reserved the right to use her replacement tonnage as she saw fit, as long as the resulting vessels conformed to the treaty's qualitative limits, implying that she intended to use the tonnage for vessels other than 35,000 ton battleships. It is therefore possible that the *croiseur porte-avion* was to be some form of combination battlecruiser-carrier. Unfortunately, no details of these vessels are available, and one is left only with their tantalysing designation.

It is, however, tempting to trace some evolutionary link to another French warship project that apparently combined heavy guns and aircraft. The genesis of this project, and its subsequent development, is uncertain; what is known is that

French heavy cruiser *Duquesne*. She and her sister, *Tourville*, were the subject of studies for never-undertaken conversion into semi-hybrid vessels (*Naval Imaging Command*)

in 1925 there was considerable discussion in French naval circles of a *croiseur de combat*. This was, in effect, a battlecruiser, capable of overwhelming any 8in gun cruiser and able to show a clean pair of heels to anything larger. The resulting design was by all descriptions as *outré* as the Rota project.

This sort of 'cruiser-killer' was an idea that received a great deal of attention between the wars, but most naval powers considered their capital ship tonnage too scarce to expend on such vessels. The French Navy, however, had to consider two completely different types of war: in the Atlantic, against Britain (still regarded with deep suspicion by the French Navy), whom it could not hope to match in numbers of ships, and in the Mediterranean, against Italy, whose antiquated battle fleet was on a par with its own. In this situation, the *croiseur de combat* could act as commerce raider in an Atlantic war while filling the role of capital ship in the Mediterranean.

Eventually, the *Conseil Supérieur de la Marine*, the body charged with formulating warship characteristics and policy, ordered the *Service Technique Constructions* to design such a vessel. Although the particulars of the design have been lost, the general outline of the ship has survived. Displacing 17,500 tons (allowing two such ships in place of a single 35,000 ton treaty battleship), it would have a maximum speed of 34 to 36 knots, making it the fastest capital ship in the world. Propulsion would perhaps have been a combination of steam turbine and diesels, for a long cruising range. Armour would be sufficient to withstand 8in gunfire, and armament would be eight 12in guns in two quadruple turrets with a secondary battery of dual-purpose 5.1in guns.

The design's outstanding feature was the placement of the 12in turrets *en échelon* amidships to allow catapults (and presumably hangars) at bow and stern. As many as eight aircraft may have been considered. Echeloned turrets were an innovation of the great Italian naval architect Benedetto Brin in his battleships *Lepanto* and *Italia* of the 1880s. The arrangement had enjoyed a brief vogue, being duplicated in various Italian, British, American and Brazilian vessels. More recently, it had been used in the midship turret arrangements of several dreadnoughts. In theory, echelon placement permitted full broadside fire on both beams, but in practice this was scarcely possible because of the danger of damage from blast; this same consideration also severely limited fore and aft fire. However, this danger was minimal if the echelon-turret ship could outrange and outspeed, and thus outmanoeuvre, an opponent. This was exactly what the *croiseur de combat* was designed to do *vis-à-vis* an 8in-gunned cruiser. To give it even greater advantage over its prey, its 12in guns were to be a new and powerful model, firing a 970lb shell to an extreme range of 48,000 yards.

Discussion of a vessel with these traits in French naval periodicals alarmed British naval analysts Hector C Bywater and Maurice Prendergast, leading them to speculate on the potential of such a ship in a joint article in the November 1925 *US Naval Institute Proceedings*. They first criticised the design because of the turret arrangement, pointing out that while it permits the concentration of heavy armour in a small central citadel, it leaves much of the rest of the vessel unprotected, restricts arcs of fire, and complicates machinery and magazine layout. Then they indulged their imaginations in a frightening scenario in which a *croiseur de combat*, fictively dubbed *Indomptable*, is loosed on the sea lanes at the start of a war with Britain. In an eight-week rampage in the South Atlantic and West Indies, she sinks four cruisers and a score of merchantmen, easily escapes in a brush with the battlecruiser *Renown*, and totally disrupts British oceanic commerce.

Bywater and Prendergast assign no role to the *croiseur de combat*'s aircraft, although they note that the echelon arrangement of the main battery would allow some form of flight deck forward and/or aft. Logic suggests that aircraft would prove valuable in scouting out merchant prey and avoiding concentrations of enemy warships. Given the great range of the 12in guns, aircraft could also

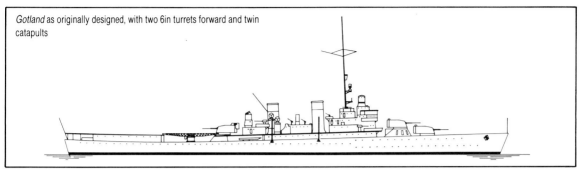

Gotland as originally designed, with two 6in turrets forward and twin catapults

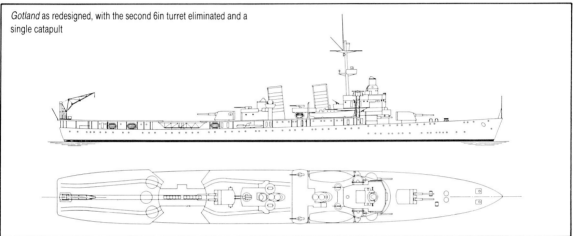

Gotland as redesigned, with the second 6in turret eliminated and a single catapult

perform usefully as spotters during an engagement.

The fictional fear raised by this article became real a few years later with the arrival of the German *Panzerschiffe*, which, like the *croiseur de combat*, were thought capable of outfighting anything they could not outrun. In fact, in the first months of the Second World War, *Graf Spee* haunted the sea lanes almost as effectively as the fictional *Indomptable*.

' Ironically, it was the advent of the *Panzerschiffe* that led to the abandonment of the *croiseur de combat*; to counter this threat to its own commerce, the French Navy began to investigate larger, more heavily armed and armoured schemes, leading eventually to *Dunkerque* and *Strasbourg*.

One other French proposal for a hybrid-like vessel was broached before the Second World War: a study during 1935–36 of converting the first two French treaty cruisers, *Tourville* and *Duquesne*, into carriers. These, it was felt, could be spared from the cruiser ranks with little loss; very much 'political' ships, hastily built in reply to the Italian *Trento* and *Trieste* before experience had been gained in what could be done within the 10,000 ton limit, they were lightly armoured and were soon outclassed by subsequent treaty cruisers.

Four alternative conversion schemes were drawn up: two of them retained one 8in turret forward, a third kept one turret aft, and a fourth eliminated the turrets altogether. Flight decks in all the versions retaining an 8in turret would have measured 456ft by 72ft 2in, but hangar dimensions varied. AA armament in all three schemes would have been twelve 3.9in (12 × 1) and four 37mm, aircraft capacity would have been twelve to fourteen machines, and the remodelling would have increased the displacement to 12,000 tons standard. These conversions would have produced vessels more readily described as heavily armed carriers than hybrids. The flight decks, 100ft longer than those on the roughly contemporary American flying-deck cruiser designs (see Chapter 9), would have been adequate for the vintage and outmoded aircraft then equipping the French Navy. Nothing came of the proposal, however; it was revived in 1944–45, again with no action taken.

★   ★   ★

The third navy to consider a hybrid vessel was that of Sweden, and the result was the only such ship to be constructed by a European nation between the wars.

The genesis of *Gotland*, as the vessel was

Gotland as completed. A Hawker Osprey is on the catapult with another under the aft crane. Guns of the aft turret are at extreme elevation, showing their capability for AA fire (*Royal Swedish Navy, courtesy of Stellan Bojerud*)

eventually named, can be traced to 1925, when the Ministry of Defence decided upon replacing two old ships, the cruiser *Fylgia* and the minelayer *Klas Fleming*. A committee was appointed to study the matter of replacement and future naval needs in general; one of its recommendations, given in December 1926, was for a small (4500 ton) seaplane carrier with a capacity of twelve aircraft. The Naval Construction Board, however, was not pleased with the idea, and altered the concept to one of a vessel combining cruiser, seaplane carrier and minelayer functions.

Plans were accordingly drawn up for a 5000 ton

ship armed with six 6in guns in three twin turrets, a speed of 28 knots, equipped with two catapults and carrying eight aircraft. The design was finalised in January 1927 and on 13 May the *Riksdag* (parliament) authorised 16.5 million kroner in construction funds.

Unfortunately, this was not enough. When tenders were invited in March 1928 it was found that no Swedish shipbuilding firm would undertake construction under such a tight budget. So the Naval Construction Board designers marched back to the draughting table to scale the ship down. A major change was a shorter hull, reducing displacement and forcing elimination of the superimposed turret forward. Its guns were instead mounted in casemates abreast the superstructure, the last time such mountings were employed on a major naval vessel. The redesign also eliminated one of the catapults, partly for economic reasons, partly because it was feared

Three of *Gotland*'s Ospreys ranged alongside her centreline Heinkel catapult obtained after negotiations for an American catapult failed (*Royal Swedish Navy, courtesy of Stellan Bojerud*)

that outboard placement might make them difficult or impossible to use in moderate seas. A single centreline catapult was substituted; for some years afterward, however, foreign naval reference works persisted in showing the ship with the two catapults of the original design.

A construction contract was awarded on 7 June 1930 to two well-known Göteborg shipbuilding firms, Götaverken as the main builder and Lindholm Mekaniska Verkstad och Varf as sub-contractor for hull and machinery. *Gotland*, officially rated as a *flygplankryssare*, was launched on 14 September 1933 and commissioned the following December, eight years after presentation of the original plan.

As completed, her particulars were

Displacement:	4750t standard, 5500t full load
Dimensions:	437ft 6in oa × 50ft 7in × 16ft 6in (mean), 18ft (max)
Machinery:	2 sets geared turbines, 4 boilers, 2 shafts, 33,000shp = 27.5kts (27.53kts at 32,768shp on trials). Oil 760t normal, 880t max, 4000nm at 12kts
Armour:	1.125-2in deck and turrets, 2in conning tower, 1.125-2in bulkheads, uptakes and hoists
Armament:	six 6in (2 × 2, 2 × 1), four 3in/60 AA (1 × 2, 2 × 1), four 25mm MG; six 21in TT (2 × 3), 80-100 mines
Aircraft:	1 catapult, 11 aircraft max
Complement:	449

Gotland's equipment had a distinctly international flavour; there was even a brief possibility that her catapult might have been American. Acting on instructions from his government, the Swedish naval attaché in Washington, Commander Erik D Torén, on 16 December 1929 addressed a request to Captain A V Johnson, Director of Naval Intelligence, for information about catapults and where they might be purchased in the United States. Catapults were needed for the cruiser of 'about 5000 tons' soon to be laid down.

The request was passed on to Rear Admiral William A Moffett, chief of the Bureau of Aeronautics, who pointed out that the only American manufacturer of catapults was the US government. However, Moffett was quite amenable to selling surplus Type A Mark I compressed air catapults that had been removed from *Omaha* class cruisers. He put the purchase price of such a catapult at $20,000, including cost of overhaul, and forwarded the recommendation to the General Board. Its members did not see things in quite the same way and instructed Johnson to reject the request, which he did in a 20 January 1930 letter to Torén. Johnson informed the Swedish attaché that 'the catapults at present in

use in the United States Navy are of Government design and manufacture, and it is not considered advisable to make them available to foreign governments. There are no commercial firms in the United States engaged in the manufacture of catapults'.

Thus balked, *Gotland*'s builders turned to Germany's Ernst Heinkel Flugzeugewerke GmbH, which had been a pioneer in catapult development. Heinkel had sold some catapults abroad in addition to starting to equip the German Navy, and was glad to have the Swedish order, which was contracted on 21 April 1933. As installed on *Gotland*, the catapult was a compressed air expanding type, 49ft 9in long when stowed and extending to 65ft 6in for launching.

Gotland's fire-control equipment was also of German manufacture, while all the guns were made by Bofors. The turreted 6in guns could elevate to 60 degrees for AA use; the casemated guns abreast the bridge were, of course, far more constricted in both arc of train and elevation.

From her bow to a little bit aft of amidships, *Gotland* had the appearance of a normal, albeit somewhat stout, cruiser. Aft of the second 6in turret she became an aviation vessel, with a centreline catapult immediately forward of a long seaplane-carrying and handling deck. There was a heavy-duty crane right aft. Eight aircraft could be accommodated on the deck, with stowage space for three more below. Aircraft were brought to the catapult on three fore-and-aft rails, each seaplane mounted on an individual electrically powered trolley; launchings could be accomplished at two-minute intervals. For seaplane recovery in less than calm seas, *Gotland* was equipped with a *släpsegel* (drag sail), the Swedish version of a Hein mat. It was trailed from the stern and aircraft were disengaged from it by the stern crane.

Gotland never carried the number of aircraft she was fitted to accommodate because of budgetary restrictions, and those she did employ were not embarked until several months after her commissioning. They were British Hawker Ospreys, two-place biplane reconaissance-fighters, which saw service in the Royal Navy both as capital ship and cruiser floatplanes and, with wheel undercarriages, aboard carriers. The Osprey was a 'navalised' version of the versatile Hart, which the Swedes had used in developing their dive bombing techniques. Four Ospreys were ordered from Hawker Aircraft Ltd in 1933, with two more subsequently ordered. The first four arrived on

2 September 1934 and the others on 17 July 1936. Although constructed in Britain, the Swedish machines were given 600hp British Nohab Mercury II radials built in Sweden under licence in place of the usual in-line Rolls-Royce engines. *Gotland*'s Ospreys were given the Swedish type designation S.9 and bore serial numbers 401 to 406.

Prior to the outbreak of the Second World War, *Gotland* made a number of foreign cruises; after the war began she and her aircraft were employed in neutrality patrol in the Baltic, the Skaggerak and the Kattegat, also serving as a training ship. By this time her value as an aviation vessel was at an end, primarily because a narrow sea such as the Baltic could now be completely dominated by land-based aircraft greatly superior in performance and range to her floatplanes. Her Ospreys, one of which was lost with its crew in an operational accident in January 1940, were hopelessly outmoded, their replacement impossible, and their store of spare parts diminishing.

Nevertheless, *Gotland* did perform one vital service: on 20 May 1941, while on passage to Gothenburg on Sweden's west coast, she sighted *Bismarck* and *Prinz Eugen*. This information was passed by friendly Swedish officers to the British naval attaché and was the first report the Admiralty received indicating that the German ships were on their way to the Atlantic.

Beginning in late 1943, *Gotland* was transformed from aircraft vessel to AA vessel. The catapult, crane and all other aviation equipment were removed; what had been the aircraft deck was extended over the former catapult well and eight 40mm/60 AA guns were placed on it in four twin mounts, supplemented by two 25mm/70 AA machine guns. The added armament increased her complement to 543 by the time the vessel re-entered service in April 1944. Her Ospreys were transferred to harbour bases, where the last of them served until 2 December 1947.

Gotland resumed her foreign cruising after the war, until 1954, when she again underwent reconstruction. Her new guise was as a training and fighter-direction vessel, to which end her 6in casemate guns were removed, along with all the AA guns except two 25mm, and she was rearmed with a homogeneous suite of thirteen 40mm/40 AA guns in four twin and five single mounts. Searchlights were removed in favour of an illuminating-rocket launcher and radar fire-control was installed. Complement was reduced to 401. She resumed service in 1955.

Except for one cruise along the coast of west Africa in 1956, *Gotland* remained in home waters after her refit. Her days were numbered; in spite of a further refit that included improved fire-control and search radars, plus sonar, all of British manufacture, she was stricken on 1 July 1960, sold on 1 April 1962 and broken up at Ystad in 1963.

For many years, *Jane's Fighting Ships* persisted in describing *Gotland* as a 'well-conceived and exceedingly useful type of warship'. This may have been true in 1926, when the original design was undertaken, but her usefulness as an aviation vessel was seriously eroded during the eight years it took to get her into the water, and continued even more rapidly from then to the outbreak of the Second World War. By 1939 technological advances in aviation had made the shipboard floatplane superfluous for naval war in such a narrow sea as the Baltic; in fact, the Ospreys were practically obsolete the day they were delivered.

Gotland also suffered from the attempt to achieve three ships in one hull. The results of this parsimony are plain: scaling down the original design to meet an inflexible financial limit led to a less efficient gunnery arrangement, and continued stringency denied the vessel her full complement of aircraft. However, even had *Gotland* been built to the original design and given a full aerial contingent, her loss of value as an aviation vessel was inevitable. This points to a problem that has, until fairly recently, plagued hybrid schemes, but which many designers nevertheless failed to recognise: because aircraft had a much shorter technological life than warships, a hybrid could lose much of its effectiveness long before the ship itself was ready for the scrapper's torch.

CARRIERS, CRUISERS AND TREATIES

The US Navy's interest in hybrid vessels in the 1920s and '30s is a fabric woven of many separate threads; to understand the whole, it is necessary to follow both the individual strands and the complex patterns of their intertwining.

The first thread is that most basic of military questions, who is the enemy? In the early part of the century, Germany had played this role, but she had been eliminated as a naval power by the provisions of the Treaty of Versailles. There was some concern about Britain — called 'Red' in the US Navy's colour scheme of international conflict — based on Mahan's theories about the rise and fall of mercantile empires. Japan, however, was seen as the real threat.

Even before the end of the First World War, American naval planners regarded Japan with suspicion. They distrusted her ambitions on the Asian mainland, clearly demonstrated by the '21 Demands' presented to China in 1915 and the occupation of Siberia during the Russian civil war; they were anxious about the defence of the Philippines, especially as there was no other substantial naval power in the western Pacific to distract Japanese ambitions. Most of all, the American planners were aware of the vast reach of ocean between the United States and its territories on the periphery of Asia.

This stretch of ocean forms a second thread which will run through this story. The imposing vastness of the Pacific assumed an even more forbidding aspect after the Treaty of Versailles 'mandated' the former German Caroline and Marshall Islands to Japan. The route a US fleet would have to take to the Philippines was flanked for 2000 miles or more by the Mandates, and the American planners assumed that these isles and atolls would be swarming with Japanese aircraft, submarines and light surface forces in any future conflict.

The response of the US Navy's planners to this strategic problem was the Orange Plan, orange being the colour-code for Japan. The earliest version of this plan was devised in 1907; although it was often revised and modified during the next three decades, the basic outline remained unchanged through all its incarnations. While defensive forces held the ring in the Philippines, the US main fleet would sally forth 'to establish, at the earliest practicable date, United States naval power in the Western Pacific in strength superior to that of Orange and to operate offensively in that area'. Although later versions of the plan recognised that the Japanese would probably overrun the Philippines before the fleet could arrive, this only changed the navy's trans-Pacific mission from relief expedition to reconquering force. The Orange Plan was studied almost to the point of obsession throughout the interwar period.

The next thread was the 'treaty system', the series of naval disarmament treaties whose provisions determined to a large extent the shape of the world's navies between the wars. The first and most successful of these treaties grew out of the Washington Conference. The Four Power Pact ended the American nightmare of a war against both Britain and Japan by terminating the Anglo-Japanese Alliance, but the same pact also forbade any increase in fortifications west of Hawaii, thereby denying the US Navy a secure forward base in a war with Japan. This strategic puzzle was complicated by the Five Power Treaty, whose famous '5:5:3' ratio limited the size of the US battle fleet in comparison to that of Japan. Although the treaty ratio limited the tonnage of the Imperial Japanese Navy's (IJN) battle fleet to only 60 per cent of the American, US planners believed that a fleet fighting far from its bases — as the US Navy would in any war with Japan — needed at least a two-to-one superiority to ensure victory.

The penultimate thread in this strategic tapestry was the rapid growth of naval aviation between the wars. Many naval officers saw in aviation the solution to many of their other problems. Aircraft could scout for the fleet, protect it from Japanese aircraft and light forces based in the Mandates, and provide a welcome tactical edge by spotting the fleet's gunfire when it finally confronted the IJN somewhere in the western Pacific. Even before the Washington Treaty, consideration had been given to the conversion of one of the incomplete *Lexington* class battlecruisers into an aircraft carrier. These schemes played a large part in the American insistence on a large maximum size for carriers during the Washington Conference. The demand for large carriers backfired, however, as the treaty allotted the United States a maximum of only 135,000 tons in that category, almost half of which would be absorbed by the huge *Lexingtons*. To fight the Orange war, the navy wanted more flight decks, but the remaining tonnage would allow only a limited number of new carriers.

The final thread was a purse-string. The parsimony and pacifism of the successive Harding, Coolidge and Hoover presidential administrations and their Congresses continually delayed or postponed new construction, keeping the navy well short of its treaty-mandated strength. Desperate for the carriers it would need in an Orange war, the navy got only the *Lexingtons*, which ended up costing far more than originally planned; all other attempts to add to naval air strength proved fruitless. The cruiser situation was just as bad; the navy's own prewar fixation on capital ships, the First World War's imperative demand for destroyers and anti-submarine craft, and finally the Washington Treaty's cancellation of the postwar building programme, successively prevented the navy from acquiring modern cruisers. There were a number of armoured and protected cruisers in commission, but some of these dated back to the Spanish-American War. The only modern vessels were the ten ships of the *Omaha* class, the first and only light cruisers to join the fleet since the three *Chesters* of 1907; they were absurdly few in number for the world's second-largest battle fleet.

All these threads would weave in and out of the US Navy's plans between the wars, and all played a part in the navy's frequent search for a hybrid solution to the strategic conundrums it faced.

Although its strategic situation forced the US Navy to an early appreciation of the value of aviation, this appreciation did not automatically settle questions about the optimum size, armament, speed and protection of aircraft carriers. At one end of the scale, it was suggested in 1920 that one of the incomplete *Omahas* be converted into a flight-deck carrier, but it was eventually decided that it would not be wise to lose a badly needed cruiser for the sake of a small and probably inadequate carrier. At the other end of the scale were the *Lexingtons*; in early 1922, as designs for their conversion got under way, the US Navy's General Board — a high-level policy-making board composed of senior admirals, which also played a prominent role in the development of ship characteristics — fought a 'battle of the guns' with the Bureau of Naval Aeronautics. The bureau,

with efficiency of aircraft operations and accommodation uppermost in its collective mind, believed that a 6in calibre would be sufficient for surface action. The board was adamant for 8-inchers. Both bodies were in agreement that a strong AA armament also was imperative, although at one point the bureau came up with the radical suggestion that *all* guns be eliminated and the ship rely solely on its aircraft for defence, an idea from which the board recoiled more or less in horror. Not only did the board want 8in guns, it wanted to enhance the carriers' capability for surface combat still further by arming them with torpedoes. Four 21in tubes were included in the original preliminary design; they were, however, eventually eliminated.

The importance accorded to the big-gun armament of the *Lexingtons* is indicated by the layout finally chosen for it: four twin turrets superimposed fore and aft of the starboard island. This classic disposition permitted full broadsides on either beam and was approved in the full knowledge that portside fire would not only wreck any parked aircraft, but almost inevitably damage the flight deck by blast, perhaps to the extent that aerial operations would then become impossible. This indicated the continuing belief that aircraft would have been expended by the time the guns were needed.

The *Lexingtons* were not the only US carrier design to feature 8in guns. A parallel series of designs was sketched in 1922-23 to explore the characteristics of a carrier built from the keel. A wide range of carrier sizes was explored, from 11,500 to 27,000 tons standard. Even the smallest ship had six 8in guns, while the larger design showed eight or nine. The largest design, Scheme 282 of January 1923, had triple 8in turrets fore and aft of the island, with another triple turret mounted forward of the flight deck, which consequently ended well short of the bow.

With such batteries, it is scarcely surprising that carriers such as *Lexington* and *Saratoga* were for a short time regarded nearly as much cruisers as carriers. In 1928, the year after the big carriers commissioned, Admiral William V Pratt, a future Chief of Naval Operations (CNO) and at the time Commander Battleship Divisions, Battle Fleet, expressed the view that they were more useful as 'battle cruisers' than as carriers; Pratt's attitude at this time is worth noting, as he became a central figure in later US proposals for hybrid cruisers.

The only carriers to match the *Lexingtons* in

big-gun armament were the Japanese *Kaga* and *Akagi*, completed contemporarily with the US ships in 1927–28 and under the same Washington Treaty provision. Plans originally called for the two big carriers to be converted from battle-cruisers, but one of the intended hulls, *Amagi*, was so badly damaged by the great earthquake of 1923 that the incomplete battleship *Kaga* was substituted. As a result, although the two resembled each other in appearance and were teamed together for most of their lives, they were never true sisters.

One point of similarity, however, was their identical main battery of ten 8in guns — actually 7.9in, a true 8in calibre not being introduced into the Japanese Navy until a few years later. Four guns were mounted in two twin turrets forward, one on each beam on a level between the flight deck and what was to have been a lower take-off deck (although it was never used as such); the other six were in single casemates low on the hull aft, three to a side. While this arrangement avoided blast damage to the flight deck, it restricted broadside fire to five guns.

It was perhaps inevitable that the existence of such heavily armed carriers would lead to speculation that the rival ships might engage each other. In 1927, before any of the carrier conversions had been completed, one Captain Walter S Anderson USN, deeply disturbed by this prospect, wrote an intriguing article for the *US Naval Institute Proceedings*. He first pointed out that the complex language of the Washington Treaty allowed carriers built under the 27,000 ton limitation to mount more 8in guns than the larger ships permitted under Article IX. This was especially worrying

Saratoga, here seen steaming at high speed, represented an extreme of the heavily armed carrier, a concept that blurred the dividing line between carrier and cruiser (*R D Layman collection*)

Saratoga firing her aft 8in guns to starboard during a fleet exercise, a graphic illustration of the danger her portside fire could represent to flight deck and aircraft on it (*R D Layman collection*)

to him because of the two-gun superiority of the approximately 27,000 ton Japanese carriers over the 33,000 ton *Lexingtons*. Anderson pointed out that if one of the American carriers by damage or accident lost its speed superiority, 'Then the *Lexington* could be overhauled by an *Akagi*' and 'could then be sunk by the smaller but better armed [vessel]'.

Improbable as such an encounter was, it summons up a fascinating picture — truly eggshells pounding each other with hammers, as Winston Churchill once characterised a battleship engagement. However, the good captain need not have fretted; although unknown when he wrote his article, the *Akagi*'s two-gun superiority was squandered in an inefficient (from a gunnery point of view) arrangement. The *Lexington* class in fact had a three-gun edge in broadside fire.

The heavy gun batteries of these and other early carrier designs stemmed not from any deliberate attempt to create hybrid warships, but, like those of *Furious* and *Vindictive*, were the results of simple inexperience over just what kind of armament an aircraft carrier needed. The US Navy sorted out these questions during the late 1920s and early '30s in the 'Fleet Problems', extensive wargames involving virtually the entire navy. The value of carriers was repeatedly demonstrated during these exercises, which played a central role in pioneering the carrier task force concept. That the *Lexingtons* were believed to be well enough armed to outfight any vessels they could not outrun was perhaps one reason, although certainly not the major one, behind the decision to detach them from the fleet for independent sorties during these exercises. *Saratoga* did in fact defend herself successfully in the first of these experiments, her famous mock attack on the Panama Canal during Fleet Problem IX in January 1929. Although she managed to 'sink' an 'enemy' destroyer, the incident was a lesson in how much self-inflicted damage the main battery could cause, for the blast wrecked a torpedo plane parked 68ft from the forward turret. These exercises also demonstrated how vulnerable the big carriers were to gunfire: they kept blundering into battleships of the opposing sides with resultant 'loss' or 'damage'.

This vulnerability was one of the reasons for the trend away from large-calibre carrier armament during the 1930s, for it soon became clear that carriers should avoid encounters with heavy surface units. Carriers, inevitably large and thinly protected, simply could not stand up to battleships — or even cruisers — no matter how much artillery they carried. Another reason was the increasing realisation that the real threat to carriers would probably come from the air. This lesson might have been extrapolated from the experience of the First World War, in which aviation vessels were attacked by aircraft fairly frequently but never tangled with warships; the only aviation ship lost to enemy action, *Ben-my-Chree*, was sunk by shore-based artillery. Dual-purpose guns, able to defend against both the aerial threat and smaller warships, were better suited to a carrier's needs. However, interest in heavily armed carriers continued to surface from

time to time; both Japan and the United States were to consider construction of such ships in the early 1930s, and one, Germany's *Graf Zeppelin*, came close to completion.

The offensive value shown by the carriers during the US exercises was enhanced by the development of dive bombing. The exact origins of this form of aerial attack are obscure; suffice to say that the US Navy began formal development of the technique in 1926 and found that it was at least 50 per cent more accurate than horizontal bombing against floating targets. Dive bombing was all the more effective because, with no satisfactory early warning systems, there was no way of knowing from what direction or altitude the attackers would come; even fighters already aloft could not intercept the attackers before they struck.

A technological advance that improved the performance and dependability of the dive bomber and other US naval aircraft was the radial engine, developed during the 1920s by private industry with support and encouragement from the navy. This powerplant features cylinders arranged circularly rather than in line and is cooled by propeller-generated air flow instead of liquids. By eliminating the in-line engine's complicated cooling system, the radial could produce the same horsepower at a great saving in weight and size; its chief drawback was increased drag. By the mid-1930s radial engines of the Pratt & Whitney Wasp series and the Curtiss Cyclone family powered all US naval aircraft. The Japanese Navy also adopted the type for the majority of its aircraft.

As the US Navy's appreciation of aviation deepened in the 1920s, some officers became so convinced of its value that they wanted to complete one of the 8in-gun cruisers authorised in 1924 as a carrier. Agitation for carriers was so strong that the Secretary of the Navy proposed redesigning the 10,000 ton cruisers as small carriers. The General Board adamantly opposed any such ideas, for the same reason it had rejected an *Omaha* conversion: cruisers were still in too short supply. Of the eight authorised, only two had been laid down, *Pensacola* and *Salt Lake City*. A presidential order delayed the start of construction of the others until 1927.

It was during the extended design period of these cruisers that two schemes for a combination

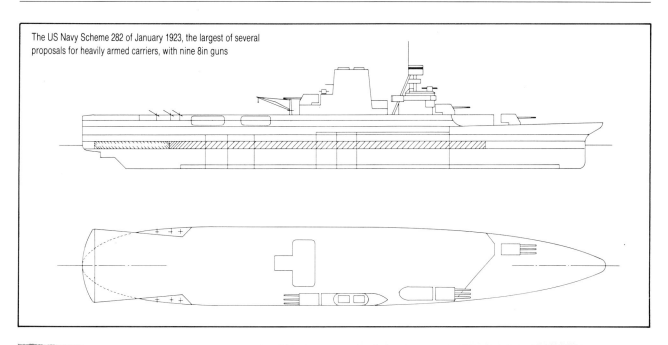

The US Navy Scheme 282 of January 1923, the largest of several proposals for heavily armed carriers, with nine 8in guns

US Navy aviators of the 1930s pinned much of their faith in the flying-deck cruiser on the offensive power of the dive bomber. Here is an early, somewhat improvised, example of the type, a prototype or early production Boeing F4B-1, first of a series of fighters adapted for dive bombing and so widely used in that role that some carrier squadrons had their designations changed from VF (fighting) to VB (bombing). The F4B series was powered by radial engines, a type that greatly enhanced performance and shipboard serviceability of US naval aircraft (*Boeing Airplane Company, courtesy of William T Larkins*)

cruiser-carrier were advanced; these were apparently the first US hybrid cruiser proposals. Unlike the earlier carrier designs, they were conscious attempts to enhance the capabilities of an existing type of ship by the addition of aviation facilities. They called for a 250ft landing deck aft and a 164ft take-off deck forward, separated by a lift and funnels. One design featured three 8in turrets, fore, aft and under the flight deck; the other had only two 8in turrets, but one of them was a quadruple. A similar design was proposed in 1925 by James L Bates, a civilian constructor in the Bureau of Construction and Repair. Bates' design had three twin 8in turrets and a capacity of fifteen to twenty aircraft. As it had with the cruiser-to-carrier conversion scheme, the General Board took a dim view of such vessels, informing the Secretary of the Navy in a 16 January 1926 memo that 'the Bureau of Construction and Repair considers it wholly impracticable to combine the qualities of the two types [ie, cruisers and carriers] in a 10,000-ton ship. This in itself eliminates it from consideration on any other ground'. As we shall see, the Bureau of Construction and Repair would soon change its views.

The General Board's opposition to cruiser conversions or hybridisations was not based on some deep-seated antipathy to aviation; in late 1927, it submitted to Congress a request that included, in addition to twenty-five cruisers above and beyond those existing, under construction or authorised, five 13,800 ton carriers, which would exhaust the tonnage allowed by the Washington Treaty. The board wanted both carriers *and* cruisers; they believed, however, that cruiser-sized carriers would be too small to be effective.

The General Board's request met with an immediate legislative stone wall. By 6 March 1928, when an appropriations bill was reported out from the Committee on Naval Affairs of the House of Representatives — the lower chamber of Congress where all monetary measures must originate — the programme had been reduced to fifteen cruisers and one carrier. The ensuing debate was enlivened by one of the oddest suggestions for a hybrid warship yet broached.

This scheme was the brainchild of a member of the Naval Affairs panel, Representative James V McClintic, a Democrat from Oklahoma. McClintic disagreed so strongly with the trend in naval appropriations that he tacked a one-man minority report onto the full committee's recommendations. His report asserted that 'The foundation of the proposed naval legislation, calling for 15 cruisers, rests upon the assumption that England has far greater cruiser strength than the United States'.

McClintic set about refuting this 'assumption' under the peculiar belief that any warship between 1000 and 5000 tons displacement was a cruiser. *Ergo*, destroyers were cruisers, or 'cruisers, destroyer type' in McClintic's scheme of things; ergo, because the United States had more of this type than Britain it actually enjoyed a 99,924 ton advantage in this category; ergo, it was unnecessary to build more cruisers. McClintic therefore proposed to substitute fifteen large submarines and, in lieu of a carrier, to

authorize the expenditure of $1,000,000 on each of . . . 18 battleships for the purpose of providing an extra platform, constructed immediately above the turret guns, suitable for aircraft purposes, thereby making each of these ships its own aircraft carrier, having in mind that such an addition would not obstruct the use of the turret guns, and at the same time enable large bombing planes to be utilized in attacking an enemy for a distance of approximately 200 miles away.

He pushed his proposals to the fullest during debate on the naval measure, describing the platforms as designed to be 'hinged and raised and lowered like a drawbridge in case it is decided ever to use the big guns', an eventuality he clearly regarded as unlikely. He filled page upon page of the *Congressional Record* with statistic-laden arguments writing off the battleship as obsolete and extolling the submarine and the aeroplane as the truly important naval craft of the future.

The Oklahoman's views came under scathing and sarcastic attack on 15 March by the chairman of the Committee on Naval Affairs, Representative Frederick A Britten, an Illinois Republican. He ridiculed McClintic's report as 'so fantastic, so impossible, that Grimm's Fairy Tales never had anything so pleasant to read'. Britten, according to the *Congressional Record*, went on to say that

This minority report provides . . . for changing battleships . . . into aircraft carriers by putting a deck over the top of the turrets. The deck, according to the best expert figures, will be about 320 feet long, so that it will go over the bow . . . and over the guns. When the big guns are to shoot, the flying deck will be raised like a jackknife bridge; and as it is only a little more than half as high as the Washington Monument, it will not weigh over a thousand tons. . . . When you raise it up the captain on the bridge will not be able to see through it, and the men in the fire-control mast will not be able to see over it, so that in all probability the minority report will have to be modified so as to provide that this deck shall be made of glass. Wired glass so that it will not splinter when hit. When the wind hits this thing standing up in the air, of course, the battleship will overturn. But they will probably amend the minority report again and provide that when the ship overturns it will be a submarine.
(Laughter).

The next day, when the naval measure finally came up for a floor vote in the House, the undaunted McClintic offered an amendment that would have altered the bill entirely by substituting submarines for the cruisers and providing for installation of 'aircraft launching platforms' on eighteen battleships in graduated steps during the fiscal years 1929–34. The amendment was defeated by a vote of 129 noes to 22 ayes.

McClintic can be credited with recognising the rising power of the submarine and the aeroplane, and the diminishing power of the battleship, in naval warfare, but his bizarre notions of what constituted a cruiser and how capital ships could launch aircraft made his arguments ludicrous. He claimed that his aircraft platforms were deemed feasible by naval experts, but he would never identify these experts publicly, as he was pressed to do on 15 March by Representative Thomas S Butler, an Independent Republican from Pennsylvania. The defeat of his amendment the next day put a quietus on what was probably the first formal proposal for an American hybrid battleship; but this is not the last we shall hear of American hybrid capital ships or the gentleman from Oklahoma.

★   ★   ★

When the naval measure passed all legislative hurdles, including McClintic's alarums and diversions, in February 1929, it was with the proviso that the entire programme could be halted if further world naval disarmament was agreed upon. The US Navy could still hope to build the carriers and cruisers the Washington Treaty allowed it, even if the government was slow to finance them. Oddities like hybrid cruisers were all but forgotten; however, proposals continued to surface from time to time. For example, a December 1929 Bureau of Aeronautics scheme called for a relocation of the seaplane facilities on 8in cruisers to their sterns; by moving the after turret forward 38ft and extending the upper (forecastle) deck aft to the counter, a flush-decked ship with an enclosed hangar would be created. This hangar could accommodate eight seaplanes and

A Martin BM-1, the US Navy's first specialised dive bomber. Going into production in 1931, it was a type that would have been operated from the flying-deck cruiser. The one seen here has an auxiliary fuel tank under the fuselage in partial lieu of its 1000lb bomb load (*Glenn L Martin Company, courtesy of William T Larkins*)

Another early US Navy dive bomber that would have gone aboard the flying-deck cruiser: the Curtiss F8C-4, the famous original 'Helldiver'. This one, belonging to a *Saratoga* squadron, carries an auxiliary fuel tank in place of its 500lb bomb and its underwing bomb racks are empty (*National Archives, courtesy of William T Larkins*)

would be served by a lift right aft. The aircraft would be launched by a double-ended athwartships catapult. The idea was eventually given up due to its weight; it was revived, in somewhat different form, in the light cruisers of the *Brooklyn* class in the mid-1930s. Another proposal found its way to the desk of the Secretary of the Navy in a 6 January 1930 memo from Captain J K Taussig, Acting President of the Naval War College; Taussig was forwarding a bizarre suggestion by one Commander W A Glassford for double-ended

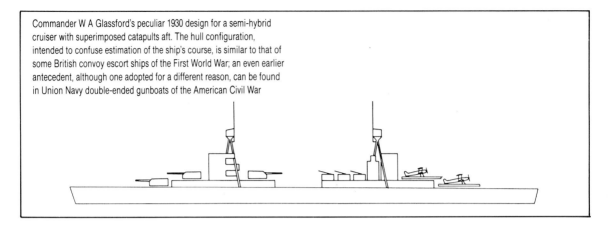

Commander W A Glassford's peculiar 1930 design for a semi-hybrid
cruiser with superimposed catapults aft. The hull configuration,
intended to confuse estimation of the ship's course, is similar to that of
some British convoy escort ships of the First World War; an even earlier
antecedent, although one adopted for a different reason, can be found
in Union Navy double-ended gunboats of the American Civil War

cruisers, the idea being that an opponent would have a hard time estimating the ship's course. Strange as it was, the scheme featured superimposed catapults aft, and Taussig noted that 'Should the arrangements aft for carrying aircraft permit of flying on, the value of the design would be enhanced'.

Such schemes received little attention, however. There was, after all, a carrier under construction, and cruisers to design. What changed this situation was the intersection of two of the threads that form the background pattern of this story: the 'treaty system', in the form of the London Naval Conference; and the growth of naval aviation, as personified by Rear Admiral William Adger Moffett.

Moffett, frequently called 'the father of American naval aviation' (although this title might be more aptly applied to Captain Washington I Chambers), was born four years after the end of the American Civil War, the son of a Confederate army hero. He first went to sea on the venerable eighteenth-century frigate *Constellation*, still in use as a cadet training ship in the 1880s, and was graduated from the Naval Academy in 1890. As an ensign in 1898 he served aboard the cruiser *Charleston*, taking part in the seizure of Guam and the capture of Manila during the Spanish-American War. As a commander in 1914 he skippered the cruiser *Chester* during the landing at Vera Cruz, winning the Medal of Honour for his accurate navigation and gunfire. From mid-1914 to late 1918 he was commandant of the Naval Training Station at Great Lakes, Illinois, presiding over the growth that made it the largest institution of its kind in the world. It was here that Moffett was first exposed to aviation, when a naval air training station was established in mid-1917.

In late 1918, promoted to captain, Moffett was given a choice post: commander of the brand-new battleship *Mississippi*. His interest in aviation grew when that vessel was fitted with turret-top launching platforms and he soon became a dedicated apostle of naval aviation, the cause to which he devoted the rest of his professional career.

In July 1921, upon creation of the Bureau of Naval Aeronautics, Moffett was appointed its chief, with promotion to rear admiral to give the new department some bureaucratic clout. No armchair aviation enthusiast, Moffett began his new job by taking the naval air observer's course at Pensacola, Florida, qualifying on 1 July 1922 — no mean feat for a man fifty-two years old (although other flag officers were later to emulate him). This was three years before the law stipulating that only naval aviators or observers could command aviation vessels and air stations. Altogether, Moffett went aloft 367 times during his career, logging 1273 hours of flight time.

When Moffett sailed for London on 9 January 1930 aboard the liner *George Washington*, the earlier schemes for hybrid cruisers may have been percolating somewhere in the back of his mind. Certainly he would soon bring the hybrid cruiser to the attention of the world, becoming its most articulate advocate. Moffett, more than any other individual, would be responsible for bringing it so near to realisation. And it was he who would bestow on it the name by which it was known in the US Navy — the 'flying-deck cruiser'.

Moffett introduced the flying-deck cruiser (only occasionally was it called the 'flight-deck cruiser') on the centre stage of international diplomacy, the London Naval Conference. Intended to reduce the navies of the world still further in the spirit of the 1928 Kellogg-Briand Pact, or 'Pact of Paris for the

Renunciation of War', it convened in London in January 1930, with Admiral William V Pratt, Commander-in-Chief, US Fleet, as senior naval adviser to the US civilian delegation and Moffett as adviser for aviation.

The London Naval Conference produced the 'International Treaty for the Limitation and Reduction of Naval Armament', signed on 22 April 1930, which had profound effects on the three major naval powers: Britain, the United States and Japan. It established national tonnage ratios for cruisers, destroyers and submarines, vessels for which the Washington Treaty had established qualitative limits only. Perhaps even more significant was its redefinition of the cruiser into two classes: 'heavy cruisers', carrying guns between 6.1in (155mm) and 8in calibre; and 'light cruisers', carrying guns of 6.1in or less. (One immediate consequence of this new division was the redesignation of all US 8in-gun cruisers afloat or building from CL to CA on 1 July 1931.) The Washington Treaty's 10,000 ton limit on individual cruiser size was retained.

An important American objective at the conference was to obtain more carrier tonnage, but this was not achieved; in fact, the US delegation was hard-pressed to retain the 135,000 tons allowed under the Washington Treaty. Ramsay MacDonald, the British Prime Minister and chairman of the conference, hoped to reduce the carrier allotment to 100,000 tons for Britain and the United States. This was unthinkable to the American naval advisers, who were only too aware of the inhospitable stretch of ocean between Hawaii and Manila.

With no hope for an increase in carrier tonnage, Moffett devised an alternative. In a memo of 31 January, he proposed that the delegation work for a provision allowing flight decks on all combatant vessels. Pratt needed little convincing, and the issue became a major concern of the conference. There were two naval constructors attached to the American delegation, Captain A H van Keuren of the Bureau of Construction and Repair, and his assistant, none other than James L Bates, who seems to have been present at several critical points in the history of the flying-deck cruiser. They soon set about sketching cruisers with flight decks to explore the feasibility of the idea, and eventually came up with a 31 knot ship armed with nine 6in guns in one triple turret forward and two aft, with a flight deck in between; the AA battery consisted of eight 5in guns.

Their efforts were not limited to 10,000 ton

cruisers; Admiral Pratt, in exploring British proposals for a reduction in the size of capital ships, also directed them to develop a flight-deck battle-cruiser; the result was a 30,000 ton ship capable of 33 knots, armed with nine 12in guns and protected against 12in gunfire.

The American delegates meanwhile strove to incorporate Moffett's scheme in the treaty. In the end, the American campaign succeeded only in part; Part I, Article 3, Section 2 of the final draught stated, 'The fitting of a landing-on or flying-off platform or deck on a capital ship, cruiser or destroyer, provided such vessel was not designed or adapted exclusively as an aircraft carrier, shall not cause any vessel so fitted to be charged against or classified in the category of aircraft carrier'. But the very next section forbade such a deck on any capital ship existing as of 1 April 1930. Because the treaty's first article extended the Washington Treaty's ban on capital ship construction for five years, the possibility of a hybrid battleship-carrier was ruled out for the immediate future.

Since destroyers were clearly too small for the fitting of an efficient flight deck, only the cruiser category was left as a candidate for hybridisation. However the Americans did not get their way in this category, either. After much bargaining, including the concession of submarine parity to Japan, the best they could obtain was Section 5 of Article 16, Part III, specifying that 'Not more than 25 per cent of the allowed total in the cruiser category may be fitted with a landing-on platform or deck for aircraft'.

Before proceeding with the story, it should be noted that the language of both of the flight-deck clauses was oddly ambiguous for a document draughted by supposed experts in diplomacy and naval affairs. A strict grammatical interpretation of the phrase 'landing-on or flying-off' deck could imply that a vessel could have one but not both; that is, a deck on which an aircraft could land but from which it could not take off, or vice versa. Under the same logic, the mention in Article 16 of only a 'landing-on platform or deck' could be inferred as permitting landing but barring take-off. The possibility that a ship with a combined landing and take-off deck would constitute a violation of the treaty's language would be raised several times over the next few years. On occasion it would be suggested that the use of catapults obviated the flying-off difficulty, since aircraft so launched did not, strictly speaking, 'fly off' a deck. In the event, the matter was never put to the test.

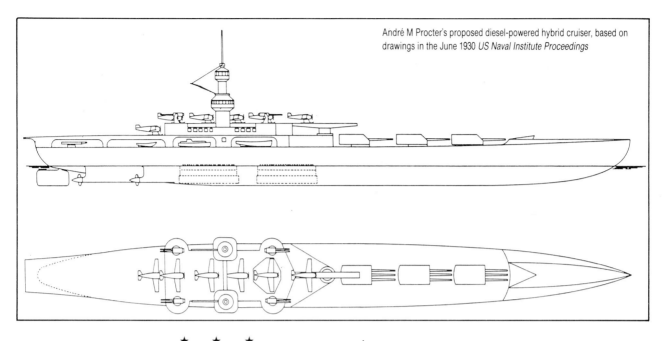

André M Procter's proposed diesel-powered hybrid cruiser, based on drawings in the June 1930 *US Naval Institute Proceedings*

★   ★   ★

Predictably, the US naval hierarchy was divided about the London Treaty, some officials opposing it because of its general limitations and the fact that it restricted US strength in 8in cruisers to eighteen vessels, other favouring the pact because it at least set tonnage targets for construction of the type of ship in which the US Navy was notably deficient.

Senate hearings on ratification of the treaty, and the desirability of building up to its limits, began in May. One of the main topics of debate was the relative merits of the 8in and 6in cruiser. Moffett was a proponent of the lighter weapon, holding that 'in single combat, one of the 6″ platform cruisers would defeat any 8″ cruiser since the 6″ gun can shoot twice as fast, and she can carry more ammunition'. This was the calibre he favoured for the flying-deck cruiser, and he seized the opportunity during early testimony before the Senate Committee on Naval Affairs to beat the drums for the type, declaring, 'I believe the placing of landing decks on 25% of the total cruiser tonnage, preferably first on the remaining 6″ gun cruisers, will make them at least equal, and in my opinion superior to the 8″ gun cruisers without landing decks'.

To objections that such a ship would be purely experimental, he responded, 'this vessel will not be as experimental as others believe. The *Lexington* and *Saratoga* are merely large flying-deck cruisers as they carry not only aircraft but eight 8″ guns. Their operation has been successful and they are of immense value to the Navy. . . We

know we can operate airplanes from cruisers that carry guns'. Moffett was willing to go even farther into the hybrid realm; asked if he would have preferred the treaty to allow flight decks on all cruisers, he responded, 'I would like to have seen it on all cruisers, and all battleships; that is, not the present ones, but future ones'.

★   ★   ★

By the time the special session of the Senate ratified the London naval treaty on 22 July by a vote of 58 to 9, the US Navy was already investigating the flying-deck cruiser. By this date, however, an unofficial scheme for a hybrid cruiser had already appeared in print.

It was put forward by Captain André Morton Procter USN (ret). Procter had had a distinguished naval career, serving in the Spanish-American War and eventually rising to the command of the battleship *Texas* after the First World War. An engineering officer, he had developed an obsessive fascination with the diesel engine and was absolutely convinced of its necessity for naval vessels. From 1925 on he contributed articles on the diesel to the *US Naval Institute Proceedings*, *Scientific American*, and any other journal that would print his opinions. The June 1930 issue of the *Proceedings* featured his article, 'A Study of the Possibilities of the Diesel-Engined 10,000-Ton Cruiser'. This was primarily an exploration of the potential of diesel propulsion for economical long-endurance cruising at relatively high speed, based on what was then known of that other type of 'hybrid' warship, the 'pocket battleship' *Ersatz*

Preussen, soon to be christened *Deutschland*.

Although most of Procter's discussion was devoted to engineering aspects, it is intriguing that he cast his proposed vessel as a flight-deck hybrid. It is unlikely that he was influenced by the American representations for flying-deck vessels at the London Conference, for he stated in his opening paragraph that his arguments were 'based on the situation existing at this time, January 1930' — Moffett's memo would not be submitted to the delegation until the very last day of that same month. It is possible that Procter's almost off-hand presentation of his diesel cruiser as a hybrid reflects the general interest in the concept in American naval circles; but there may be a more specific source for his choice. In a meeting of the American Society of Naval Architects and Marine Engineers in 1927, one Edward C Magdeburger presented a paper entitled, 'Diesel Engines for the Navy'. In reviewing earlier suggestions for diesel warships, Magdeburger mentioned a 1925 proposal of Procter to convert the battleship *Oklahoma* to diesel propulsion. Procter was therefore invited to comment on Magdeburger's paper. Also commenting on the paper was a member of the institute, none other than James L Bates. Although Bates did not mention hybrid ships in the published discussion, it is entirely possible that he mentioned it to Procter some time in the course of the meeting.

Whatever his inspiration, Procter theorised a ship with the following characteristics.

Displacement: 10,000t standard, 13,500t full load
Dimensions: 600ft (wl) × 60ft × 40ft depth of hull
Machinery: four 12-cylinder direct-drive diesels; 4 shafts, 80,000shp = 31kts. 20,000nm (minimum) at 20kts. Oil 3500t
Armament: nine 8in (3 × 3), eight 5in AA (4 × 2), four TT (1 × 4)
Aircraft: 1 catapult, 12 aircraft
Armour: unspecified (2054t total weight)

Procter's sketch shows the vessel's general appearance; it has many features by now familiar. The main armament is concentrated forward, and the aviation facilities aft. The three triple 8in turrets are on a single level, training forward. For some reason, Procter chose to give his ship a whale-back fo'c's'le with a curiously curved cutwater. Two tall cylindrical towers, reminiscent of the military masts of French pre-dreadnoughts, are located abreast one another, connected by an arthwartships gallery. Each mast has two control decks and a derrick. The 5in guns are sited on each beam, forward and aft of the tower masts. Funnels being deemed unnecessary in a diesel-powered ship, engine room gases are exhausted through

ducts on each side of the hull.

Now, having given his ship aeronautical facilities, Procter failed to tell his readers anything about them or their function beyond specifying an aircraft complement of twelve machines, with hangar accommodation for only six, and declaring that diesel propulsion will provide 'greatly increased aero capacity, without sacrificing gun power'.

It is possible to say a little more about the aviation features of the design, based on the sketch. Taking the 600ft waterline length as a basis, Procter's drawing indicates that the aft aircraft deck, which overhangs the stern, would be about 150ft long. The upper aircraft deck would run approximately 135ft. Here the first glaring fault appears: 150ft was scarcely long enough for a 1930s aeroplane to land on. Almost as bad, an aircraft attempting to land would have been badly buffeted by turbulence from the upper deck and the twin towers; moreover, waving off an aircraft would have been virtually impossible as no matter which way a pilot veered, he would be confronted by a tower.

The upper aviation deck, too short for landing, is a handling and staging area for aircraft to be launched from a trainable catapult immediately forward of it. The catapult extends forward over the aftermost turret, hence the necessity of mounting all turrets on one level. There is a lift just abaft the catapult. This arrangement would have permitted rapid transfer of aircraft to the catapult and so speeded launching considerably; however, because Procter has given hangar space for only six aircraft — and even then the space allowed seems inadequate — the others are shown in his drawing lined up in a row of four behind the aircraft already on the catapult, with another at the forward end of the landing deck. This is presumably the position in which they would have been carried while their more fortunate brethren sheltered below, secure from the elements.

There are a few bright spots in the design. The lack of a superimposed turret and the use of a catapult would have minimised the danger from turbulence in launching, and even the dual superstructure — that menace so many early aviation ship designers fell victim to — would not have imperiled catapult take-offs: On the whole, however, the design is dreadful; it could have been redeemed only by extending the two aircraft decks aft to the stern, the upper to form a flight deck and the lower a hangar deck. This would have permitted at the least a doubling in the aircraft capacity.

Further rectification would remove one of the towers, and the relocation of the AA guns on that beam below the level of the flight deck.

Perhaps the best that can be said of Procter was that he was an officer of long service who had come to appreciate the value of aircraft. His efforts to mate the diesel engine with aircraft and artillery did not end with this hybrid cruiser; we shall have occasion to examine another of his curiosities in a subsequent chapter.

Procter's cruiser, with all its doubtful aeronautical features, was clearly an amateur effort; but the experts of the Bureaux of Construction and Repair and Aeronautics were already hard at work on a far more feasible version of the flying-deck cruiser, and it is to their efforts we must now return.

'THE FORERUNNER OF FUTURE MEN-OF-WAR'

In May 1930 the flying-deck cruiser was still only a byproduct of an unratified treaty, but Moffett was already pushing hard to get the idea tested and a ship built. On 28 May, a few days after his Senate testimony in support of the London Treaty, he directed a long memorandum on carrier and cruiser construction to Secretary of the Navy Charles Francis Adams, routed through the Assistant Secretary for Aeronautics, David S Ingalls (who, incidentally, was the only US naval fighter ace of the First World War). In it, Moffet presented many of the arguments that he and others would later use in advocating the flying-deck cruiser.

Moffett began by asserting that the London Treaty, which he obviously assumed would be ratified by the United States, 'has so modified the naval forces available to the United States in a possible future overseas expedition that it seems desirable that our new building program provide vessels of the greatest offensive usefulness in the execution of the Basic War Plans [which] recognize our dependence on the successful use of large numbers of offensive aircraft'.

He therefore recommended construction of five 13,800 ton carriers (exhausting the treaty-allotted tonnage), each with a capacity of seventy-six aircraft. Then, turning to cruisers, he noted that

Assuming that it is the [Navy] Department's intention to build ultimately eighteen 8″ gun cruisers, there are left available for 6″.1 [sic] cruisers 73,000 tons [under the London Treaty limits]. It appears to be the sense of the . . . treaty that it is permissible thus to augment the scouting and offensive power of vessels which may be expected to perform . . . the multitudinous duties of 6″.1 [sic] cruisers, but which would not be readily useful for the more restricted but weightier offensive duties of Fleet aircraft carriers.

The 6″.1 [sic] cruiser has a variety of uses where their full gun powder will be employed but rarely. Among these are: blockade duty, visit and search, distant scouting and observation, convoy through waters where submarines may be expected, but not heavy surface forces, and trade control in distant waters. The radius of usefulness of one such vessel would in all these duties be greatly increased by aircraft that can be launched and recovered at will. In addition, light cruisers with aircraft decks and suitable aircraft would be more adaptable than ordinary 6″.1 [sic] cruisers for battle tactical scouting, for controlling our own and repelling enemy destroyer attack, for developing contacts and maintaining touch with enemy operations, and for protecting aircraft from other vessels. There may also be mentioned the greatly increased safety to the aircraft of other Fleet units that would be afforded by an additional number of landing decks.

Preliminary studies indicate the practicality of building cruisers of 10,000 tons, about 30 knots speed, armed with six to nine 6″ guns, eight 5″ anti-aircraft guns, and six anti-aircraft machine gun emplacements, and fitted with landing decks and hangars capable of accommodating thirty to forty airplanes of various types. This matter has been taken up with the Bureau of Construction and Repair and they are now making a study of the proposed ships.

Moffett concluded by recommending construction of seven 10,000 ton flying-deck cruisers, CL42-CL48, to be laid down between 1930 and 1933 and completed between 1933 and 1936.

Up to this time, the work on hybrid cruisers had proceded on an exploratory basis, some of it perhaps done by members of the Construction Corps attached to the Bureau of Aeronautics (naval constructors were often the only trained engineers available in the early days of aviation, and served in several navies as aircraft designers and advisers). Much of the material prepared by the Bureaux of Aeronautics and Construction and Repair at this time has apparently disappeared over the years; all we have is a bare outline of the tentative characteristics proposed by Moffett at about this time for a flying-deck cruiser.

Displacement:	10,000t standard
Dimensions:	560ft (wl) × 66ft (wl)
Flight deck:	234ft (excl lift)
Machinery:	90,000shp = 31kts
Armament:	nine 6in (3 × 3); eight 5in
Aircraft:	20
Armour:	4-2.5in belt, 2-2.25in deck, 6in turret faces

There is nothing to indicate why Moffett cut the aircraft complement to twenty in these characteristics.

Pratt fully supported Moffett's scheme, but the General Board was less enthusiastic. Although its members agreed to the necessity of all five carriers, they had less confidence in 6in cruisers, suggesting only five such ships and stating that they did not want 'any 6-inch vessels until all 8-inch vessels proposed are built or actually building'. As for the flying-deck vessels, 'No plans for a combination cruiser-carrier have yet been submitted. . . . A vessel of such a type is not at this time believed to best meet service needs; final opinion must be reserved until developed plans are ready and further study of the subject is made'.

Moffet was undeterred by such opposition. On 26 June 1930, he requested, and eventually obtained approval for, flight experiments on a carrier to determine 'the relative safety and efficiency of operations from . . . restricted decks' such as the proposed vessel would have. The tests were carried out aboard *Saratoga* and were evaluated by a panel composed of battle fleet aircraft officers headed by the carrier's commander, Captain Frederick J Horne. They were completed by September and the results formed the basis for the flying-deck cruiser's preliminary and final designs. The panel's recommendations were

1. That a flight deck 350ft long by 65ft wide, with two hangar decks, be provided.
2. That an express type [ie, high speed] lift be installed at forward end of flight deck.
3. That a crane be installed at each side of forward end of flight deck if a suitable type can be developed.
4. That arresting gear be installed throughout available length of flight deck.
5. That extra barriers be installed in the forward half of arresting gear.
6. That the forward edges of flight deck be of such shape as to minimize the effect of air turbulence and that wind tunnel tests be conducted to determine these air conditions and the best method of overcoming them.
7. That the flight deck extend as far aft as possible.
8. That the upper hangar be so ventilated as to permit servicing and warming up planes and that one or both be so constructed as to permit entering planes from forward provided cranes are installed.
9. That only one type of plane be operated from such a cruiser, to be a two-seater capable of efficiently carrying out the mission of the air force attached, but not to be of a special design for cruiser operations only.
10. That the maximum number of planes to be operated from this cruiser should not exceed the number that can be effectively stowed and hand led in the hangar space available.

Many of these recommendations stemmed from the conclusion that 350ft was the minimum practicable length for a flight deck. Extra arresting wires and emergency barriers were specified to make sure an aircraft could be halted in the shortest possible distance. The constricted flight deck left little or no room for a deck park, so every possible measure was needed to achieve a clear deck; this was the reason for the forward placement of the lift and its high-speed requirement. This location ensured that each aircraft could be struck below immediately at the end of its landing run, thus clearing the deck for the next one. The cranes were intended as an additional means of getting aircraft off the deck quickly. Lack of deck park space was also the reason for the recommendation that no more aircraft be embarked than hangar space could accommodate. This was a departure from normal American practice, in which the majority of the aircraft were stowed on the flight deck and the hangar was used principally for repair and servicing.

In October, Admiral Pratt became CNO, and he lost no time in throwing his weight behind the new type of cruiser. In early November he sent a memo to the Secretary of the Navy in which he said, 'There is need for the development of this type, particularly to find out its value. If its value is demonstrated it will be an asset to the Fleet. If it has no value we will prove it in a manner which is better than any argument on paper. What is needed now is to prove or disprove the value of this type, viz., proof versus expression of opinion'.

There was certainly no lack of opinion or its expression; if Pratt and Moffett supported the flying-deck cruiser, there were also powerful voices in opposition. The General Board was lukewarm at best; Admiral Frank H Schofield, Commander, Battle Fleet, an old friend of Pratt, disapproved of the idea in its entirety. Commenting on the *Saratoga* tests, he wrote to Pratt on 30 September,

> . . . I desire to submit my opinion that the general proposal for a combined gun and airplane cruiser is unsound in every way. The fire hazard will be great on these vessels, so great that we shall have even under the most advantageous conditions, a timid cruiser, one fearful of being brought into position where its guns are to be used. . . . It appears to me that a single four or five-inch shell from a destroyer might very well put one of these vessels out of action through the fire it might start in hangar and other deck spaces, where the presence of gasoline in considerable quantities cannot be avoided.

Schofield also objected that the flying-deck cruiser might well require escort by other vessels during flight operations, and concluded, 'I recommend that no cruiser tonnage be jeopardized by the building of hybrid vessels'.

The debate was not confined to the navy's hierarchy; it was soon a topic of discussion in the pages of the *Proceedings*. An early consideration of the merits of the flying-deck cruiser appeared in its November 1930 issue in an article by Lieutenant Commander Forrest Sherman on 'Some Aspects of Carrier and Cruiser Design'. Sherman, who would himself rise to the post of CNO after the Second World War, was an intellectual officer with a deep appreciation for history, and his analysis of the role of aircraft in naval warfare bears evidence of a very close reading of Sir Julian Corbett's *Some Principles of Maritime Strategy*. In fact, as his theme he chose a quote from that work: 'The classes of ships which constitute a fleet are, or ought to be, the expression in material of the strategical and tactical ideas that prevail at any given time'. Sherman saw this 'expression in material' leading to four distinct categories of aviation ships: battle line support carriers of moderate speed, pure aircraft carriers for offensive use, small scout carriers of very high speed, and carrier-cruisers 'carrying light bombing planes and a fair 6-inch battery'. These latter would function in what we would now call 'sea control' duties: tracking and destruction of enemy commerce raiders, convoy and screening. He drew on examples from the sailing ship era and more recent history to bolster his case.

> A carrier cruiser . . . would have changed the story of Coronel. A carrier cruiser in the forces trailing the *Goeben* and *Breslau* in 1914 might have had a far-reaching effect on the course of the World War. One with von Spee at the Falklands would have prevented him from walking into the trap awaiting him.

Even when his essay is read today, Sherman's use and understanding of naval history make his case for the 'carrier cruiser' very convincing; it was only the exponential growth in the offensive capacity of aircraft that eventually eliminated the need for all of his carrier classes save the 'large . . . powerful and . . . high speed' vessels.

Others were less excited by the prospect of flying-deck cruisers. The *Proceedings'* 1931 Prize Essay, published in the April issue, was entitled, 'Elements Contributing to Aerial Superiority'. Its author, Lieutenant Franklin G Percival USN (ret), quoted another naval historian, Alfred Theyer Mahan, in arguing against the hybrid cruiser: 'In

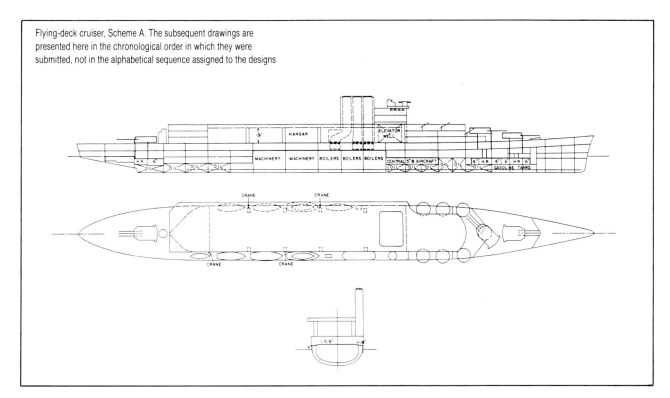

Flying-deck cruiser, Scheme A. The subsequent drawings are presented here in the chronological order in which they were submitted, not in the alphabetical sequence assigned to the designs

the design of the individual ship of war ... exclusiveness of purpose ... is the secret of great military success'. Percival pointed to the 'inevitable quantities of gasoline [which] would add greatly to the fire hazard in the hybrid cruiser'. Furthermore,

> The flying deck would probably not last long in a gun engagement, while the large hangar would use up valuable displacement and center-line space, block the effective arc of fire of the guns, and add to the size of the target. If the cruiser is to use its guns effectively, the course it steers will be dictated by the necessities of the gun action. This course will rarely permit flying operations. ...

Percival was willing to concede one role for the hybrid cruiser, however: it would make an 'ideal' fleet flagship. In such a role it would not usually be in the forefront of the action, but it might be subject to air attacks, so 'an unusually strong antiaircraft battery of 6-inch and smaller guns' would be valuable. The flight deck and aircraft would be necessary 'for observation by members of the staff'.

Commander Richmond Kelly Turner, like Sherman destined to become an admiral, disagreed. Turner was in the Bureau of Aeronautics at this time, and was closely involved in the development of the flying-deck cruiser design. In the May 1931 issue of the *Proceedings*, he pointed out that 'fighting is incidental' to the accomplish-

ment of many of the cruiser's various tasks. Therefore, 'For most of these purposes the flying-deck cruiser's planes will make her far superior to ordinary cruisers'.

Another observer, Lieutenant L A Kniskern of the Construction Corps, also involved in the flying-deck cruiser design, outlined various possible cruiser programmes in an article in the September 1931 issue. He was one of the few writers of the time to use the term 'flight-deck cruiser', but otherwise had little to add to the debate; he proposed building two such vessels because of their 'promise of having great strategic value'.

★   ★   ★

Whatever their promise, the debate within the navy had been settled by this time; Pratt and Moffett had gained the General Board's grudging approval, at least as far as agreeing to the construction of one flying-deck cruiser for experimental purposes. The board included one such vessel in a modest construction programme for the fiscal year 1932 submitted to the Secretary of the Navy on 16 October 1930.

At this point, the actual configuration of a flying-deck cruiser was still only hazily defined. Construction and Repair and the Bureau of Aeronautics had been exploring the idea in a preliminary way but it was not until 29 October that

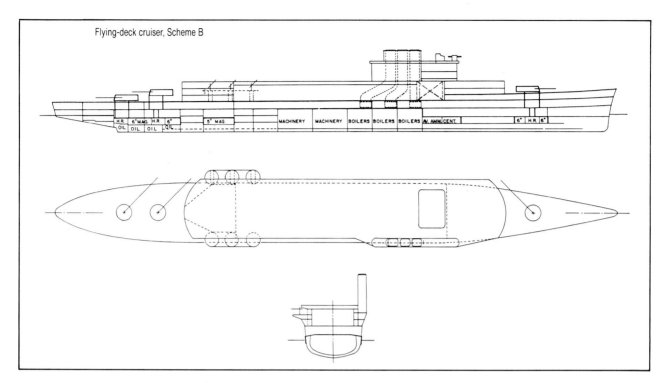

Flying-deck cruiser, Scheme B

Moffett, addressing Pratt and the chief of Construction and Repair, Rear Admiral George H Rock, wrote, 'it is recommended that design studies be undertaken on ... arrangements of aviation facilities to be incorporated in a 10,000 ton cruiser'. The early design work had explored a great many possibilities: 8in gunned ships, ships with four quadruple 6in turrets, short ships and longer ones. Moffett now tried to set some basic parameters for the design work; in this, however, he did not keep entirely to the recommendations established by the *Saratoga* panel. He suggested study of three types of vessel, all to feature a high-speed forward lift, a 65ft wide flight deck extending to the stern, and 'stacks on the side only, to be of the folding [hinged] type'.

The first type called for a vessel with a capacity of thirty-six aircraft and double hangar decks, the upper one ventilated, and a 360ft flight deck; the second called for a single hangar, partially ventilated, for twenty-four aircraft, and a 330ft flight deck; the third envisaged a single ventilated hangar for eighteen aircraft (exclusively fighters) and a 300ft flight deck.

Admiral Rock of Construction and Repair wrote to Pratt on 3 November, saying that Moffett's recommendations 'will furnish a convenient basis for attacking the problem of a cruiser with flying deck, since they furnish a range of flight deck dimensions'. Rock declared, 'This Bureau believes there are possibilities inherent in a cruiser with flying deck which should be developed by the actual construction of a few vessels of this type', and promised to get to work on design studies as soon as designs for destroyer leaders and destroyers were out of the way. But then came a fly in the ointment: 'In all studies of cruisers with flying decks the Bureau proposes to keep in mind as the basic requirement, that this type of vessel must be primarily a cruiser, with characteristics as to battery, protection and speed as far as it is possible to obtain the same in combination with the landing platform'. This statement presaged the tussle that would soon develop over the compromises that are inexorably required in hybrid design.

The General Board requested that the Naval War College conduct board games pitting flying-deck cruisers against conventional cruisers. The results were given by Rear Admiral Harris Laning, the college president, in a document dated 3 December. He reported that in three games 'nothing startling has as yet been developed', but opined that, 'Considering the three main war functions of cruisers, (a) on the tactical field with the Fleet, (b) as scouts for the Fleet, and (c) as commerce raiders or protectors, it appears at present that under (b) and (c) this type [flying-deck cruiser] will prove of great value, while under (a) it will meet its greatest handicap'. He concluded that 'the type has value' and recommended that it have a speed of at least 33 knots, a battery of nine 6in guns at minimum, protection against 8in shellfire if possible and carry no fewer than twelve aircraft — six fewer than Moffett considered the minimum requirement; he held that a flying-deck cruiser unable to accommodate at least eighteen aeroplanes was not worth building.

By late 1930, official opinion on the flying-deck cruiser (or 'CLV', for ' Cruiser, Light, Aviation'), if not unanimous, was for the most part squarely behind it; the battle to bring it into existence therefore shifted to new fronts. In the Preliminary Design branch of the Bureau of Construction and Repair, a reasonable design had to be worked out, while in the committee rooms and on the floor of Congress, the legislators had to be convinced of its value.

In many ways, the latter proved easier than the former. The flying-deck cruiser found its way into Congress as part of House of Representatives bill 14688 of the third session of the 71st Congress, which was put before the House Committee on Naval Affairs on 8 December 1930. This bill proposed the construction of 'One flying-deck cruiser to cost, including armor, armament, ammunition, and airplanes, not to exceed $20,780,000'.

Hearings soon began on the measure. Admiral Rock later noted 'how favorable all the members of the Committee were for the flight-deck cruiser. It appeared to me that if we could get any ship through the Committee it would be a flight-deck cruiser'. Testimony before the committee bears out Rock's observation. Admiral Pratt was closely questioned by the committee's members over several sessions, but the flying-deck cruiser was not the chief object of their scrutiny. The legislators devoted more time to inquiring as to the value of the smaller pure 6in cruiser also included in the bill. They found arguments for the value of a small, handy cruiser to back up destroyer squadrons in fleet work unconvincing, and kept coming back to the ship's inferiority in a one-on-one engagement with an 8in gunned heavy cruiser. As for the flying-deck cruiser, the Congressmen generally expressed themselves favourably inclined toward it. Pratt testified that he 'would like to see all of the excess tonnage go into the . . . flying on deck cruisers because that type of ship, I think, although it is entirely experimental, is going to be one of the new coming ships and if it turns out to be what we hope it will be, it will be a very fair match for the 8-inch

cruisers'. He would rather have had two flying-deck cruisers to start with, and envisaged an eventual total of six.

Admiral Rock testified for Construction and Repair on the technical feasibility of the ship. The committee members, always concerned about the superiority of individual ships in one-on-one encounters, pressed him for reasons why an 8in gunned flying-deck cruiser was not proposed. Rock outlined the difficulties of weight and space involved in combining the heavier gun with a usable flight deck, and then went on to state that, 'The 6-inch landing-on-deck cruiser . . . offers such tremendous possibilities for the future that personally I do not hesitate to say it may almost revolutionize ship building'.

Moffett, of course, was wholly in favour of the new type of ship. In trying to dispel the uncertain, 'experimental' image of it, he called the *Lexington* and *Saratoga* 'merely large flying-deck cruisers'. The underlying rationale for the flying-deck cruiser was clearly given when Moffett offered a historical parallel.

> I believe that a fleet on an expedition, unless it has a great many aircraft, will stop as soon as it gets within range of land-based aircraft or even of another fleet equipped with greater numbers of aircraft. Ships have never been able to to operate within range of shore fortifications, and they can not now operate within range of enemy aircraft unless these can be defeated.

The 'expedition' Moffett had in mind was unquestionably the trans-Pacific journey the fleet would have to undertake in a war with Japan; the 'enemy aircraft' the fleet would have to defeat would be those based in the Mandates.

Moffett's public support of the flying-deck cruiser was not confined to committee hearings; he pressed his case at every opportunity with a vigour that has led one writer to label his touting of the type sensationalistic. In a 19 February memo written for a speech by the Secretary of the Navy, Moffett declared the flying-deck cruiser 'the forerunner of future men-of-war . . . it will play a vital role in Fleet tactics and . . . a properly balanced Fleet should include a strong force of this craft'.

By this time the bill had been reported out of committee favourably but had yet to be voted on by the House. Our friend Representative McClintic both supported the measure and muddied the waters by resurrecting his proposal for fitting take-off platforms on battleships. During Admiral Pratt's testimony McClintic had

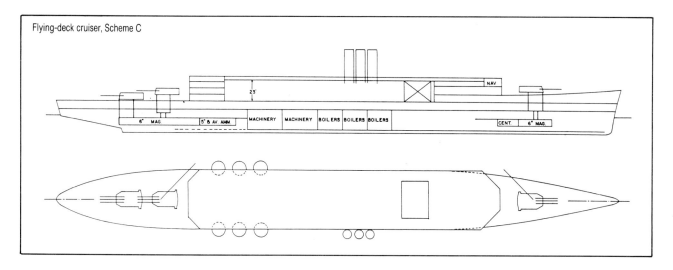

Flying-deck cruiser, Scheme C

raised the question as to whether it would not be advantageous to test an aircraft deck on a battleship. Pratt tried to point out both the expense of such a scheme, and the London Naval Treaty's specific banning of landing-on decks on existing capital ships, but McClintic had clearly thought this problem through, for he had a ready answer: while he agreed that the treaty did prohibit landing decks, 'as far as take-off deck [sic] is concerned, there is nothing to prohibit such construction'.

He carried his fight for hybrid battleships to the floor of the House. On 26 February he read to his colleagues a naval press release quoting Pratt as saying that recent manoeuvres off Panama showed, *inter alia*, 'the necessity for cruisers, especially those of the flying-deck type'. With, as he thought, naval opinion firmly behind hybrid vessels, he asked rhetorically what it was Admiral Pratt wanted? 'More airplane deck ships or flying-deck ships. . . . And if the admiral is in favor of that as a principle on cruisers, why would he not be in favor of it on a type of ship that would make it possible to carry more bombing planes than can be carried on a ship of this type? What is the difference? One is just a little smaller than the other'.

'Right now I have in my possession', McClintic had declared dramatically in earlier oratory that day, 'plans and specifications for an addition to battleships which would make it possible for each one of them to carry not less than 20 bombing planes, and when an addition of this kind is added to a battleship it means that 15 battleships in our Navy thus equipped would be able to fly 300 bombing planes a distance of 200 miles and strike the enemy, when if an addition is not made to such ships they are old, superannuated, floating grave-

yards, and the majority of the people of this Nation know this to be true'.

McClintic buttressed the latter assertion by having read into the *Congressional Record* a list of 306 newspapers which in their editorial wisdom had decided the battleship was, as the Congressman put it, 'a relic of the dark ages and should be forever abolished'.

McClintic's call for hybrid battleships had little influence on the course of the debate, other than to consume a great deal of time, and after this appearance the McClintic flight-deck battleship seems to have sunk without trace.

Meanwhile, over at the Bureau of Construction and Repair, draughtsmen were busily churning out tentative flying-deck cruiser designs. In December 1930 a spectrum of designs was sketched in an effort to reconcile the often antithetical demands of the various US Navy bureaux. These included, besides Construction and Repair itself, Aeronautics, Engineering, and Ordnance. All saw their interests as paramount, and controversies arose over placement of main battery as well as the heavy and light AA batteries, island *vs* flush-deck configuration, degree and disposition of protective features, low *vs* high fire-control positions, and hinged *vs* fixed funnels. Many people in the Bureau of Aeronautics wanted what would be essentially a carrier, with multiple lifts and a catapult or two, requests that were quickly quashed due to the excessive weights entailed. The bureau also wanted low fire-control positions to minimise interference with flight operations; Ordnance wanted high positions for more efficient direction of gunfire.

The sharpest and longest-lived controversy

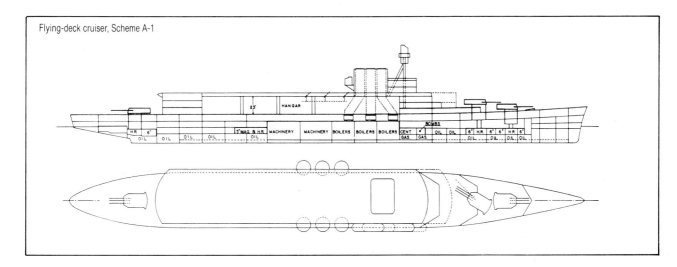

Flying-deck cruiser, Scheme A-1

centred on funnels. Moffett wanted a hinged type; the flush deck would allow aircraft to begin their take-off runs off the centreline without fear of hitting the island. This would make for faster launching than if each aircraft had to be spotted on the exact centre of the deck before it could begin its take-off run. It would also allow the ship to launch aircraft with the wind a little off the bow, giving her a wider range of courses should she have to get the aeroplanes off while under fire. The Bureau of Engineering was adamant that fixed funnels were more efficient, and Construction and Repair agreed. There was some experience supporting Engineering's stand; the hinged funnels on *Langley* had not been particularly successful, and the CLV required a far more powerful machinery plant, with a far greater volume of gases to exhaust. A more advanced hinged funnel was under development for the carrier that eventually became USS *Ranger*, but there was no guarantee that it would be any more successful — and in fact would also prove disappointing. Construction and Repair's objection to hinged funnels was due to their weight, which was initially estimated to be 100 to 200 tons greater than that of fixed funnels because of the counterbalancing weights required, the increased electrical loads and additional motors and gearing. In a design as tight as that of the CLV, even 100 tons could be decisive.

The General Board held several hearings on the characteristics of flying-deck cruisers during December 1930. In the course of these hearings, Construction and Repair developed a series of sketches, running from A to G. It should be emphasised that these sketches do not represent a logical progression, but rather a series of alternatives; G was not necessarily more advanced in

conception than A — quite the reverse, in fact. Although each addressed different points raised regarding the desirable traits for a flying-deck cruiser, the designs all shared certain features, such as a long hull, and the machinery arrangement, which in all cases consisted of three boiler rooms in a block with the two engine rooms aft of them.

The first design was A, presented to the board at its 4 December hearing. In this design one turret was sited aft of the flight deck, which was the layout strongly favoured by Construction and Repair. A's flight deck was only 60ft wide, rather than the specified 65ft, and to make matters worse, it was reduced to 45ft forward of the lift to allow for the 5in AA guns. It also had a low island superstructure and a fixed funnel. The flight deck was offset to port to balance the weight of the island, a feature that would recur throughout the series. Design A was not liked by the aviators, who had seen it the day before the hearing and prepared their own sketch for comparison. This had all three turrets forward and, surprisingly, a flight deck 40ft shorter than the Construction and Repair design. It naturally had a flush deck, and to get the folding stacks farther aft the engine rooms were placed forward of the boilers. Construction and Repair objected to the latter feature because it would mean raising the boilers to get the shafts under them, and the tops of the boilers already projected above the waterline. There was much discussion of telescopic fire-control masts for flush-decked designs, the best way to defend against dive bombers, fire-fighting features, and some brief consideration of how the ship was to be fought. Rear Admiral Mark L Bristol, president of the board, thought the CLV would probably run away from an enemy ship, and so should have the

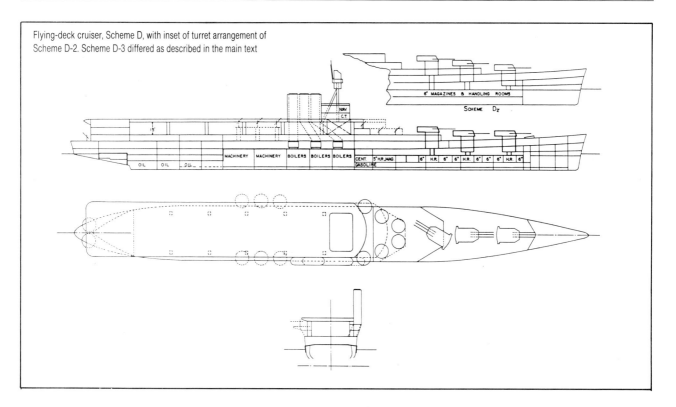

Flying-deck cruiser, Scheme D, with inset of turret arrangement of Scheme D-2. Scheme D-3 differed as described in the main text

majority of her main battery aft instead of forward. This would also have the beneficial effect of placing the after end of the flight deck closer to the centre of the ship, and so reduce the degree of pitching a pilot would face when coming in for a landing. Several of the Aeronautics people attending also felt that the farther forward the flight deck was the better an aviation ship it would be; these comments would lead to a very odd design before long.

Construction and Repair returned the next day with two hastily prepared sketches, dubbed B and C. In these, two turrets were aft and only one forward, as had been discussed the previous day. This allowed greater freeboard forward, since the one turret could be higher than a superimposed arrangement allowed, and also increased the vertical clearance between the flight deck and the turret, which the aviators considered desirable. Apart from the reversed gun arrangement, these schemes were similar to A; B had a 366ft by 65ft flight deck and moved the 5in guns aft on sponsons, while C featured the same battery arrangement as B but had three hinged funnels in place of the fixed stack. The island was eliminated, the bridge being located under the forward end of the flight deck. The flight deck was 355ft by 65ft.

During this hearing, Sir George Thurston made a brief, albeit anonymous, appearance. In discuss-

ing the various configurations, Assistant Secretary Ingalls remembered a hybrid cruiser design in the 1923 Brassey's, and someone was told to go and look it up; but the board never returned to this topic. Ingalls was probably confusing Sir George's 1923 'experimental battleship' with a later article he wrote on cruisers in which he proposed an all-forward arrangement for the main battery, but no aviation facilities. In fact, Sir George did not like ·aircraft on cruisers at all, believing that they interfered with the ship's guns to an unacceptable degree. His only concession was to suggest that 'a modified cruiser type with equal or greater speed [compared with other cruisers], but with a reduced number of guns should be designed' to provide the aviation element for cruiser squadrons. A tepid endorsement indeed coming from the man who had proposed so many hybrid battleships.

The representatives from Construction and Repair left this hearing with a whole new set of suggestions, and the draughtsmen were soon busy again. At the next hearing, on 23 December, Construction presented a wide range of schemes: A-1, D, D-1 and D-2, E, F and G. It should be noted in passing that James L Bates was present at this hearing, although he did not testify; Captain van Keuren represented Construction and made a strong pitch for the bureau's favourite battery disposition. A-1 was an improved version of A, with the flight deck's width increased to 65ft, but

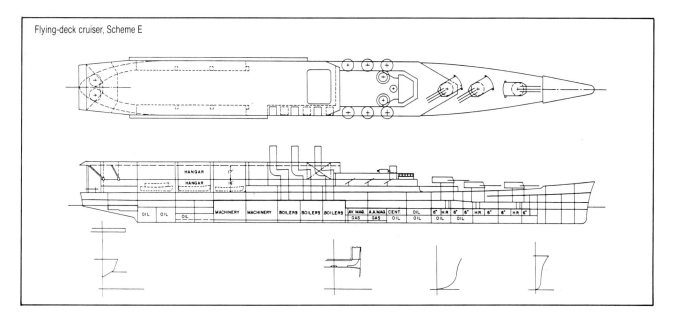

Flying-deck cruiser, Scheme E

its length reduced from 370ft to 336ft due to an increase in the arc of fire of the forward guns from 135 to 150 degrees on each beam; it was noted on the drawing that if the 135 degree firing arcs were accepted, the flight deck could be extended 30ft and the island moved forward 14ft. The 5in guns were on sponsons aft, and the hangar height was increased from 19ft to 23ft. Also added was a tripod fire-control mast.

The D series was similar to the Bureau of Aeronautics scheme proposed at the 4 December hearing, with the entire 6in battery located forward of the flight deck. D had its 5in AA guns sited just forward of the 344ft by 65ft flight deck, with two more on the fantail. These last had fairly good sky arcs because the flight deck did not extend all the way to the stern. D-1 had its 5in battery abaft the island on sponsons, allowing an increase in flight deck length to 370ft; the hangar height was increased from 15ft to 23ft, and the two aft 5in guns were deleted. Both D and D-1 had only the third 6in turret superimposed; D-2 introduced a triple-tiered arrangement, but the resulting increased weights would have required a 63 ton reduction in the protective features. D-2 was in all other respects a repeat of D-1.

Scheme E was based on suggestions from the Bureau of Ordnance. It resembled Scheme D, but had hinged stacks and no island. The flight deck length was reduced to 316ft, and an extra deck level was added so that the bridge just abaft turret no 3 had a view over the turret. This increased the height of the flight deck above the waterline to 53ft 3in. The flight deck extended over the stern, severely limiting the AA capabilities of the two

after 5in guns. Ordnance liked the arrangement of the AA directors, which were located near the 5in guns on the superstructure forward of the flight deck. This reduced the correction necessary between directors and guns and made for more accurate fire control.

The next design in the alphabetical sequence, Scheme F, can best be described as a monstrosity. Following on from the earlier proposal to place the flight deck forward, all 6in turrets were aft, the foremost turret superimposed. Between the turrets and the flight deck were the boat deck and, at a higher level, the fire-control positions and AA guns. There were three separate hinged funnels to starboard. The bridge was forward, with the flight deck overhanging it; it had wing extensions on each beam to allow some view aft.

To land on this aberration, an aviator would have to negotiate all the turbulence generated by the turrets and other clutter, then touch down on a flight deck 318ft long. Once halted, the aircraft would have to be trundled back to the lift, which was placed at the after end of the flight deck. It is difficult to see how any of the Aeronautics representatives could have ever favoured such a hazardous arrangement, and at this hearing there was no support for the idea.

If Scheme F was a freak, Scheme G was a throwback, almost *Vindictive* all over again. It was based on the December 1929 studies for improved aviation facilities on cruisers and represented, as van Keuren noted, 'the ultimate development of the cruiser with minimum amount of aviation facilities'. The turrets were forward (the third superimposed), followed by a large

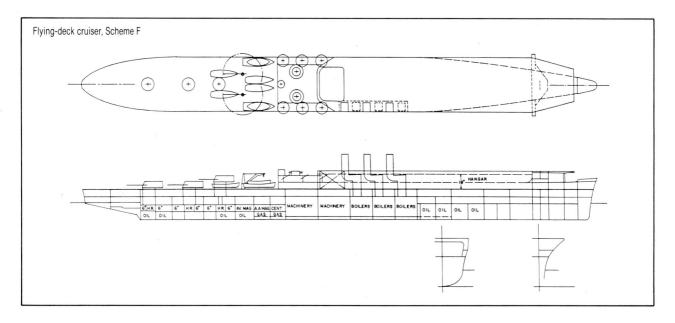

Flying-deck cruiser, Scheme F

centreline superstructure complete with tripod mast; these unlikely arrangements were finished off by a large centreline funnel. The flight deck stretched 264ft from the stern to a lift aft of the funnel. It would have been a rare and exceptionally gifted pilot who could have alighted on such a platform, as had been amply demonstrated on *Furious* thirteen years earlier. As take-off was obviously impossible from the deck, there were two athwartship flush-deck catapults on the hangar deck, with 44ft wide spaces between the flight deck supports to allow for the wingspan of the aircraft. The AA guns were sited abreast the funnel and lift. As expected, the design received no support whatsoever from the aviators; Captain John H Towers of Aeronautics characterised the design as 'entirely outside the category of the flying-on cruisers'.

Admiral Bristol made a pitch for something even closer to *Vindictive*: a cruiser with a forward flying-off deck, centreline superstructure amidships, and a landing-on deck aft. As in *Vindictive*, there would be gangways around the superstructure to move the aircraft. Captain Towers diplomatically agreed that the design might be 'workable', but quickly pointed out that it would probably not be possible within the 10,000 ton limit. The idea was dropped.

Throughout the hearings the issue of whether the ship was a cruiser or really a carrier in disguise had come up for discussion. At the 23 December hearing Rear Admiral William D Leahy, head of the Bureau of Ordnance, stated that the CLV 'is an aircraft carrier regardless of what you call it'. He was willing to accept a reduction in gunnery efficiency on that basis and so conceded that the ship would be built 'for the aviators and we should build the ship to suit the aviators and it ought to have a flush deck if we can possibly do it'. Coming from the head of Ordnance, this must have been a surprising concession.

The aviators, of course, saw the ship's main punch as coming from the aircraft. They believed that the 'bombers would get through' no matter what sort of a defence you had. In pre-radar days, fighters could not intercept them because there was no way of knowing from what direction or altitude the attackers would come, 5in guns fired too slowly to deter dive bombers, and peacetime trials indicated that the dive bombers could score about 60 per cent hits (most of the aviators believed it would be half that in wartime, but this would still amount to a devastating number of hits). The dive bomber, or, in the case of the CLV, fighters and scout aircraft equipped for dive bombing, would provide the flying-deck cruiser with a considerable offensive punch, but by the same token the ship would have no effective defence against such an attack. Machine guns, close-in defence, were the only answer; Towers wanted to 'plaster the ship with machine guns'. Even so, he did not think they would be terribly effective.

By the end of December, the General Board had looked over the first series and decided in favour of a ship with all guns forward. Two sketches were prepared to meet the new characteristics, H and H-1. A third design, A-2, prepared on Construction's own initiative, was also submitted. Admiral Rock explained in his cover memo that, 'Although this scheme is basically that one with two turrets

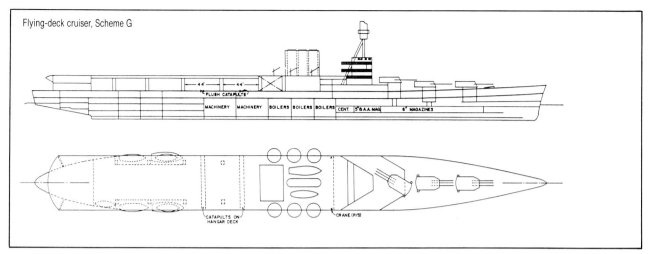

Flying-deck cruiser, Scheme G

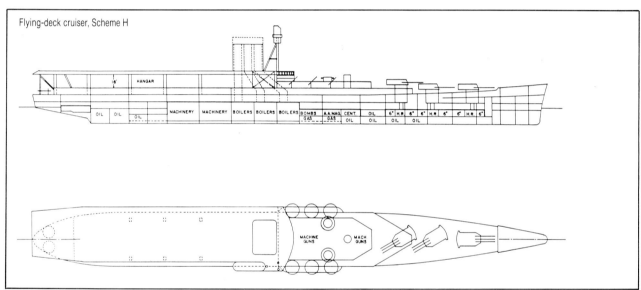

Flying-deck cruiser, Scheme H

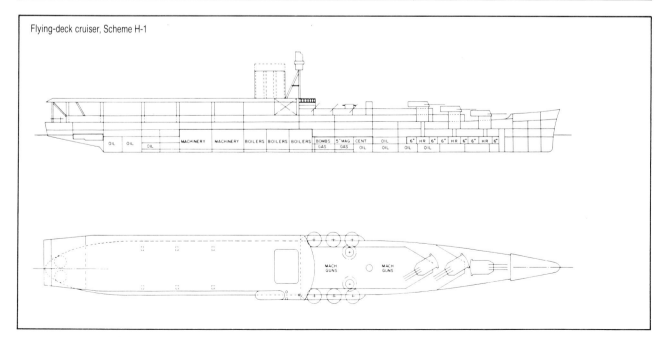

Flying-deck cruiser, Scheme H-1

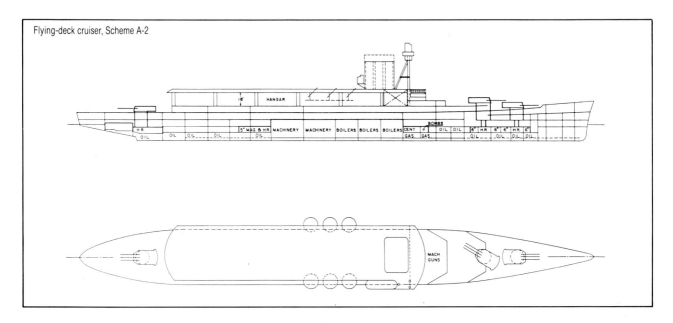

Flying-deck cruiser, Scheme A-2

foward and one aft [A-1] which did not meet favor with the General Board, and does not meet the characteristics for location [of the main battery] as given [by the board], the Bureau feels so strongly as to the merits of this typical arrangement that a further detail study leading to this scheme was made'. A-2 was, in fact, almost identical to the earlier A-1. The only substantial difference was the moving of the bridge from an island to the now generally accepted position below the forward end of the flight deck. The fixed funnels and tripod mast were retained.

H and H-1 were developed from Scheme E. In both designs, all 6in turrets were forward, H having the first two turrets on the same level with the third superimposed, H-1 having all three superfiring. H's flight deck was only 316ft long; H-1 had a 327ft deck, the all-superfiring arrangement allowing the turrets to be shifted forward slightly. The 5in guns were sited abreast the forward superstructure, the deck flaring out from the ship's side to provide sufficient area for them. Their directors were on the superstructure deck inboard of the guns, as were the AA machine guns and the secondary 6in director. There were two 5in guns right aft, under the flight deck. As in the very similar D series, the three superfiring turrets required a reduction in the weight of protection.

Rock compared the three designs in his memo, emphasising whenever possible the superiority of the A-2 battery arrangement over the all-forward placement of the other schemes. He considered that 'scheme H-1 is so low in its protective features that [it] must be taken out of the cruiser class without question'. On the other hand, 'although

the general type from which scheme A-2 was drawn did not meet favorable criticism before the General Board, scheme A-2 is decidedly better than either scheme H or H-1, and represents a better all around cruiser with flying deck than any other of the schemes considered'.

The admiral concluded with a plea that 'detail points such as type of smoke pipe, arrangement of AA fire control and machine guns be not rigidly specified . . . but that the general desires or intent of the General Board be given, with freedom of improvement and development as the detail design may eventually proceed'.

★   ★   ★

Eventually, the General Board forwarded its criteria for the hybrid sought in the 1932 programme to the Secretary of the Navy. The characteristics were anything but rigid; many were in fact couched as pious generalities — 'the best possible' this, 'all necessary' that — but specifically the board sketched out a vessel of no more than 10,000 tons standard displacement, with a flight deck not less than 65ft wide 'and as near 350 feet long and clear of obstructions as possible', a hangar for the full complement of twenty-four 'light type' aircraft and a high-speed forward lift.

Armament was to consist of nine 6in guns 'in three triple turrets forward, in single vertical echelon', six 5in/25 AA guns and 'the best practicable battery of automatic machine guns'. Protection was to be 'as nearly as possible equal to that of a cruiser, without flying deck, of latest design'. Speed was specified as not less than 32.5 knots,

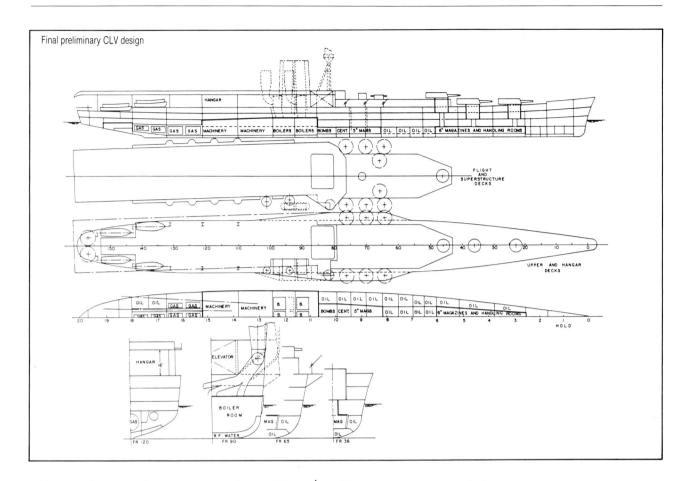

Final preliminary CLV design

with an endurance of 10,000nm at 15 knots. There must also be 'The best possible method of disposing of boiler gases compatible with good flying-on conditions'. Fixed funnels were favoured 'unless improvement in design develops a hinged stack giving manifestly improved ship characteristics'.

In the meantime, Pratt had presided at a 19 January conference on the final design attended by the Assistant Secretary of the Navy for Aeronautics, the chiefs of the Bureaux of Ordnance, Construction and Repair, Engineering, and Aeronautics, the Assistant CNO and the head of the War Plans Division. Rock's recommendations were overridden and Scheme H-1 was selected for final development, but modifications were suggested. These included slight changes in the placement of the 6in turrets and the two forward AA guns, replacing the stern 5in guns with 6in guns, and extending the flight deck aft 'as much as practicable'. Also asked was consideration of a 'high spot' on a tripod mast for the main battery, a 'low spot' for the secondary guns, hinged stacks, a flush deck except for the mast, and a bridge under the flight deck. If hinged funnels were not feasible, 'stacks as high as reasonable to avoid smoke interference with flight

facilities' were recommended.

Pratt reported the results of the meeting to the Secretary of the Navy three days later. 'The ship should be primarily a cruiser', Pratt asserted; 'As a fighting unit the Chief of Naval Operations is of the opinion that this type of ship will fight bow on, closing the range as rapidly as practicable — therefore, it is essential that her main battery be concentrated forward.... She should avoid broadside action, therefore her main armor belt is of relatively less importance than in straight cruisers'.

Over the next six months, Construction and Repair hammered out the details of the design. There was one especially intriguing moment during this phase: on 23 June 1931, Moffett requested a study by the Bureau of Engineering on the possibilities of full diesel or half-diesel, half-steam propulsion for the flying-deck cruiser 'because of the very beneficial operating conditions to be derived from a reduction or elimination of the smoke and smokestack interference'. Perhaps he had just got around to reading Procter's article; however, the request was withdrawn a week later and no documents have been found to explain why. So the US Navy never designed a

FLYING-DECK CRUISER DESIGNS, DECEMBER 1930–JANUARY 1931

	Scheme A 1 Dec	Scheme B 4 Dec	Scheme C 4 Dec	Scheme A-1 11 Dec	Scheme D 10 Dec	Scheme D-1 10 Dec	Scheme D-2 10 Dec
Displacement:	All schemes 10,000t standard						
Dimensions:	All schemes 630ft wl × 65ft (at main deck; sponsons and other projections not included)						
Machinery:	All schemes geared turbines, 80,000shp = 32kts. 10,000nm at 15kts						
Armament:	All schemes nine 6in (3 × 3)						
	six 5in	six 5in	six 5in	six 5in	eight 5in	six 5in	six 5in
Flight deck:	370ft × 60ft	366ft × 65ft	355ft × 65ft	336ft × 65ft	344ft × 65ft	370ft × 65ft	370ft ×65ft
Aircraft:	c20	?	?	18	18	24	24

diesel flying-deck cruiser.

By this date, the final preliminary design was ready. Forwarded to the Secretary of the Navy on 2 July, it was clearly a descendent of H, although it showed many changes in detail. Perhaps the most interesting of these was the incorporation of a slightly angled flight deck, allowing the full width of 65ft to be maintained abreast the island without the use of an offset deck. The characteristics of the design were

Displacement:	10,000t standard, 11,580t trials
Dimensions:	637ft (wl) × 62ft 6in (wl) × 19ft 5in
Flight deck:	332ft × 65ft
Machinery:	6 boilers, 4 sets geared turbines, 80,000shp = 32.5kts. 10,000nm at 15kts
Armament:	nine 6in (3 × 3); eight 5in/25; 16 AA machine guns
Aircraft:	24
Armour:	belt 3.5in; deck 1.375in; barbettes 3in; turret face plates 5in; sides 1.75in; roof 1.25in
Complement:	693 plus 186 aviation personnel

The machinery arrangements had been revised, with the boilers concentrated in only two compartments; this may have been possible because the inner bottom was now continued up only just above the turn of the bilge, rather than to the full height of the compartment as in the earlier designs. Provision was still made for hinged stacks, but a fixed stack was very definitely favoured by Construction and Repair. There was to be a fire-control mast in each case, but no island as such. The aviation petrol tanks apparently wandered during the design process; one drawing in the General Board files shows them abaft the machinery spaces, but Rock's memo placed them 'outboard the after group of magazines in the bilges', ie, forward of the machinery spaces. This latter location was not liked; Rock noted that, 'The outside water furnishes their only protection'.

There was an alternative, however: fixed stacks would save about 40 tons over the hinged type, making it 'practicable to transfer the gasoline tanks to the space between the longitudinals . . . [between] frames 48 and 65' — that is, abaft the 6in magazines and forward of the 5in magazines. This relocation would allow the provision of 'deck protection over and longitudinal bulkheads alongside of the same thicknesses proposed for the magazines, viz., 55 lbs and 120 lbs to 80 lbs. The Bureau strongly favors this change'. Overall, the protection was intended to provide immunity against 6in gunfire between 10,000 and 20,000 yards on a 60 degree target angle.

Superimposing both no 2 and no 3 turret proved impossible due to the weights involved, so nos 1 and 2 were mounted on the same level. No 2 turret could fire directly ahead at ranges of 15,000 yards or more, while at 0 degree elevation it was restricted to an arc of fire between 21 and 150 degrees on each beam. The 6in guns aft proved impossible, and there was no fire-control station for the two 5in/25 mounted in their place. There was a conning tower just forward of the flight deck, and a bridge under the forward edge of the flight deck 'extending entirely across the ship and arranged so as to secure vision directly aft as well as forward and on the beam'.

Rock closed his memo by pointing out that 'The Bureau is now engaged upon the contract plans for this vessel and will be materially assisted in their further development by early action on the part of the Department' regarding the preliminary drawings.

There were two more General Board hearings to consider the design, on 16 and 17 July. Tinkering with the design continued at the hearings, leading Admiral Rock to complain that 'the design has

	Scheme E 12 Dec	Scheme F 12 Dec	Scheme G 13 Dec	Scheme A-2 7 Jan	Scheme H 29 Dec	Scheme H-1 30 Dec
Displacement:	All schemes 10,000t standard					
Dimensions:	All schemes 630ft wl × 65ft (at main deck; sponsons and other projections not included)					
Machinery:	All schemes geared turbines, 80,000shp = 32kts. 10,000nm at 15kts					
Armament:	All schemes nine 6in (3 × 3)					
	eight 5in	six 5in	six 5in	six 5in	eight 5in	eight 5in
Flight deck:	318ft × 65ft	318ft × 65ft	293ft × 65ft	316ft × 65ft	316ft ×65ft	327ft × 65ft
Aircraft:	18	12	12	?	?	?

been continuously subjected to a sort of stretching process first on one account and then on another and I think from the tenor of the comments this morning that the end is not in sight. . . . I merely want to emphasize that the design as submitted has practically no margin of weight'. There was some comment on the need, or lack of it, for a conning tower; Rear Admiral W R Sexton from the CNO's office noted that on the *Omaha* class cruiser *Concord* the conning tower was used as a sewing room. The hinged *vs* fixed stack controversy was apparently winding down; Rear Admiral S M Robinson of the Bureau of Engineering felt that the hinged stacks were 'a technical problem . . . that is really impossible of solution in a satisfactory manner. I don't say you can't build stacks that will revolve, but they will probably jam and bind and leak gases'. Commander Richmond Kelly Turner of Aeronautics surrendered gracefully: 'We want hinged stacks but we want them [the flying-deck cruisers] to be successful. We do feel in this that we must defer to the Bureau of Engineering'.

Captain A B Cook, acting chief of the Bureau of Aeronautics, was less sanguine. In a memo written one day before the hearings began, he expressed 'general agreement' with the design and praised its 'considerable ingenuity'. He was willing to accept the reduced flight-deck length, although he made a point of emphasising 'that this reduction will reflect itself in reduced efficiency in flight operations'. He was even willing to acquiesce on the fire-control mast, but there was one feature with which he most heartily disagreed: Aeronautics could not 'concur with the idea that the further addition of fixed stacks to this restricted flight deck will result in only slight reduction in efficiency'. Cook's heartfelt protest is

a measure of the frustration Aeronautics must have felt over the continual retreat of the aviation element in the design: 'These concessions are cumulative and it is essential that they be kept below a point where the aviation arm is so throttled that it cannot be depended upon in service. It is strongly urged therefore that the hinged stack feature be retained'.

Aeronautics was answered by a terse memorandum from the Secretary of the Navy: 'While the aviation facilities on the flying-on deck cruiser must not be neglected . . . the fact still remains that the ship is a cruiser and not a carrier and therefore all elements which go to make up cruiser efficiency must be given their proper weight'.

This ended the controversy once and for all. It remained only for Construction and Repair to finish its contract design; at the 16 July hearing Rock had estimated that this would take some four months. The design that eventually emerged showed numerous differences in detail from the final preliminary design. The island was reinstated, but there was no fire-control mast; instead, a director similar to that fitted in the *New Orleans* class heavy cruisers was located atop the island. The conning tower and AA directors on the deck in front of the flight deck were eliminated, perhaps to reduce air turbulence during take-offs. The aviation petrol tanks were moved to the recommended position between the 5in and 6in magazines. The angled deck was retained, and the armament, protection and machinery were unchanged, as were the minor flaws, chief among them the fact that the flight deck was too short for take-off by fully fuelled bombers. On the whole, however, the ship was almost precisely what it was intended to be; it was, perhaps, the most feasible, practicable hybrid design to emerge

HEAVILY ARMED CARRIER DESIGNS, 1931

	Scheme J	Scheme L	Scheme M	Scheme O
Displacement:	25,000t standard 28,000t trial	20,000t standard 22,700t trial	15,200t standard 17,400t trial	27,000t standard 30,250t trial
Dimensions:*	800ft × 88ft	740ft × 81ft	665ft × 78ft 5in	830ft × 89ft
Flight deck:	540ft × 86ft	500ft × 80ft	445ft × 80ft	555ft × 86ft
Machinery:	138,000shp = 32.5kts	105,000shp = 31kts	108,000shp = 31kts	140,000shp = 32.5kts
Armament:	nine 8in eight 5in	six 8in eight 5in	four 8in eight 5in	ten 8in eight 5in
Aircraft:	65	60	45	68

*Length in all cases is length on the waterline

during the era of naval artillery, a reasonable blending of cruiser and carrier characteristics.

As the flying-deck cruiser design was being finalised, there was a brief flurry of interest in another type of hybrid: the heavily armed aircraft carrier. The idea never went very far, but it demonstrates the extent of interest in hybrid vessels at the time. It is also a reflection of the similarity, and occasional confusion, of the perceived roles of carriers and cruisers. A substantial gun battery would make a carrier more independent and flexible — more like a cruiser, in fact. This, at least, was the theory.

Like that of cruisers, carrier design was complicated by the treaty situation; the United States began with 135,000 tons under the Washington Treaty, but *Lexington* and *Saratoga* consumed 66,000 tons of that (*Langley*, as an experimental vessel, did not count); this left 69,000 tons, and the navy planned to build five 13,800 ton carriers with that — the smallest effective carrier in order to get the maximum number of flight decks. The first, and only, carrier built to this tonnage, *Ranger*, lacked protection and was regarded as too small by some officers even before she was completed. If a larger size was desired, choices were limited to three carriers of 18,400 tons or two of 27,000 tons, the maximum displacement permitted under the Washington Treaty.

The General Board began the process of working out the new carrier design in May 1931, expressing interest in larger, better protected ships. Several sketches with protection against cruiser gunfire were worked out by Construction

and Repair during the summer of 1931. It was the Secretary of the Navy who took the idea of a protected carrier one step further by proposing well-armed carriers. Perhaps influenced by the arguments for the flying-deck cruiser, he asked for studies of 8in gunned carriers in early September 1931. The result was a series of schemes for 8in and 6in gunned carriers ranging in size from 15,200 tons to 27,000 tons. Their characteristics are summarised in the accompanying table.

The necessary corollary to the installation of a heavy gun battery was a substantial reduction in both the flight deck size and the number of aircraft that could be embarked. A design such as Scheme J of 25,000 tons lost nearly 200ft of flight-deck length compared with a conventional design of the same displacement; it could carry only sixty-five aircraft as opposed to the 100 of the conventional carrier.

For a navy desperately seeking to increase its aircraft strength, this was a damning indictment. In its 10 December response to these designs, the General Board pointed out that 'Large planes, heavily loaded, which at stalling speed are quite sluggish, may not have gained sufficient flying speed by the time they reach the end of the flight deck. This danger may be augmented by eddy currents set up by the turrets'. The flying-deck cruisers, intended to carry only light aircraft, could make do with a short flight deck, but the very reason for a large carrier was its ability to launch offensive aircraft, and to be effective these aircraft had to carry heavy ordnance. To jeopardise this capability for the sake of a few 8in guns was clearly a bad bargain.

A few 6in gunned designs were prepared, but

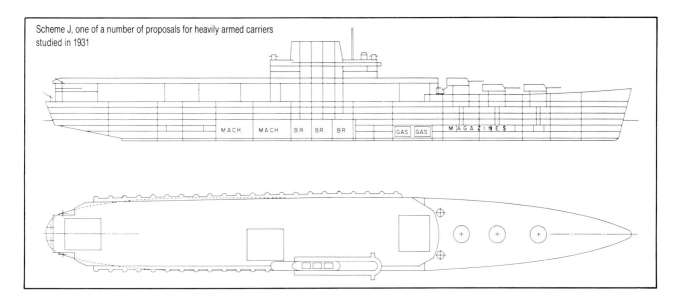

Scheme J, one of a number of proposals for heavily armed carriers studied in 1931

they were even worse than the 8in ships. The lighter gun was not much liked by the General Board to start with; to sacrifice aviation capacity in return for a small number of 6in guns did not sit well at all.

The sketch designs demonstrated that a heavily armed carrier was not much of a carrier, and the US Navy needed effective carriers very badly. The Secretary of the Navy got the message, and the idea was quickly dropped, but this incident highlights the very factor that made the flying-deck cruiser so attractive, for while the heavily gunned carrier reduced the potential number of aircraft the fleet could take to sea, the flying-deck cruiser increased the fleet's aviation capacity. Hence the quick rejection of the carrier schemes, and the tenacity of the CLV. The carrier-with-guns also demonstrates just how pervasive the hybrid idea had become; over the next few years, the navy's designers would be trying other combinations of aviation and guns.

The navy had devoted a great deal of time to developing the flying-deck cruiser's design and was confident that such a ship would be built, but larger forces soon intervened. The 71st Congress had ended without making an appropriation for warship construction of any sort; the Great Depression touched off by the stock market collapse in 1929 was beginning to scourge the country, and with the nation's economy in near-chaos, expenditure of public funds for naval construction appeared an unjustifiable luxury. Nevertheless, on 4 January 1932 Representative Carl Vinson of Georgia, the new Democratic chairman of the House Naval Affairs Committee, proposed bill 6661 of the 72nd Congress, First Session, which again included provision for one flying-deck cruiser. Hearings were held on the bill, and eventually it was endorsed by the Naval Affairs Committee on 25 January – endorsed but not forwarded to the House for a vote. The committee decided, in view of the 'abnormal economic situation', to hold the bill until the results of the Geneva Disarmament Conference were made known.

Moffett, of course, pushed hard for the flying-deck cruiser. In a press statement released in January, he declared that

> . . . in spite of the great importance to the fleet of aviation, only 3 out of a total of 14 permitted vessels are built or building. I, therefore, urge the early construction of the remaining aircraft carriers and of the eight flying deck cruisers. If expectations of the capabilities of the latter type are realized, their construction will add tremendously to the effectiveness of the Fleet.

Moffett's hopes were soon to be disappointed. Vinson's bill never made it to the floor of the House for a vote, despite the failure of the Geneva Conference. President Hoover declared that he would approve no new construction and Vinson's own party leadership, equally economy-minded, manoeuvred to keep the bill from going anywhere. Once again the flying-deck cruiser had just missed obtaining legislative approval, but the hybrid idea had taken root in the US Navy and would be resurrected in a variety of shapes before the decade was out.

ACROSS THE PACIFIC

While the US Navy was developing the flying-deck cruiser, the Imperial Japanese Navy was also experimenting with warships that combined heavy guns with aircraft; but these ships differed in one important respect from their American counterparts: instead of aeroplanes, the IJN favoured seaplanes in its hybrid and near-hybrid vessels.

The IJN's love affair with the shipboard seaplane was close and enduring. It began before the First World War with the acquisition of French and American floatplanes as the IJN's first aircraft and continued into the 1920s — logically enough then, for by the end of the First World War the seaplane had become a vital component of naval air arms everywhere. The Japanese carried the romance to an extreme during the next decade, however, sticking catapults onto all manner of warships, including submarines, and building large, fast seaplane tenders, two of which were eventually converted into flight-deck carriers.

The reason for this attachment to the type lies largely in the profound influence of the Washington Treaty of 1922 on Japanese naval strategic and tactical thought.

In the early 1920s, as the US Navy's planners pondered how to project American sea power into the western Pacific, their Japanese counterparts worked on ways to keep it out. The IJN developed a strategy that envisaged an initially defensive posture, based on the valid assumption that the US fleet would have to cross the entire Pacific to threaten Japan in any meaningful way. After steaming thousands of miles, the US fleet would meet the IJN in The Decisive Battle — the great, all-out clash between lines of capital ships that the writings of Mahan taught would confer 'command of the sea' upon the winner. Belief in such a battle as the ultimate goal of naval warfare was widely held in all quarters in the early 1920s, but it was nowhere more avidly embraced than in Japan, with good reason: less than two decades earlier, Togo had won what was perhaps naval history's greatest victory of annihilation at Tsushima. An American fleet would face a journey similar in extent to Rozhestvensky's before it could come to grips with the IJN.

Japanese staff planners happily anticipated an American trans-Pacific advance, for it would permit The Decisive Battle to be fought in or near home waters, a situation that would bestow all the advantages of proximity to friendly harbours and dockyards on the IJN, while the American supply lines stretched for thousands of miles, with its repair facilities equally distant. The Japanese main fleet would therefore take no offensive action until this geographical advantage had been attained; then it would sortie for the big battle which, given equal odds, the Japanese were certain they could win.

It was with The Decisive Battle in mind that even before the end of the First World War Japan embarked on a huge naval construction programme centred on giant battleships and battle-cruisers. Then came the Washington Treaty, ending such programmes and establishing the famous 5:5:3 ratio in capital ships for Britain, the United States and Japan, respectively.

This ratio completely upset Japanese calculations. The study of naval history, plus fleet manoeuvres, showed that not even a geographical advantage was sufficient to achieve victory in a battle where one fleet was approximately 30 per cent inferior in capital ship strength.

A new strategy was developed. Under it, the main fleet would remain passive in home waters at the beginning of the campaign, as before, but now a vigorous, sustained offensive would be mounted against the US fleet during its Pacific passage, with emphasis on torpedo attack by cruisers, destroyers, submarines and aircraft. This strategy sought to wear down American battleship strength prior to The Decisive Battle; by that time the Japanese hoped to have parity or even superiority in battle fleet strength.

This whittling-down process, or 'diminution operation' as it was called, was essentially a larger-scale version of the strategy adopted by the German Navy early in the First World War. The German aim then had been to isolate and destroy a portion of the Grand Fleet, thereby achieving equality with the British battle line. The vast expanse of the Pacific offered greater possibilities for such a strategy than the North Sea had allowed the Germans, granting as it did more opportunity for manoeuvre and surprise.

As we have seen, projected American strategy

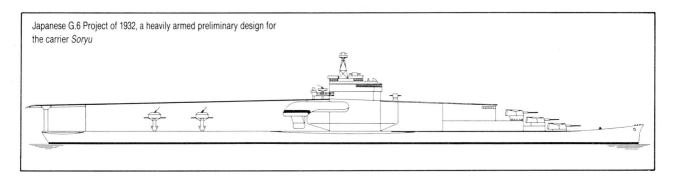

Japanese G.6 Project of 1932, a heavily armed preliminary design for the carrier *Soryu*

dovetailed precisely with Japanese expectations. The trans-Pacific advance was the centrepiece of War Plan Orange, and was the major inspiration for the US Navy's interest in flight-deck cruisers in the early 1930s.

The Japanese change in strategy toward 'offensive defensive' demanded a shift in tactical emphasis that influenced the types, numbers, design and characteristics of warships built after the Washington Treaty. Submarines had obvious value, especially long-range types. Another type seized upon eagerly by Japan was the 'treaty' cruiser: 10,000 ton, 8in gun armed ships. As we have seen, the treaty imposed limits on the displacement and gun calibre of individual cruisers, but it placed no restrictions on the number of these vessels that could be built. Japanese tacticians reasoned that such cruisers could help compensate for the numerical inferiority in battleships, and scarcely was the ink dry on the treaty when the first two were laid down, followed by another pair in 1924. By the end of 1932 Japan had twelve of them afloat, compared with seven for the United States.

Aircraft also were allotted an important place in the 'diminution operation', again with the aim of helping to compensate for battleship inferiority. With no international agreement limiting the number or type of aircraft a navy might possess, the IJN was free to develop air strength to any maximum desired. It proceeded to do so with a vengeance. No one save a few radicals believed that aircraft could by any means replace one's own battleships, or sink the enemy's, but they could help inflict the damage and casualties that were the aim of the wearing-down strategy.

The foundation for a naval air arm had been laid by a British aeronautical mission in 1921–23. Japan soon produced the world's first built-from-the-keel flight-deck carrier to enter service, *Hosho*. Aviation took on an ever increasing importance, spurred by keenly air-minded officers, the most notable of whom was Admiral Isoroku Yamamoto. British aircraft designs had at first dominated IJN flight decks and catapults; in 1932 Yamamoto instituted a programme to replace them with aircraft of all-Japanese design and manufacture. The result was the production of naval aircraft that were probably the world's finest for their time, including the types that figured so prominently in the early years of the Pacific war.

For aircraft to function in the far reaches of the Pacific they would obviously have to operate from ships or fixed bases, preferably both. For the former, the Washington Treaty was a stumbling block, as it limited Japan to inferiority in aircraft-carrier tonnage compared with the United States. The Pacific island groups mandated to Japan by the Treaty of Versailles — which the US fleet would have to pass through or near on its trans-Pacific trek — could provide excellent aircraft bases, but they lacked the landing fields required by wheeled aeroplanes. Contrary to a belief still widely held in America, until 1939 Japan respected Article XIX of the Washington Treaty forbidding preparation of naval bases on the islands.

However, the many Pacific atolls provided ready-made bases for seaplanes and their supporting ships, requiring no preparation save perhaps for some dredging. This was the first reason for the IJN's attachment to the seaplane.

A second stemmed from Japanese carrier doctrine. Carriers were to take part in the 'diminution operation', with special attention given to knocking out their American opposite numbers, but the carriers were not to operate as a combined unit; the carrier task force concept came late to the IJN — the First Air Fleet, the carrier force that hit Pearl Harbor and later swept the Indian Ocean, was not created until 10 April 1941. Carriers instead were to function independently, although preferably within air support distance of each other. To ensure the greatest possible offensive punch from the limited number of carriers, their complements consisted largely of torpedo planes and bombers, with a low ratio of fighters. Fighter complements were not increased until 1937, when severe losses were inflicted on unescorted carrier planes in China, including one occasion when eleven out of twelve bombers from *Akagi* were downed by Chinese fighters.

By the same token, the IJN did not wish to sacrifice potential offensive strength by employing carrier aircraft for reconnaissance, but aerial reconnaissance was essential; consequently it was to be carried out by aircraft from other ships, aircraft that perforce had to be seaplanes. This was the doctrine maintained throughout most of the Pacific war, even after the treaty restrictions on carrier tonnage had been thrown off. Carrier planes were reserved for the strike role; seaplanes from cruisers and/or other ships were to perform reconnaissance. Although the US Navy often saw a similar role for aeroplanes based on flying-deck cruisers, the lack of such vessels forced the carriers to use their own aircraft for reconnaissance. In the end, this may have been less of a disadvantage than prewar tacticians had thought; the aptly designated US 'scout-bombers', flying what might be called armed reconnaissance, nearly always carried a bomb or two for targets of opportunity, a policy whose advantages were demonstrated at the Battle of the Santa Cruz Islands in October 1942, when two aeroplanes on a scouting mission from *Enterprise* knocked out carrier *Zuiho*'s flight deck even before the main action was joined.

Despite this strong Japanese interest in seaplanes, the first hybrid design considered by the IJN was for a heavily armed flight-deck carrier. As we have seen, the London Naval Treaty of 1930 created, on paper at least, the flying-deck cruiser. There was a curious offshoot of this largely American concept in Japan: the G.6 Project of 1932, one of the preliminary designs for the carrier *Soryu*.

The G.6 design was a flight-deck carrier with an armament of six 8in guns in three twin turrets superimposed forward of the flight deck. This entailed a considerable loss in aviation capabilities, since it greatly reduced the length of the flight deck. The G.6 also featured a large island on the starboard side amidships, a unique feature for a Japanese carrier in 1932; perhaps experience with the island-less *Akagi* and *Kaga* showed that it was required for effective fire

control of the 8in guns. The single funnel emerged horizontally just below the island, curving downward as on other contemporary Japanese carrier designs. AA guns of unspecified number and calibre were carried on sponsons on each side aft. The design displaced 17,500 tons and was to measure 787ft 5in on the waterline; engines were to be geared turbines of 150,000shp.

The configuration somewhat resembled the original design of carriers *Kaga* and *Akagi*, which featured a three-deck arrangement forward with two twin 8in turrets on the second level. The flight deck's unusual profile also showed a link to the *Akagi*; like that of the earlier ship, it angled upward from an open stern, reaching a peak amidships abreast the island, then sloping gently downward until its termination just abaft the uppermost 8in turret. At this time the IJN used neither arresting gear nor catapults on its carriers, so the 'uphill' roll after landing was intended to slow aircraft, while the 'downhill' take-off run would give an aircraft a little extra speed in getting airborne. In spite of these similarities to earlier Japanese carriers, however, the G.6 was even more similar to the American 8in armed carrier schemes of 1931 (see Chapter 6). Both the American and Japanese designs bear a resemblance to the Thurston schemes described in Chapter 2 and shared many of the same faults, including the air turbulence that the turrets forward would have kicked up in the face of an aircraft trying to take off. The G.6 also shows an apparent narrowing of the forward portion of the flight deck to broaden the training arcs of the big guns.

It is impossible now to determine just how seriously the G.6 design was taken. Some Japanese officers may have seen this heavily gunned carrier as a useful vessel for independent missions during the 'diminution operation'. The London Naval Treaty barred Japan from building any more 8in gunned cruisers, a type the IJN held in high regard; perhaps this design was an attempt to get more of these guns into the fleet. The most probable explanation is that it was sketched as a response to American flying-deck cruisers that never materialised.

Whatever their genesis, the gunnery arrangements disappeared in the next *Soryu* preliminary design, the G.8 Project of 1933; its only touch of the hybrid was a low-angle battery of five 6.1in guns in two back-to-back turrets (a triple and a twin?) on a low open fo'c's'le, above which the flight deck was supported on stanchions. Even this vestigial

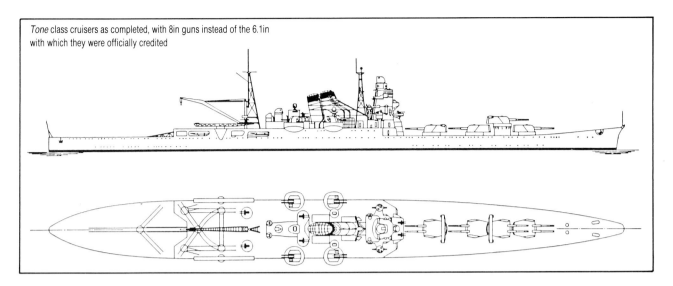

Tone class cruisers as completed, with 8in guns instead of the 6.1in with which they were officially credited

low-angle armament vanished in the next, and final, *Soryu* design.

The G.6 was a definite aberration in Japanese carrier design, and the IJN's hybrid leanings until after Midway would be toward seaplane-carrying cruisers, but it had to find the tonnage to build them. The London Naval Treaty of 1930 closed the loophole that had permitted unlimited numbers of cruisers by placing total tonnage restrictions on the type upon Britain, the United States and Japan. The treaty established a 10 to 6 ratio for the United States and Japan in heavy cruisers and a 10 to 7 ratio in light cruisers. Japan's twelve heavy cruisers exhausted its allotted tonnage in that category, but there were a couple of thousand tons remaining unused in the light cruiser allotment. Coupled with the tonnage of overaged cruisers that Japan was allowed to replace after 1936-37, this gave the IJN 50,995 tons to play with. This tonnage was devoted to six new light cruisers, four authorised in 1931 and two in 1934.

However, the IJN really wanted heavy cruisers, or Type A cruisers as they were designated, for two important strategico-tactical roles. First, they would form an 'advanced force' to help harry the US fleet during the 'diminution operation', then lead destroyer squadrons in night torpedo attacks on the enemy battle line, using their guns to pierce the American screen and joining in the attack with the strong torpedo armament that was a feature of all Japanese treaty cruisers. So the first four light cruisers, the *Mogami* class, were designed to permit the replacement of their fifteen 6.1in guns with ten 8in. This was done in 1939, so secretly that it was not known until the *Mogamis*

were encountered in combat in 1942. Nor was it known that their original displacement was more than 1000 tons heavier than the officially released figure.

The next class of cruisers also began as 'light' cruisers. Authorised in 1934, they were named *Tone* and *Chikuma*. The intended role and unusual configuration of these two vessels has almost universally caused them to be labelled hybrid warships, for while all the Japanese heavy cruisers carried aircraft, these arrangements were carried a step further in the two new ships. The earlier cruiser classes had one or two catapults and one to four seaplanes; *Tone* and *Chikuma* had far more elaborate aircraft handling facilities and a larger than normal complement of seaplanes in order to form a special division to act principally, although not entirely, as the aerial eyes of the 'advanced force'.

Tone was laid down on 1 December 1934, *Chikuma* on 1 October 1935, the latter delayed to permit redress of some of the structural problems encountered in the *Mogami* class; they were completed on 20 November 1938 and 20 May 1939, respectively. They were certainly unusual ships, with their entire main armament concentrated in four turrets on the fo'c's'le. The second turret was superimposed above the first, with the after pair, on the same level as the first, training aft. The stern portion was given over completely to seaplane facilities, with parking and traversing rails, turntables, two catapults and a handling derrick on the mainmast. The aft portion also housed four triple torpedo tubes, which were mounted as far from the bridge structure as possible for fear of explosion by enemy gunfire.

It has frequently been stated that this unusual

Tone sunk in Kure habour, *ca* October 1945 (*Naval Imaging Command*)

design was intended solely to facilitate seaplane carriage and operation, thus proving the ships' hybrid nature, but this is only partially true; the forward grouping of the guns was also intended to improve the concentration of salvoes. This was not simply a minor bonus of the extensive seaplane facilities aft; salvo dispersal was a problem of great concern to the IJN. Earlier cruisers, with their light, long hulls, flexed and twisted and caused the gun mountings to lose alignment, especially between the widely separated forward and after groups of turrets. Widely dispersed salvoes reduced the chances of hitting a target, and so this problem received a great deal of attention in the later cruiser designs.

The stern layout, however, certainly was advantageous from the standpoint of air operations. It offered ample, unhampered space for seaplane stowage and handling and it freed the aircraft from the danger of blast damage or destruction from the main battery, another problem on earlier cruisers. This permitted aircraft to be launched after a gunnery action had begun; in earlier cruisers it was necessary to launch before the big guns opened up or risk loss of the aircraft.

Although there was more than enough space for a hangar, none was installed; instead, the aircraft were exposed to the elements, carried on deck or catapult. This accorded with Japanese thinking that the risk of weather damage was

justified by the somewhat faster launching this permitted. Belowdeck space that might have been devoted to aircraft repair and maintenance equipment was instead given over to the torpedo tubes and their reload gear. In anticipation of damage to the unprotected aircraft, spare wings were carried.

The armament was originally to have been twelve 6.1in guns (4 × 3) but on 29 December 1934, less than a month after *Tone* had been laid down, Japan announced its withdrawal from the Washington Treaty effective 31 December 1936. With treaty restrictions thrown to the winds, Japanese naval architects were free to design and arm ships as they pleased, and one consequence was that the *Tones* were given 8in guns from the start without the necessity of conversion *à la* the *Mogamis*. Likewise, their displacement soared far above the officially announced 8500 tons. The fiction of the lighter armament, however, was maintained for reasons of political expediency and was widely reported in Western naval literature. The truth was not discovered until the Battle of the Santa Cruz Islands in October 1942.

Principal particulars of the *Tone* class as completed were

Displacement:	11,205t standard, 15,200t normal
Dimensions:	661ft 6in oa × 60ft 6in × 20ft 6in
Machinery:	geared turbines, 8 boilers, 4 shafts, 152,000shp = 35kts. 10,000nm at 18kts
Armament:	eight 8in (4 × 2); eight 5in (4 × 2); twelve 24in TT (4 × 3)
Armour:	4in main belt, 2½in deck, 3in turrets
Complement:	850

Light AA armament was originally twelve 25mm and four 13mm, but as in all Japanese warships the number, calibre and placement of these guns varied during the war.

Original plans called for a fifth twin 5in mount on the quarterdeck, but this was later dropped, probably because it interfered with aircraft arrangements as well as presenting blast problems.

There are great discrepancies as to the number of aircraft that the *Tones* could carry, or did carry, or did not carry. Reportedly, they were originally intended to stow eight, a number later reduced to six as maximum and finally to the five that is usually listed as their standard complement. It would seem, however, that seldom if ever were this many actually embarked; two or three was the customary number, and toward the end of the war only one was carried, probably because of the shortage of aviation personnel.

In 1941 Japanese naval strategy underwent a radical change when Yamamoto pushed through his plan for crushing the US Pacific Fleet with a massive aerial attack at its Hawaiian base. This did not alter the tactical role assigned to *Tone* and *Chikuma*; as Cruiser Division 8 they were attached to Vice-Admiral Chuichi Nagumo's First Air Fleet to provide advance aerial reconnaissance. They did this quite successfully during the Pearl Harbor operation, when two seaplanes, one from each cruiser, scouted the location of target ships without being detected.

During the return passage the cruisers were detached to support the seizure of Wake Island, and some of their aircraft took part in the attack.

Reattached to the First Air Fleet in January 1942, *Tone* and *Chikuma* operated extensively in support of Japanese advances southward and westward, taking part in the capture of Rabaul and the raids on Port Darwin and Ceylon. On 1 March *Chikuma* sank a merchant vessel by gunfire and later that day joined *Tone* and battleships *Hiei* and *Haruna* in a torrent of overkill that sank the hapless US destroyer *Edsall*. On 5 April a scout plane from *Tone* sighted the British heavy cruisers *Cornwall* and *Dorsetshire* in the Indian Ocean and guided the carrier aircraft to them; both cruisers were quickly sunk.

Cruiser Division 8 did not cover itself with glory during its next operation, however. As the First Air Fleet approached Midway on 4 June 1942, two seaplanes from each of the cruisers were assigned to carry out dawn searches for enemy vessels. They were delayed by a catapult malfunction and engine trouble, and one aircraft had to turn back because of bad weather. Several scouting flights were made later, and a *Chikuma* seaplane is credited with the sighting that led to the aerial attack on the carrier *Yorktown*. Most of the aviators' reports, however, were vague, misleading, or incorrect. They either underestimated or overestimated the number of enemy ships spotted, misidentified them, or failed to provide information as to the type of vessels sighted; all in all, their reports may have been more harmful than helpful. Their inept performance may have been the result of the IJN's prewar emphasis on offensive air operations; reconnaissance was considered a routine topic and naval aviators were given no special training in it. Midway was the first operation where aerial reconnaissance was a matter of vital importance, hence the first where the lack of training became disastrous.

Singly or together, both cruisers took part in

Chikuma under US attack off Samar, October 1944. A portion of the stern has been blown away (*National Archives*)

most of the remaining major actions of the war. *Chikuma* was badly damaged by US carrier aircraft on 26 October 1942 during the Battle of the Santa Cruz Islands, suffering casualties of 190 killed and 154 wounded. This was the first damage to be inflicted on either cruiser and laid her up for repairs until March 1943. She was sunk by US surface and air action off Samar on 28 October 1944 during the Battle of Leyte Gulf. *Tone* was sunk at Kure by a series of air attacks in August 1945.

The next Japanese warship generally accepted as a hybrid is the light cruiser *Oyodo*. Authorised in 1939 under the Fourth Replenishment Programme, she had the announced purpose of serving as a flagship for submarines, operating six high-speed seaplanes to reconnoitre for them. Construction of the ship and development of its aircraft apparently were to proceed in tandem, for a contract for the special seaplanes was given to the Kawanishi Aircraft Company in July 1939.

Oyodo was laid down on 14 February 1941 and completed on 28 February 1943. Her hull form followed the general lines of the *Agano* class light cruisers also authorised in the 1939 programme, but she was 1500 tons heavier. Published sources give varying particulars for this ship, especially for beam, draught and armour thicknesses; those given seem the most generally accepted.

Displacement:	8164t standard, 11,433t full load
Dimensions:	620ft 1in wl, 630ft 3in oa × 54ft 6in × 19ft 6in
Machinery:	4 sets geared turbines, 6 boilers, 110,000shp = 35kts. Oil 2360t; 10,600nm at 18kts
Armament:	six 6.1in (2 × 3); eight 3.9in AA (4 × 2); twelve 25mm (6 × 2)
Armour:	belt 2in, deck 1.4in, turrets 1in

Two features have caused *Oyodo* to be termed a hybrid: a large hangar, unique among Japanese cruisers, sited aft of the single funnel, and an exceptionally large catapult, 149.5ft long, on the quarterdeck. These features caused the main battery, six 6.1in guns in two triple turrets (removed from the *Mogamis* when they were converted to 8in guns) to be mounted forward. Heavy AA armament consisted of eight 3.9in guns (4 × 2), and twelve 25mm machine cannon made up the original light AA battery. *Oyodo* was also unique among Japanese cruisers in possessing no torpedo armament.

The ultra-powerful catapult, and the two extremely sturdy aircraft derricks sited to port and starboard of the hangar, were required to handle the ship's proposed seaplanes, the Kawanishi E15K1 *Shiun* (Violet Cloud, given the Allied code name Norm), which had a full-load weight of 10,803lb, considerably heavier than other Japanese shipboard floatplanes.

The E15K1 was an unusual craft, in advance of its time in many ways. A two- or three-place single-engine low-wing float monoplane, it was intended to operate in enemy-dominated areas and was therefore designed to be fast enough to outrun enemy land-based fighters. To accomplish this, it was given a unique system of retractable wingtip floats and a jettisonable main float, the dropping of which was calculated to add about 58mph to the top speed of approximately 290mph. It was powered by a 1620hp engine, later replaced by an 1850hp version, driving two contra-rotating propellers, a first in Japanese aero design. Intended purely for reconnaissance, it was armed defensively with only a single flexible machine gun.

Despite the ingenuity of its design, the E15K1 was a total dud. Its development was plagued with a long series of accidents and problems involving the dual propellers and the float mechanisms, which failed to function properly. Between October 1942, when the prototype made its first unsuccessful flight, and February 1944, only fifteen models were produced. None went aboard

Oyodo; six were assigned to Palau in the South Pacific, where all were quickly lost to the enemy fighters they could not outrun.

By the time *Oyodo* was completed her intended role was long outdated. Not only were her special aircraft unavailable, but the ill-managed Japanese submarine service had been reduced largely to supplying isolated island garrisons. Earlier, an authorised sister, never named, had been cancelled before laying down. (The 'name' *Niyodo* or *Nyoyodo* sometimes quoted in Western naval reference books for this ship simply means '*Oyodo* number two'.)

During late 1943 and early 1944 *Oyodo* was converted to a fleet flagship, with the hangar remodelled into staff and communications quarters, the large catapult replaced by a standard model, the aircraft complement reduced to two and light AA increased to fifty-four 25mm guns.

Oyodo became headquarters for the Combined Fleet on 30 April 1944, but the conversion proved inadequate and she ended that service after five months. She went into action for the first time on 25 October 1944 as a unit of Vice Admiral Jisaburo Ozawa's First Mobile Fleet, the decoy squadron intended to draw US forces north during the Battle of Leyte Gulf. She was slightly damaged by air attack, and Ozawa transferred his flag to her after the carrier *Zuikaku* was hard hit. She was damaged again from the air on 24 December in 'a bizarre raid that served no purpose', an attempted amphibious assault on Mindoro airfields. Returning to home waters, she was badly damaged by US carrier aircraft at Kure on 19 March 1945. Temporarily repaired, she was transferred to Edachi, where she was sunk by another carrier attack on 28 July.

Were the *Tones* and the *Oyodo* really hybrids? Both Western and Japanese opinion is nearly unanimous in claiming that they were, but for the *Tones* at least a strong argument can be made to the contrary. The oft-cited belief that the placement of their main battery was entirely to facilitate aircraft operation is incorrect; good gunnery was also a large factor in that placement. As it turned out, the all-forward arrangement was not as helpful as hoped, and the design of the final Japanese heavy cruiser, the never-completed *Ibuki*, reverted to the earlier five-turret arrangement, with three forward and two aft. Nor were the aircraft facilities particularly advanced over

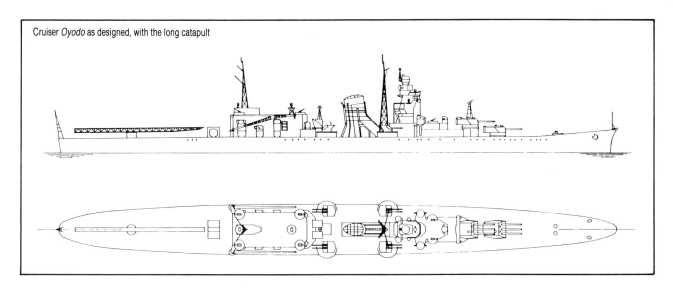

Cruiser *Oyodo* as designed, with the long catapult

those of earlier cruisers apart from offering more deck space for a somewhat greater number of aircraft.

It may well be concluded that the *Tones* do not meet the criteria that define a hybrid, but were simply cruisers able to carry two or three more aircraft than other Japanese cruisers. Perhaps they could best be described as 'semi-hybrids', if such a creature can exist.

Oyodo has more claim to be considered a hybrid. The all-forward placement of her main battery, unlike that of the *Tones, was* dictated entirely by the aircraft facilities, which were more extensive and specialised than those of the *Tone* class. These facilities caused a considerable sacrifice in firepower, for without them *Oyodo* could easily have carried a third triple 6.1in turret, and perhaps a fourth.

Oyodo soon after completion in 1942 (*Naval Imaging Command*)

Her intended tactical role has been accepted uncritically by naval historians, but given a little thought seems impractical. Co-operation between submarines, which could at best make about 20 knots on the surface and barely half that submerged, with a 35 knot ship would have been difficult, to say the least. And if *Oyodo* were to operate in areas of enemy air superiority, how was she to defend herself against aerial attack while equipped with seaplanes possessing no offensive power?

With the demise of her purpose even before she was completed, *Oyodo* was unable to serve any useful function. Despite her conversion to a command vessel, she failed in that role also. In her short life span, *Oyodo* probably saw less active sea service than any other major Japanese warship, for there was nothing she was equipped to do well. It is difficult to quarrel with Oscar Parkes' evaluation of her as 'the outstanding failure amongst modern cruisers'.

Japanese prewar hybrids, if such they were, were intended to fulfil a specific mission: scouting, either for the fleet or for submarine flotillas. As such, they were the products of a fully developed tactical doctrine. The same could not be said for the next generation of Japanese hybrids, those created in the aftermath of Midway. Their story, however, is reserved for another chapter.

ON THE TRADE ROUTES

In both the United States and Japan, the 'decisive action' formed the focal point of naval thought. Although Britain, the senior member in the small club of great naval powers, was likewise concerned with the lessons of Jutland and the clash of great battle fleets, it had also to consider the problems of the defence of commerce. These problems had been greatly complicated by the restrictions imposed by the naval limitation treaties, and it was in the area of trade defence that the hybrid made its tentative appearance in the Royal Navy's discussions.

Unlike its continental neighbours, the Royal Navy showed no interest in hybrid vessels during the 1920s; this is, perhaps, a reflection of the unhappy experiences with *Furious* and *Vindictive*. The Royal Navy also avoided the heavily gunned carrier; although some sketches of carriers armed with turreted 8in guns were run up in late 1923, no such ship was ever seriously considered for construction. *Courageous* and *Glorious*, the two remaining 'large light cruisers', were converted to carriers in 1928 and 1930 respectively, and were armed only with AA guns. By early 1939 even *Furious*' 5.5in had been replaced by twelve 4in AA.

The only British schemes for hybrid warships in the 1920s to come to light are purely unofficial, but certainly interesting, and among the most unusual of the breed. And it is scarcely surprising to find Maurice Prendergast, whom we met when discussing the French *croiseur de combat*, right in the thick of it all.

The French naval historian Henri le Masson once said of Prendergast that he 'had a great talent for drafting sketches of warships which were remarkably precise and plausible . . . sometimes of existing ships and sometimes of "projects," products of his imagination which he worked out with great facility'. Prendergast had a lot of information to draw upon in draughting these 'projects', for he was the editor of *Jane's Fighting Ships* for many years. He also seems to have had a habit of naming his creations — *Indomptable* is one example of this tendency; in the same vein, he dubbed his hybrid cruiser design *Boscawen*. Prendergast began work on a model of this ship in 1923; the model was still incomplete when he described his ship in the October 1926 issue of *The Navy*.

Boscawen was Prendergast's answer to the question, 'What is the best possible type of fleet scout'? He pointed out that 'a few aeroplanes, in a few hours, can con over a space which a squadron of light cruisers could only sweep over in a day'. On the other hand, small carriers such as *Hermes* and *Hosho*, while ideally sized for the role of fleet scouts, suffered from a 'poverty of . . . armament'; the answer was 'a vessel of about 10,000 tons, having a large capacity for aircraft, but powerfully enough armed to take care of herself '. This implied a battery of 8in guns to deal with the Treaty cruisers his scout was likely to encounter; the secondary battery was fourteen 4in or 4.7in guns. Prendergast described his vessel as a 'centaur-ship'; like its mythical namesakes, it would combine in one body the features of two dissimilar creatures.

Prendergast's model shows a ship with a very high freeboard and two triple turrets forward of a tall tower mast. Abaft the tower is a third triple turret, and aft of that is a landing-on deck. In many ways, the ship is a mixture of other vessels: the flight deck aft is clearly based on that of the carrier *Hermes*, including the hump-like after end, while the tower seems based on early illustrations of *Nelson*'s superstructure. He gave his ship twin funnels and masts, which were also in no way novel; but Prendergast did propose one irrefutably unique feature, his aircraft launching arrangement.

The flight deck was linked to the tower by a light bridge over the third turret, which led to an 'archway' through the tower, thence to the catapult atop B turret. This rather clumsy arrangement was intended to reduce interference between the guns and aircraft. Complicating matters still further was the fact that the bridge to the tower was some 10ft higher than the flight deck; this necessitated a lift to raise the aircraft to the higher level, in addition to the lift serving the hangar below the flight deck. Prendergast used this discontinuity in deck levels to provide a covered area between the funnels for an 'emergency re-fuelling station'. He estimated the aerial complement at ten to twelve machines: one 'ready-use' aircraft on the catapult, one in the 'archway' (which could be closed off fore and aft by roller doors to form a one-machine hangar), one above and one inside the 're-fuelling station', two on the flight deck itself, and four to six machines in the hangar.

Boscawen clearly would not have been a workable proposition. The turbulence over the landing deck, from both the centreline tower and the twin funnels, would have precluded safe landing operations, while the single catapult would have taken twenty or thirty minutes to launch all twelve of the ship's aircraft. It is also open to question whether nine 8in guns and a flight deck could have been achieved on a ship of less than 10,000 tons; a few years after Prendergast's *Boscawen*, the US Navy's Bureau of Construction and Repair would conclude that nine 6in was the greatest battery that could be squeezed into a reasonable treaty cruiser (see Chapter 6).

An anonymous naval correspondent of the *Naval and Military Record* liked the combination Prendergast had put forward, and outlined a very similar 'super-cruiser' in the 8 September 1926 issue of that journal. He envisaged a 19,000 ton

Maurice Prendergast's freakish 'centaur-ship' *Boscawen*, based on a photo of his model appearing in the October 1926 issue of *The Navy*. Note the twin parallel funnels and the 'archway' through the tower mast by which aircraft were to be transferred to the catapult atop B turret (*drawing by John P McLaughlin*)

version of the *Boscowen*, identical in general configuration but armed with nine 12in guns; the ship was to be unarmoured, and capable of 33 knots or more. Its role would be rather different from Prendergast's 'best possible fleet scout'; it would act as a cruiser-killer, and the author maintained that such a ship would be 'ideal for such a mission as the chasing of a hostile raiding squadron'. To some degree, the 'super-cruiser' was inspired by the recent reports of the *croiseur de combat*, although the author believed 'the "defensive" school holds the reins at the Rue Royale', and so thought it unlikely that France would build such offensively oriented vessels.

Consideration of the security of the Empire's trade routes certainly motivated the author of the super-cruiser, with its suitability for hunting raiders clearly spelled out. Oddly enough, Prendergast did not see *Boscawen* in that role, even though he was gathering a portfolio of proposals for convoy protection vessels at the same time as he was working on his 'centaur-ship' model. Eventually, he published a critique of the trade protection proposals he had collected, and among them was a hybrid ship combining the features of a monitor, a cruiser and a carrier. Its anonymous designer gave it the unfathomable name *Tishy's Ghost*.

At 8800 tons, this vessel would have a hull similar to that of the First World War monitors *Erebus* and *Terror*, but with somewhat finer lines and greater freeboard. Its huge bulges for torpedo protection would limit speed to 19 knots, but this was more than sufficient for convoying merchant ships. In peacetime, main armament would be limited to a single turret for 8in guns, to conform to the Washington Treaty, but once war began it would be replaced by a twin 12in turret. The turret is mounted atop a redoubt housing a secondary battery of nine 6in guns. Six AA guns of unspecified calibre are mounted in sponsons, three to each beam. The vessel also was to carry an anti-submarine howitzer for launching depth charges to a range of 2000 yards.

Aft of the tower superstructure is an aeroplane landing deck, patterned on that of *Hermes*. Engine room gases would be vented in a manner similar to *Argus*; despite this feature, landing on a ship of this configuration would have been almost as hazardous as on *Furious* and *Vindictive*.

Aircraft take-off arrangements are not clear, although there is apparently a catapult atop the main battery turret, and it is probable that the large derricks sited abreast the tower would be used to swing aeroplanes to the catapult from the aft deck.

If the combination of characteristics embodied in *Tishy's Ghost* makes it an oddity even among hybrids, an additional feature renders it truly unique in hybrid history — it was to be equipped to operate small airships. Thus there is a tall mooring mast, and broken lines on the drawing above the flight deck almost certainly indicate collapsible wind screens to shelter one or more airships.

This idea had real merit, for it was both technologically feasible and militarily sound. Small non-rigid airships had made their debut well before the First World War, but the idea of employing numbers of them for anti-submarine patrol was a brainstorm of Lord Fisher in early 1915. Britain churned out swarms of such craft for the rest of the war; the type was adopted by the French Navy in 1916 and by the American in 1917.

These airships have been credited with great usefulness in the campaign against the U-boat; carrying a few bombs and a machine gun or two, they patrolled the sea lanes to the limit of their endurance, protecting convoys by spotting U-boats and leading surface craft to them, and by diverting convoys from likely areas for submarine attacks or mine fields. No submarine was ever directly sunk by an airship (save a British boat destroyed by a French airship through mis-identification), but they unquestionably prevented many U-boat attacks.

The lighter-than-air gas that provided their lift enabled the 'blimps', as they were soon nicknamed, to remain in the air far longer than even the largest aeroplane or flying boat, but their radius and endurance were limited by their fuel capacity and crew fatigue. Consequently, the Royal Navy experimented fairly extensively and quite successfully with refuelling and remanning airships while they were towed by cruisers (although this was for the purpose of reconnaissance for the Grand Fleet rather than anti-submarine work). In 1918 an airship landed successfully at least once on the aft flight deck of *Furious*.

The anonymous creator of *Tishy's Ghost* was obviously aware of the value of airships for convoy escort, perhaps through personal experience during the war. It is also possible, depending on when the design was drawn up, that he might have been influenced by the Spanish aviation vessel *Dédalo* or the American oiler *Patoka*, both of which were fitted with airship mooring masts, the former in 1922 and the latter in 1924.

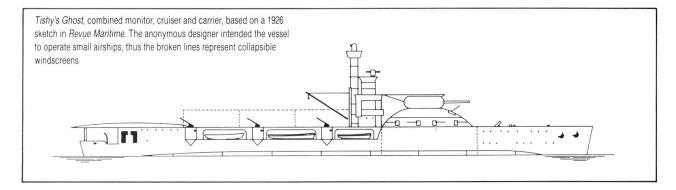

Tishy's Ghost, combined monitor, cruiser and carrier, based on a 1926 sketch in *Revue Maritime*. The anonymous designer intended the vessel to operate small airships, thus the broken lines represent collapsible windscreens

Whatever the inspiration, the notion makes a good deal of sense, for it would have permitted operation of airships even in mid-ocean. In fact, an airship-equipped hybrid seems far more feasible than one intended for aeroplane take-off and landing. The bulk of even the smallest airship is far greater than that of an aeroplane, enabling it to weather the turbulence stirred up by a ship far more safely than a heavier-than-air craft. Its extremely slow landing speed is another factor in its favour. The feasibility of an airship-surface ship combination was proved not only by the British First World War experiments but in post-Second World War practice in the US Navy, when airships were towed and replenished by vessels ranging from aircraft carriers to submarines.

Apart from its unfortunate landing deck, *Tishy's Ghost* had many of the ideal attributes of a convoy escort: guns big enough to ward off raiding cruisers, good protection against underwater attack, and effective anti-submarine weapons. Nevertheless, Prendergast considered it too complex and elaborate, and there is some justice in this criticism. Leaving aside the vessel's questionable status under the naval treaties, it is doubtful whether any country would have been willing to invest in the construction of the considerable number of such ships that trade protection would have required, and it could certainly not be mass-produced in time of war. Its low speed would have barred *Tishy's Ghost* from work with a fleet; its only possible duties would be convoy escort and shore bombardment.

It might be said that *Tishy's Ghost* walked again during the Royal Navy's deliberations regarding the hybrid cruiser in the early 1930s, for official consideration centred on its value in trade protection, although not specifically for convoy escort.

British interest in such ships arose from the

Operation of airships from *Tishy's Ghost* would have been quite feasible, as demonstrated in this photo of an experiment on 27 May 1918 in which naval airship SSZ.59 landed aboard HMS *Furious* (*J M Bruce/G S Leslie collection*)

American agitation for flight-deck vessels at the London Naval Conference in 1930. It was almost a year, however, before the matter of 'flying-deck' vessels was seriously taken up. This delay was almost certainly the result of the traditional Admiralty policy of not initiating construction of new types of warship; until the US Navy actually laid down the hybrid ships Moffett had fought so hard to legitimise at the London Naval Conference, the Sea Lords were content to wait upon developments. This attitude did not preclude discussion of the alleged merits and faults of hybrid ships, however, and in March 1931 the Commander-in-Chief, Mediterranean, Admiral Sir Ernle M Chatfield, forwarded to the Admiralty a proposal by the Rear Admiral, 1st Cruiser Squadron, for a 'semi-aircraft carrier' with eighteen torpedo-carrying aircraft to be launched by catapult. This proposal stimulated considerable debate among the members of the Naval Staff.

This debate began in late 1931 when the Board of Admiralty asked the commanders-in-chief of the Home and Mediterranean Fleets for their opinions of the value of a 'flying-deck cruiser'. The Home Fleet C-in-C, Admiral Sir John D Kelly, ruled the type out for work with the fleet because it 'will presumably only be developed at the sacrifice of fighting power, and will be at a disadvantage in action, particularly at night or in low visibility'. However, he judged that such vessels would be 'of great use on trade routes and on reconnaissance sweeps owing to their ability to operate and recover their aircraft in weather conditions which prohibit the use of seaplanes'. Despite this usefulness, he believed that construction of a hybrid would be 'premature' and recommended instead that 'designs for a flying-deck cruiser should be produced and that the question of building them should be reviewed in the light of progress made'.

Chatfield, C-in-C Mediterranean, agreed that 'designs of cruiser-carriers should be prepared', but also recommended that 'designs should be prepared showing what can be done in the way of a small carrier to work with our cruisers on the trade routes'. Either method of getting aeroplanes to work with the cruisers was preferable to the use of seaplanes because 'cruiser borne float or boat planes . . . can never be reliable in ocean weather', an opinion with which generations of naval officers would heartily agree. Whether tonnage should be devoted to small carriers or cruiser-carriers 'depends on the design of the latter'.

Chatfield included a list of questions about the design of such ships that were virtually identical to those being asked by US naval officers at this same time.

'How many aircraft of what types could be carried?
'How many aircraft could be operated at one time?
'What guns both H.A. and L.A. will be possible?
'Comparing the cruiser-carrier with the HERMES type carrier, will the reduced size of hangar in the cruiser-carrier be compensated for by the increase of gun power due to a larger gun deck?
'Will the hybrid cruiser-carrier be able to defend herself against a cruiser of equal tonnage?
'Will better reconnaissance, aircraft spotting, and a possible air striking force counterbalance her lesser gun power and possibly increased vulnerability?'

His final comment, too, mirrored American concerns; bearing in mind that since 'once a cruiser is built it must last us for twenty years', the navy might end up stuck with 'a ship of inferior gun power and protection'.

In his report Chatfield had also raised an issue that would play a role throughout the British discussion of hybrid cruisers, noting 'That it is an important consideration whether the development of this type will be more to our advantage in protecting trade and finding raiders than to the enemy in attacking it'. This was a vital question that would surface every time the matter of building hybrids was debated, and was at the heart of the frequently expressed desire not to 'lead the way' in the construction of such new types of warship.

The mild endorsements of the hybrid from the two fleet commanders formed the basis for a strong recommendation of the flying-deck cruiser advanced by the Director of the Naval Air Division (DNAD), Captain C E Turle, in a long minute dated 21 March 1932. His argument began with a *prima facie* assumption of the 'great value of aircraft in co-operation with surface craft on the trade routes in defense of maritime communications'. Turle considered aircraft only minimally useful in attack; scouting was the *raison d'être* of trade protection aircraft, and in this role 'one ship working aircraft is equal in reconnaissance value during favourable weather and by day, to at least 2 ships without aircraft', a statement remarkably similar to Admiral Jellicoe's declaration that during the First World War each German airship was 'in *favourable weather* equal to at least two light cruisers' for scouting.

'In its ability to attack ships', Turle continued, 'the aircraft has less marked advantage. Bombs and torpedoes from the air are like shell and torpedoes from ships — many miss; thus many are required in order to obtain one's object of destroying or damaging the enemy . . . aircraft in attack hardly achieve anything that the cruiser herself could not achieve.'

This attitude ran directly counter to the major theme of the American flying-deck cruiser proponents, that it was the *offensive* potential of its aircraft that made the CLV a worthwhile proposition. US naval aviators expected 60 per cent of the bombs delivered by dive bombers to hit, a far different assumption from Turle's expectation of many misses.

Having outlined the advantages of aircraft in scouting, Turle believed that the only matters to be considered were 'the type of aircraft required . . . and how to get them to the right spot at the right time in the right numbers'.

The type, it was immediately concluded, should be strictly a reconnaissance craft, able to carry some bombs unless this 'would involve too great a sacrifice in reconnaissance'. As to how to get them to the right spot, Turle outlined several methods: aeroplanes could be flown from the decks of carriers, merchant vessels or cruisers, or seaplanes could take off from the water or be launched by catapult. He ruled out carriers because of the limited number available under the terms of the Washington Treaty and the vital necessity of keeping them with the main fleet; also eliminated were mercantile carriers because of the delay involved in converting and equipping them. Seaplanes were dismissed because of their total dependence on favourable weather and sea conditions.

This left only 'a floating aerodrome . . . i.e., a flying deck' [cruiser], which offered the advantages of 'greater speed in operation of a number of aircraft' and their more frequent availability for use. Turle recognised that arguments against the hybrid ship would centre around the fact that 'such a cruiser will mean a less efficiently gunned or armoured or engined ship, and that we cannot afford to sacrifice such qualities in view of our now restricted [cruiser] numbers'. However, 'the reply . . . is that our cruisers seldom, it may be said never, work singly on the trade routes'.

After expatiating on the advantages of the hybrid cruiser, Turle suggested that 'If a flying deck cruiser were built, it would be possible to judge its capability both actually and comparatively'. As we have seen, Admiral Pratt had made exactly the same point in arguing for the construction of at least one hybrid cruiser by the US Navy.

Turle concluded by recommending that 'the design of a flying-deck cruiser should be examined forthwith . . . and that the construction of such a cruiser shall receive early consideration'.

He appended a list of proposed characteristics for the cruiser; they make an interesting contrast to those advanced by the US Navy.

'Stowage for 12 aircraft to be provided at a minimum, 18 for preference.
'Hangar space is not essential, but preferably hangar space for at least 1/3rd of the aircraft where major maintenance can be effected.
'A catapult might be required.
'Smooth flow of air over the flying deck to be given special consideration.
'Length of flying deck to be 250 feet made up as follows: —
'50 ft. abaft the after arresting wire.
'100 ft. (5 wires 25 ft. apart).
'100 ft. before the foremost wire, i.e., the length necessary to pull up a 55 knot aircraft with 1 g. with a 20 knot deck wind.
'Breadth of flying deck to be at least 60 ft.
'No superstructure to be abreast after 200 feet of flying deck.'

The proposed length of the landing deck — some 100ft shorter than the American naval aviators generally considered the minimum — was clearly geared to small and relatively low-performance reconnaissance aircraft, and in fact Turle's appendix outlined an aircraft suitable for the vessel: a two-seater of about 5000lb with a full wingspan of 37ft and a folded span of 15½ft. This was a lighter and smaller aeroplane than the then-standard British shipboard reconnaissance-spotter, the Fairey IIIF; the characteristics more nearly approximated those of the Fairey Seafox, a light catapult floatplane that went into production in 1936 and is remembered chiefly for the role one played in the Battle of the River Plate.

It is interesting to note that while the restricted flight deck of the American CLV forced British-style aviation operations on its aircraft — hangar stowage for all, and high-speed lifts to strike them down rapidly — Turle recommended an almost American style of operations, with aircraft permanently stowed on deck and the hangar reserved for major maintenance and repairs. One member of the Naval Staff concurred with Turle's paper but pointed out one of the problems with such operations, arguing 'that hangar accommodation for all . . . aircraft is necessary in order that the ship may be capable of fighting without [?] damage to aircraft carried', presumably from the blast of the ship's own guns.

Other members of the Naval Staff were not as enthusiastic. The Director of the Tactical Division, Captain C D Burke, agreed 'it would be desirable to investigate the design of a flying deck cruiser', but believed that such a vessel might well be inferior in armament and armour to a conventional cruiser.

In April, Captain H C Rawlings replaced Turle as DNAD. Rawlings lost no time in voicing his support for the hybrid in a minute of 27 April 1932, relying heavily on the mildly favourable opinions of Chatfield and Kelly and proposing that 'a preliminary investigation of the design for a Flying [Deck] Cruiser now be commenced'.

Admiral Sir Dudley North, Director of Operations, responded to Rawlings' minute on 24 May. He 'fully concurred' with the value of aircraft on the trade routes and that their function there should be reconnaissance, but disagreed with the assertion in Turle's original paper that trade protection cruisers would never be required to operate singly: 'the conditions which may necessitate their doing so are certainly not decreasing'. This, North wrote, involved 'the question of whether to concentrate a squadron's air resources in one unit, or whether to make each ship self-supporting with regard to the air together with as little sacrifice as possible in other respects'. This was a question that has been asked time and again during the history of shipboard aviation, and is still being asked to this day.

North's recommendation was that investigation of the hybrid cruiser be delayed pending forthcoming trials of a new type of carrier arresting gear, adding 'An additional reason for postponement would seem to be that our policy may have to be dictated to a certain extent by the results of the Disarmament Conference'.

This reference was to the General Disarmament Conference under way in Geneva. The conference had opened in February and had still produced no tangible results; it was eventually adjourned in June without reaching any agreements. Yet it continually promised (or, as naval men in every nation saw it, threatened) to produce some new limitations on cruisers. The conference was also being used in the United States as an excuse for suspending Congressional consideration of naval appropriations that included funds for flying-deck cruisers, the real problem being one of economics rather than diplomacy.

In August the Director of Plans (D of P), Captain J H D Cunningham, noted that the Board of Admiralty had decided that 'we should support a Japanese proposal at Geneva to prohibit the fitting of flying-on decks', a position that would presumably be taken at the next disarmament conference, scheduled to take place before the expiration of the Washington and London treaties in 1936. 'Under these circumstances', the minute continued, 'it would appear that there can be no question of our leading the way by *building* a flying-deck cruiser at present' and furthermore it appeared that 'the U.S. are not actually proceeding with the building of their much-advertised flying deck cruiser' and that 'the U.S. Naval authorities are weakening in their advocacy of the type'. Therefore, 'the preparation of design could well wait until the actual laying down of a vessel of this type by the U.S.A. or another State makes it necessary to give further consideration to the subject'.

Rawlings, faced with a board decision against the type and the uncertainties created by the hazy disarmament situation, on 13 December 1932 had to 'concur . . . that preparation of this [flying-deck cruiser] design should be deferred'.

Yet the Director of Naval Construction's department apparently did prepare a sketch design for a cruiser-carrier in 1933, although no details of it have survived. It was rejected by the board, at least in part because of the fear that other nations would follow suit. The hybrid would not only make an effective trade protection vessel, but, as Chatfield had mentioned, a good commerce raider as well, and the Admiralty did not want to give anyone ideas along that line.

The hybrid resurfaced in 1936; consideration at that time was again being given to various ways of hunting down commerce raiders. By this time the quantitative restrictions of the treaties had lapsed, so capital ship tonnage no longer had to be carefully reserved for the battle fleet; this made a battlecruiser-carrier attractive as an anti-raider vessel, and a sketch design was drawn up, but again all details have been lost and no such ship was ever recommended for construction. Perhaps this vessel would have mounted the new 12in/50 gun; a prototype of this gun had been completed in 1933, and Vickers Armstrong had produced plans for a triple turret using it. Such a hybrid might very well have proven effective in hunting down commerce-raiding pocket battleships.

The hybrid's final appearance in the prewar Royal Navy was entirely unofficial: several students at the Greenwich school of naval architecture worked out theoretical hybrid designs during their courses there. All trace of these projects has apparently been lost. The hybrid would not make another appearance in the Admiralty until 1940, but by then its rationale would have absolutely nothing to do with trade protection.

That many of the issues raised during the Royal Navy's discussions of the hybrid cruiser in the 1930s were also being examined by the US Navy at this time has been noted, but the differences in the national approaches to the hybrid should also be pointed out. Whereas the US Navy thought the type valuable for both fleet work and trade protection, the British concentrated entirely on the latter. Given this emphasis, it is odd that the Royal Navy gave no consideration to the hybrid in anti-submarine operations, a topic repeatedly mentioned across the Atlantic. This lack of interest may well have been due to what Arthur Marder has described as an 'exaggerated confidence' in asdic (later termed sonar), which was often seen as the answer to the underwater menace.

Another and perhaps more significant difference was the general British attitude that a hybrid cruiser's aircraft, while very useful in reconnaissance, would be of little value offensively. Throughout this period the Admiralty was mired in controversy with the Air Ministry over control of the Fleet Air Arm, as the Royal Air Force's naval component was designated in 1924. Among the consequences of the navy's repeated defeats in that battle were the lack of up-to-date strike and fighter aircraft and the resulting lag in RN experience with and understanding of the potential of shipboard aviation in the offensive role. The men who could have supplied the expertise and nurtured the understanding, the naval fliers of the First World War who had pioneered integration of aviation into sea power, were no longer in the navy at all; almost without exception they had chosen to remain with the RAF that had co-opted them in 1918. Their reasons for joining the new service were varied but valid: lack of appreciation of their efforts by the Admiralty (often exaggerated, but definitely a factor), greater chances for promotion, the adventure and challenge of developing a new service, the sheer love of flying.

The lack of experienced aviators within the Royal Navy's hierarchy led to a perhaps inevitable underrating of the offensive value of aircraft; even the Director of Air Material dismissed the value of aircraft in attack. In contrast, it was precisely because aircraft, especially dive bombers, were seen as offensive weapons that the US Navy gave such serious consideration to the hybrid cruiser in the early 1930s.

It is a measure of the Royal Navy's concern over commerce protection that a vessel considered markedly inferior to conventional types was discussed at such length; but without senior officers to back the idea, any British flying-deck cruiser scheme stood little chance of realisation. Chatfield succinctly summed up the opposition case a few years later in rejecting proposals for large destroyers: 'Hybrids are always failures'.

'NEITHER FISH NOR FOWL'

In 1932 America's Great Depression was approaching its nadir. Naval construction was in limbo; Congress, desperate to cut expenditure, even considered a bill to take all battleships out of commission. The bill did not pass, but it is indicative of the alarm the legislators felt over the economic crisis.

Conditions for the navy were to change soon. Rightly or wrongly, the American electorate held Republican President Herbert Hoover responsible for the nation's economic wreckage, and in November voted Democrat Franklin D Roosevelt into the White House in a landslide.

Roosevelt was without question the most nautically knowledgeable president in US history. The study of ships and navies had been his passion since boyhood, when he had considered applying for appointment to the Naval Academy; he had written on naval history and affairs, had gained a near-professional comprehension of naval technology, and, during his eight-year tenure as Assistant Secretary of the Navy under Josephus Daniels, had acquired an intimate understanding of Navy Department procedure. As his naval secretary, Roosevelt chose seventy-one-year-old Claude Swanson, a former chairman of the Senate Committee on Naval Affairs and himself a considerable authority on maritime matters. Swanson's age and poor health, however, led Roosevelt to remark once that he was his own secretary of the navy, and it was an added duty he clearly relished; among other things, he became personally involved in the design of the *North Carolina* class battleships.

One of the many extensive public works projects that Roosevelt initiated was a naval construction programme. Like so many of Roosevelt's economic ideas, it was not original to him; Moffett had earlier suggested that shipbuilding could play a significant role in relieving unemployment, as had Hoover's outgoing naval secretary, Charles Francis Adams. The idea was not implemented, however, until Roosevelt allocated $238 million for

naval construction in June 1933 under the National Industrial Recovery Act. Now the navy could finally begin to build the ships it had so long planned; within the year, the carriers *Yorktown* and *Enterprise* and five cruisers had been authorised. In November, an additional $7.5 million was allotted for the acquisition of naval aircraft and their equipment. This impetus continued into 1934, with passage of the landmark Vinson-Trammel Act authorising naval construction to the limit of the Washington and London treaties.

Progress was not confined to legislation; during 1933–34, there were significant technical advances in naval aviation — improved carrier catapults and arresting gear were developed, and contracts were issued for the first monoplane carrier dive bombers and torpedo bombers.

There were, however, setbacks, especially for the cause of the flying-deck cruiser. Among them was the resignation of David S Ingalls as Assistant Secretary of the Navy for Aeronautics, and the retirement of Admiral William Pratt as CNO. Both men had supported the flying-deck cruiser; Pratt's replacement as CNO, Admiral William H Standley, did not back the hybrid with anything like Pratt's vigour and enthusiasm, while Ingalls' former post would remain vacant until 1941, allegedly for economy's sake.

The most crucial loss of all came with the crash of the airship *Akron* in the Atlantic on 4 April 1933, for aboard her was Rear Admiral William Moffett. With this loss, the most persistent and articulate voice in favour of the hybrid cruiser was stilled. Although Moffett died within a few months of mandatory retirement age, there can be no doubt that had he lived he would have continued his crusade for the CLV as a private citizen — and he was a man who commanded considerable public admiration and support.

Within months of Moffett's death, support for the flying-deck cruiser began to wane. The loss of his advocacy, however, influential as it may have been, was not the cause. Rather, it was almost entirely because of Roosevelt's naval renaissance. That the CLV concept should fall into disfavour at the precise moment funds for it were finally available is not the paradox it would first appear, for it had been conceived in straitened political and economic circumstances, a compromise intended to bolster cruiser and carrier strength when neither type could be obtained separately. It was out of place amid the sudden abundance of

The ubiquitous Vought Corsair series of shipboard aircraft, typified by this O3U-3 version taking off from USS *Ranger*, undoubtedly would have formed at least part of any flying-deck cruiser's aerial complement. The sturdy, versatile Corsair, adaptable to both wheel and float undercarriage, was a mainstay of US naval aircraft during the 1930s, capable of performing in a number of roles including scouting, spotting and bombing (*US Navy, courtesy of William T Larkins*)

construction; compromise was no longer needed, and officers who had given the CLV their luke-warm support as the only, but certainly not the best, way to get more aircraft to sea began to turn away from it, leaving only those who liked it *per se*.

The sudden lack of interest occasioned some comment in the House Naval Affairs Committee, whose members wanted to know why the navy had not begun building any flying-deck cruisers. In January 1934, in response to what the senior member of the General Board, Rear Admiral Richard H Leigh, characterised as 'agitation' in the committee, the board circulated a series of questionnaires and held hearings on what was now generally referred to as the 'CF'. Senior officers afloat and chiefs of various bureaux were asked what they thought of the flying-deck cruiser.

The questionnaires differed according to their destination, and many of the inquiries, especially those aimed at the Bureaux of Aeronautics and Ordnance, again sought technical information on matters such as flight-deck length, placement of lifts, disposition of armament, fire control, etc. Almost for the first time, however, attention was given to what the flying-deck cruiser's true func-tion and purpose should be, both tactically and strategically. One query cut right to the heart of the issue, and was asked of almost everyone: in the absence of treaty restrictions, would the CF still be worthwhile?

Only three respondents answered 'yes' to this question. One was Rear Admiral S W Bryant of the War Plans Division, whose avowed support for the flying-deck cruiser predated the General Board's questionnaire. He had recommended the type in a memorandum to the CNO of 17 January; he now reiterated his support in both his response to the questionnaire and in testimony during the hearings held on 31 January. He believed that 'the use of these flying-deck cruisers will be limited largely to strategic problems'. For example, the CF could be used in 'the arc of scouting covering most probable routes of enemy main fleet advance and on the flanks of such a scouting line'. Another strategic role would be 'on a patrol line such as that between Mindanao and New Guinea, both for detecting merchant shipping attempting to pass through and to detect the approach of hostile naval craft, in order to give advance warning to our convoys'. While admitting the tactical vulner-ability of the CF, he believed that it could act as the advanced element of the fleet's air forces, scouting for the carriers, whose aircraft would be reserved for strikes against the enemy fleet, an almost exact parallel to the later Japanese use of cruiser-launched floatplane scouts which led to the *Tone* class heavy cruisers (see Chapter 7). Asked if 10,000 ton carriers, with more aircraft, would not be better for these jobs, Bryant responded that there was a limit to the number of aircraft required to search an area, and that having more aircraft would not increase the ship's ability to monitor that area; clearly, he did not see the CF as a vessel intended for offensive air strikes.

It is curious that Bryant, perhaps the most enthusiastic supporter of the CF, handicapped his own arguments in favour of it by following a strict interpretation of the London Treaty's 'landing-on platform or deck' passage. He apparently anticipated the use of catapults for launching; to make it clear to the world that the ship did not have a combined landing-on, flying-off deck, he suggested that 'the superstructure be made so that it would be perfectly apparent that planes could not fly off. Undoubtedly in time of war it could be converted for them to fly off too'. Everyone else, both supporters and detractors, assumed that a 'landing-on' deck implied a 'flying-off' deck as well.

Another supporter was Rear Admiral John Halligan, commander of Battle Force aircraft. He stated that from his study of flying-deck cruisers in Naval War College board games 'they were a very successful type as long as they remained out of gun range of enemy vessels'. Like Bryant, he thought 'The utility of the CF is principally in its strategical employment. For work against raiders, for convoy escort, and for search the CF is distinctly better than the CL in areas of good visibility'. He also opined that the type would be valuable in anti-submarine work and 'in the vicinity of the [Japanese] Mandated Islands' where 'air operations from vessels less important than large carriers will be useful'. He concluded with the observation that, 'It is argued that the CF is a hybrid, but so is the mule'.

Rear Admiral Luke McNamee, president of the Naval War College, shared Bryant's and Halligan's view that the flying-deck cruiser's value would be 'chiefly strategical', and that 'For distant scouting, trade protection, etc., . . . I see an advantage over ordinary cruisers, especially in the Pacific where the weather and visibility are favorable'. Their tactical use would be 'bombing the enemy light forces preliminary to battle' and providing spotting aircraft for the battle line. McNamee recommended construction of four CFs, with the first given a one-year head start so that lessons learned from its operation could be incorporated in the following ships.

McNamee buttressed his favourable opinion of the type by appending a long report on War College board games that had used the CF. Also included in these addenda was an essay by Com-

mander G B Hoey of the War College staff. Hoey echoed the arguments Forest Sherman had made in his 1930 *Proceedings* article in supporting the flying-deck cruiser as a trade protection vessel *par excellence*, but noted that high speed would not be important in this role; 30 to 30.5 knots would be adequate to permit it to overhaul virtually any merchantman and no warship could outrun its aeroplanes. By shaving a couple of knots off the generally accepted cruiser speed of 32 knots, he calculated, there would be a saving of 30 per cent in shaft horsepower and the resulting reduction in machinery weight could be put into protection, especially against underwater attack. The result would be 'a CF capable of operating without any anti-submarine screen except her own planes, [and] her own speed'. This was close to the concept of the 'one-ship task force' that Sir George Thurston had first advanced in outlining his 'experimental battleship' of 1923 (see Chapter 2), a frequent hybrid rationale.

Unlike other supporters, Hoey attributed a substantial offensive role to the CF, which had a powerful aerial punch in Naval War College board games due to the use of dive bombers. By 1934 dive bombing had become a standard US Navy tactic, and the American navy the world leader in the technique; aircraft that had pioneered it on an improvised basis were being replaced by aeroplanes especially designed for the role.

Whether dive bombers and 6in gunfire could be coordinated was, of course, a moot point. Even its supporters generally assumed that the CF would *not* attempt to coordinate them; instead, it would function for the most part as an aircraft carrier. Some, like Rear Admiral Ernest J King, Moffett's successor at the Bureau of Aeronautics, were quite prepared to admit that the CF was really a mini-carrier. 'Insofar as aircraft operating with the Fleet is concerned', he wrote in his response to the General Board's questionnaire, 'a carrier is far more satisfactory and represents a more efficient aircraft floating base than does the flying deck cruiser'. Nevertheless, he gave the CF his qualified support 'as a means of getting more airplanes afloat after all carrier tonnage has been utilized, and . . . as a vessel which offers excellent possibilities in the matter of scouting, commerce raiding, and protection of trade routes'. He recommended construction 'of one, and only one, flying deck cruiser at this time as an experimental model' with the distinct understanding that 'such a vessel is in no sense a satisfactory substitute for an aircraft carrier'.

In contrast to Hoey's image of an independent ship, almost all the CF's critics believed that it would require an escort of cruisers and destroyers. Time and again, the vulnerability of the flight deck to both gunfire and bombing attack was raised. Rear Admiral Edward C Kalbfus, commander of Battle Force destroyers and shortly to become War College president, brought up all these points, and further doubted that the substitution of aircraft would compensate adequately for the reduction in gunpower. He also pointed out the danger to the CF's aircraft from the blast of its own guns in a surface action. After presenting his view 'that the CF type will amount to nothing more than an inferior aircraft carrier', Kalbfus advanced a unique 'psychological reason why we should not build *any* [his emphasis] of the type. Should we build one, it will appeal greatly to the popular imagination. . . . It will figure prominently in our peacetime exercises and the demand for more such fine craft will be greater and greater. None of the basic disadvantages will be apparent for there will be no real gun actions. . . . For the CF type we have no historical precedent and nothing but war itself can serve to demonstrate the unsuitability of a type which now, to me, seems apparent'.

It seemed apparent to others, as well. Rear Admiral C W Cole, Director of Fleet Training, wrote, 'In my opinion, the . . . design is fundamentally wrong. A flying-deck cruiser cannot afford . . . to seek [surface] action'. The CF might be useful as a commerce raider, 'not because it is better than a regular cruiser for this purpose, but because a regular cruiser would be too valuable to assign to such duty'. He re-emphasised the unhappy mixture of the vessel's qualities: 'As a cruiser the type will be weak and timid and its tactics governed by the fear of exposing its flight deck to damage. As a carrier it will be inefficient because the number of planes is small and because the flight deck is too small to allow large bombers to take off'. Cole therefore emphatically recommended that no CF be built.

He offered one final point, which echoed an argument Pratt had used in support of building an experimental flying-deck cruiser three years before. If, despite its disadvantages, a CF were to be built, Cole advised his colleagues to 'accept from the start the possibility the type may be a failure. The hull and interior should, therefore, be so designed that the flight deck can be ripped off and additional turrets installed'.

Perhaps the most damning assault on the CF came from Admiral Joseph M Reeves, Commander Battle Force. Despite his position, he was no anti-aviation 'battleship admiral'; he had previously served as commander of Battle Force aircraft and had pioneered dive bombing tactics and the carrier task force concept. He had far more 'hands-on' experience at sea with carriers and aircraft than Moffett had ever had.

Drawing on this experience, Reeves flatly condemned 'the hybrid type as incorrect in principal and practice', and inferior for both strategical and tactical work. The 'first employment of a CF will be to function as a very inferior CV [carrier] . . . During this phase of her operations a CF will follow the now well defined tactics of a CV, avoiding gun action, and by reason of her construction can only perform these missions in an inefficient and ineffective manner as compared with a CV of equal tonnage'. Once its flight deck had been destroyed, the CF 'will function as an inferior cruiser as compared to a real cruiser of equal tonnage'.

In his summation, Reeves came down strongly on the side of purism: 'When we build a carrier I believe we should build the most efficient carrier possible. When we build a cruiser we should build a pure cruiser of the most efficient type possible. The characteristics and tactics of a carrier and of a cruiser . . . are so diametrically opposed that it is impossible to mix or combine them'.

The notional flying-deck cruiser on which this round of discussions was based was virtually the same design that had been worked out in 1931. In its reply to the questionnaire, the Bureau of Aeronautics declared that this design, with its 332ft flight deck, would no longer suffice because 'Increased performance of planes, measured by greater top speed and greater weight carrying, is attended by higher take-off speeds [which can] be developed only with a longer take-off run. . . . The longer take-off run . . . must be recognized in designing future flight decks. Figures given a few years ago can no longer be accepted as design guides today'. A CF flight deck of at least 400ft, and preferably 450ft, was recommended.

Construction and Repair had apparently already done some new sketches at the behest of War Plans, and there was some discussion during the General Board hearing of 31 January of a type with only thin deck protection and no belt at all. However, Construction soon worked out a new design, which Rear Admiral E S Land, head of the

USS *Brooklyn*, seen here anchored in New York's North River, was the name ship of the first class of 6in gun cruisers built for the US Navy since the *Omahas*. The displacement, size and hull lines of the class were attractive to designers of hybrid cruisers (*National Archives*)

bureau, presented at the board's 15 February hearing. The design was based on the *Brooklyn* class light cruisers and had the following characteristics.

Displacement:	10,000t standard, *c*11,570t normal
Dimensions:	600ft wl × 61.5 wl (moulded) × 21.1ft (moulded)
Flight deck:	364ft × 65ft
Machinery:	geared turbines; 100,000shp = 32.5kts
Armament:	nine 6in/47 (3 × 3); eight 5in/25 AA (8 × 1)
Aircraft:	24
Armour:	main belt 4.5–3in; deck 1.75in; barbettes 5.5in; turret faces 6in; conning tower sides 4.5in

The design had several unusual features. Turrets 2 and 3 and their magazines were offset to port to balance the weight of the starboard island and funnel. For the first time space was allowed for flush-deck catapults forward of the single lift. In addition to the lift, Commander A J Chantry of Construction described a novel method of getting aircraft from the hangar deck to the flight deck.

> We have a parallel motion device on which you can run a plane out of the hangar and run it on this thing and raise it up around the ramp and on to the rear end of the flight deck, so that it makes another elevator aft.

It is hard to visualise this apparatus, although it sounds a little like a navigator's parallel rulers, two sets of rails or platforms connected by pivoted supports. The aircraft would probably have been set on the device, which would then extend aft and raise the aircraft to the flight deck.

The board's members did not like the offset turrets, and asked if it would be possible to convert the ship to a straight cruiser should it fail as a flying-deck vessel. It could be done by installing two additional turrets aft and offsetting them to starboard to balance the ship, but as Land said, 'it would not be a good job'. He believed that it would be easier to convert the hybrid into a carrier.

The General Board considered the design a distinct improvement over previous types, but still did not like it. After sifting through the questionnaires and hearings, the board was able to tell the House Committee that the omission of a CF from its requests for fiscal 1936 was based on 'a growing doubt as to the value of this type of vessel'.

Construction continued to tinker with the idea. By May a new version of the *Brooklyn*-based design had been developed. This scheme, designated Design 393, was a radical departure from the earlier efforts. Four triple 6in turrets were retained, two forward and two aft; turret 2 was very slightly, and the after turrets very definitely, offset to port to balance the substantial island structure. The flight deck was only 200ft long, with 'special type' lifts at both ends, and would be used for landing only; a flush-deck catapult forward would handle all launchings. It would carry twelve to eighteen aircraft.

This new CF aroused no more support than its predecessor, and on 13 June 1934 Navy Secretary Swanson announced an official quietus of the flying-deck cruiser. As reported in the *New York Times*, his remarks were to the effect that 'Study of the [CF] idea convinced members of the General Board and officers of the Naval High Command . . . that the cost of construction of such a vessel

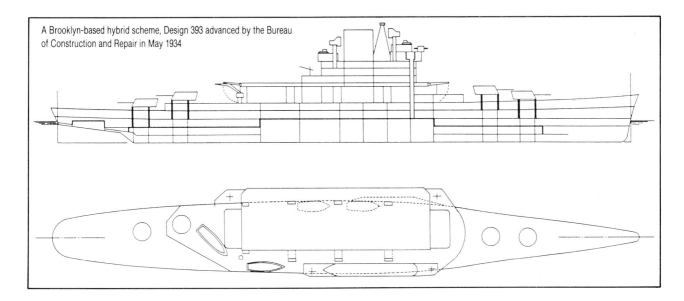

A Brooklyn-based hybrid scheme, Design 393 advanced by the Bureau of Construction and Repair in May 1934

. . . would not be justified by any distinct advantages to be derived. The weight of opinion in the [Navy] department is that a flying deck cruiser would be "neither fish nor fowl" '.

★ ★ ★

Nevertheless, the flying-deck cruiser refused to go quietly to the grave. Somewhere along the line, Aeronautics' Admiral King had become convinced that it was a worthwhile vessel, and he now supported the construction of a CF or the conversion of a cruiser into a flying-deck vessel with rather more enthusiasm than he had shown in January. His rationale was political; he feared that if the United States, after making such a fuss over the type at London in 1930, did not have at least one such vessel in prospect by the time of the next naval armament conference, other nations might try to prohibit the category altogether, as in fact the British planned to do. Given his earlier diffident support, it is hard to understand why this possibility now disturbed him, but it did. To forestall it, King was willing to mortgage away Aeronautics' traditional *sine qua non* in terms of aviation facilities; resurrecting the May CF study, he stated that 'Previous studies . . . have seriously curtailed cruiser effectiveness in an attempt to improve flight operations. [The May design] suffers very little from the above compromise. . . . The shortest safe landing deck for an airplane has been incorporated. Sacrifice has been made with respect to landing and take-off intervals but not to an extent militating against effective operation by a relatively small number of airplanes. Specially designed airplanes may be necessary'.

If a new ship was not possible, King proposed what he admitted was a 'not-too-promising' conversion of an *Omaha* class cruiser by trunking the two aft funnels together to permit extending the fo'c's'le deck aft to form a 200ft aircraft deck. Launching would be from the forward end of this deck by the vessel's existing two catapults. The configuration would have resembled in miniature form that of the later Japanese *Ise* class battleship-carriers (see Chapter 11). Moffett would no doubt have been appalled.

Reeves again took the lead for the opposition. Writing from his flagship, USS *New Mexico*, in early October, he stated that he was 'strongly opposed to the construction of a "flight deck cruiser." Each study shows it to be a hybrid type entirely unsuitable as a cruiser or as a carrier'.

As for the *Omaha* conversion, Construction and Repair scotched the idea on several grounds. To start with, the addition of so much topweight would have required 1500 tons of ballast, seriously reducing the fuel oil tankage. Most of the added weight would be toward the end of the ship, straining its light hull. Finally, the location of the engine rooms and boilers would limit the flight deck to 172ft, too short even for a landing-only deck. However, Construction did concur with King's belief that a flying-deck cruiser along the lines of the May study was worth development.

King made one last pitch at the end of October, saying that he 'considers that the flight deck cruiser as a type offers great possibilities' and again recommending 'that a ship of this class be constructed as soon as practicable'. But it was in vain; as far as the navy's hierarchy was concerned, the CF was a dead issue.

Unofficial interest was dwindling as well. In

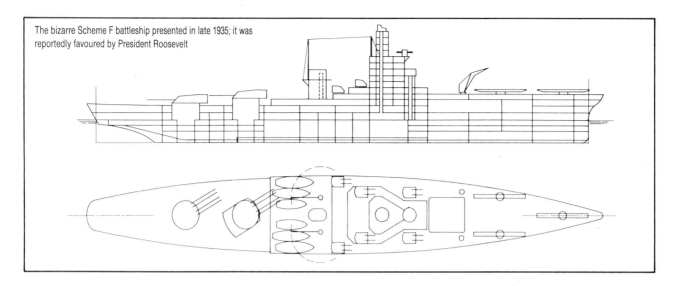

The bizarre Scheme F battleship presented in late 1935; it was reportedly favoured by President Roosevelt

the November 1934 *Proceedings*, Lieutenant (jg) John A Collett advocated the type as 'the fourth cruiser in each heavy cruiser division' to permit aerial scouting when rough weather made seaplane operation impossible. Moreover, 'The possession of a few flying deck cruisers would make it possible to remove scouting squadrons from the carriers and substitute types more capable of gaining control of the air. It would remove the conflicting missions of carriers to gain information of the enemy and at the same time conserve air power for a decisive attempt to gain control of the air and damage the enemy fleet'. Collett's article, which echoed Bryant's argument, did not even inspire a response in the magazine's 'Comment and Discussion' section.

Whether as a result of the CF studies or for other reasons, the hybrid concept continued to intrigue the Bureau of Construction and Repair. One example of this fascination came in December 1933 when Construction had studied small, fast battleships for carrier escort duty. The smallest was 19,500 tons and armed with six 12in guns; another, at 24,000 tons, carried nine 12in guns, and the largest, at 28,500 tons, had a main battery of six 14in guns. All were to have an extra-heavy AA battery, and belowdeck stowage 'for at least eight fighting or scouting planes; with facilities for taking planes aboard as in the proposed 10,000-ton, 6-inch cruisers and having two or possibly four catapults'.

Construction had proposed these carrier escort battleships of its own volition, and the idea generated no interest, but two years later the bureau returned to the hybrid battleship field. In July

1935 the General Board called for battleship studies in preparation for fiscal year 1937 construction requests, and in response Construction's Preliminary Design branch drew up a number if schemes. Most of these were fairly conventional, although several featured an all-forward turret arrangement. However, one of the sketches, Scheme F, was decidedly unconventional. Presented in late 1935, it had two quadruple 14in turrets aft and three catapults forward, one on the centreline near the bow, and other two on each beam aft of it. Each of the latter catapults had cranes to serve it, and there was a lift connecting to a hangar in which 'probably ten bombing planes of the folding-wing type can be carried'.

The design's particulars were

Displacement:	31,750t standard
Dimensions:	680ft × 101ft ×28.8ft
Machinery:	geared turbines; 160,000shp = 30kts. 15,000nm at 15kts
Armament:	eight 14in/50 (2 × 4), twelve 5in/50 AA (6 × 2), eight 1.1in AA (2 × 4), sixteen .50 AAMGs (16 × 1)
Aircraft:	10 (?)
Armour:	belt 13.5in, deck 4.5in, splinter deck 1.25in, barbettes 13.5in, turret faces 13in, tops 5.25in, funnel uptakes 2in

Extensive anti-torpedo protection included a triple bottom. It is difficult to understand why the armament was not placed forward and the aviation facilities aft, which would have permitted a flight deck for recovering the aircraft. As it stands, the ship could have carried only seaplanes. Perhaps the fact that such a flight deck could have been only marginally longer than that of the earlier CLV/CF studies led Preliminary Design to believe that a flight-deck ship would not be acceptable.

In notes accompanying the sketch, the Pre-

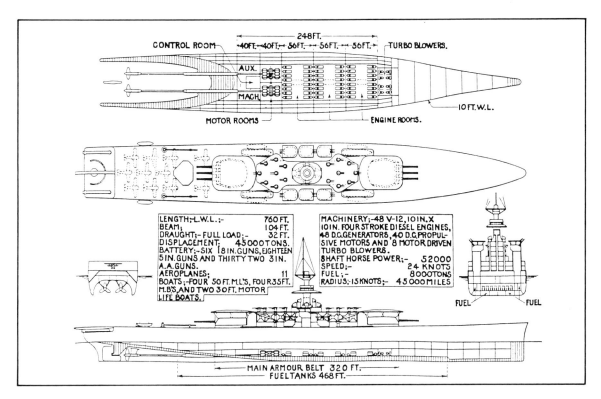

André Procter's unconventional diesel-powered battleship with hybrid features, reproduced from the January 1936 *Scientific American* (*Courtesy of Scientific American*)

liminary Design branch stated, 'This scheme is submitted only to illustrate several interesting possibilities. If the catapults with their supply of bombing planes can be considered as compensation for the loss of the forward main battery, it is believed that this design has merits warranting further investigation'.

Apparently, Roosevelt thought it had such merits; he reportedly favoured the idea. But the General Board obviously, and probably for the best, did not share this belief, and Scheme F vanished into that Sargasso Sea where hybrid warship designs go to die. The design finally selected for the first American battleships since the Washington Treaty imposed its construction 'holiday' was that of the thoroughly conventional *North Carolina*.

There followed a hiatus in the US Navy's interest in hybrid vessels. Our friend Captain Procter, however, whose flight-deck cruiser design was described in Chapter 5, still had an interest in surface combatants with a substantial aviation element. His passionate belief in the diesel engine continued unabated; he went so far as to submit diesel battleship schemes to the General Board in 1934. Its only response was to send him a thank-you note.

Undeterred, Procter published an article in *Scientific American* in 1936 on the great advantages in cruising range afforded by the diesel, and with this he provided a drawing of what may well be the oddest-looking warship proposal of all time.

The oddities of the design are, for the most part, the result of features unrelated to diesel propulsion. Protection against aerial attack was a necessity Procter had long recognised; as a defence against bombs, he equipped his ship with 'bursting hoods', weird, umbrella-like affairs supported above the turrets and superstructure by stanchions, intended to activate a bomb's delayed-action fuse and detonate it before it struck the structure beneath. Other unusual protective features included a tunnel-like hull form aft, to protect the propellers and rudders against torpedo hits. In this, Procter was well ahead of his time: German designs of the Second World War featured a hull form virtually identical to that proposed by Procter. He was also aware of the need for a substantial AA battery, and gave his ship eighteen 5in guns and thirty-two 3in guns. The main battery of six 18in guns was concentrated in two triple turrets in order to reduce to a minimum the area requiring armour. He protected the boats against the blast of this heavy artillery by placing them in covered recesses in the upper deck, not so very different from *Yamato*'s boat 'hangars' built into the hull aft. The tall, cylindrical tower mast was a feature of many of Procter's designs, and the fire-control gear resembles that of the *Nelson* class battleships, at that time among the most recently completed capital ships in the world. Whatever Procter's shortcomings in the field of aesthetic warship design, no one could accuse him of not paying attention to details.

The feature of his battleship that most concerns us is the large aircraft complement provided. Aft of the second main battery turret was a lift that provided access to a below-decks hangar for eleven aircraft. The drawing does not clearly indicate whether these were to be seaplanes or wheeled aircraft, nor does Procter specify which type he intended in his text but it seems safe to assume that they were meant to be seaplanes as no flight-deck was indicated. These aircraft were apparently to be launched via a catapult located right aft, and hoisted back aboard by two boom-like cranes on the upper deck.

Procter's ship is in many ways similar to Construction's Scheme F, although its aircraft facilities are very limited. It is perhaps not a true hybrid; yet it is one of the most unlikely designs ever put forward, and so warrants a place in this study.

With Procter's death in 1938, the diesel lost one of its most ardent proponents; he no doubt died convinced that the world would soon be see a new generation of diesel warships, and would certainly have been gratified to know of the giant diesel-powered, never-built German 'H' class and its paper successors.

While Procter sketched his diesel battleships in his rooms at the Windsor Hotel in New York, there were other matters more pressing than hybrid warships or diesel engines that demanded the attention of the navy's leadership. The American economy grew healthier in the late 1930s, and ships were sliding down the ways at an accelerating pace. However the world was becoming a more uncertain place; dictatorships were emerging in Europe, while Japan was growing ever more deeply embroiled in China, a course that seemed certain to set her against the Western nations sooner or later.

These actions led US planners to consider ways of putting pressure on the Japanese government; economic sanctions were the most frequently considered measure. Roosevelt himself proposed a 'quarantine' of aggressive powers in a speech in Chicago in October 1937; a month later, he wrote to Admiral William D Leahy, CNO, proposing a hybrid-like vessel intended to enforce such a quarantine. The ship he had in mind was a sort of aviation auxiliary cruiser; he asked Leahy if the navy had

> done anything toward developing plans for converting oil-burning merchant ships so that they could:
> (a) Remain at or near a given spot at sea for a long period.
> (b) Carry eight or ten planes to be flown every day as scouts over a wide area.
> (c) A dual purpose battery strong enough to ward off a small air attack and . . . sink a less powerfully armed merchant ship . . .

Nothing came of the idea, but it shows Roosevelt's continuing interest in unusual aviation ships. He had followed the flying-deck cruiser designs in 1934, apparently favoured the catapult-equipped battleship Scheme F in 1935, and only a few months after proposing his aviation auxiliary would be examining the Gibbs and Cox hybrid battleship design for the Soviet Union (see Chapter 10).

By this time, Japan had disavowed all treaty obligations, walking out on the Second London Naval Conference in 1936. The treaty that emerged from that conference imposed some further limitations, quantitatively and qualitatively, but was rife with escape clauses permitting them to be ignored by the signatories in the ever more likely event of war, or excessive building by a non-signatory power, or 'naval building of such a type to imperil the signer of the Treaty'. Plainly, the day of naval limitations was coming to an end, and as the treaties eroded the American navy was once again free to design the best ship for a specific role, regardless of size and armament.

A new version of the flying-deck cruiser seemed the best ship to Rear Admiral Robert L Ghormley, director of the War Plans Division. In a 5 November 1938 letter to the CNO, Ghormley made a lengthy and detailed argument for what he called a 'scouting carrier' that was in fact the flying-deck cruiser in a new guise.

Ghormley began by laying down a rationale for the type. 'Most of our thoughts concerning additions to ships to the navy', he wrote, 'have been guided by the consideration of adding to the power

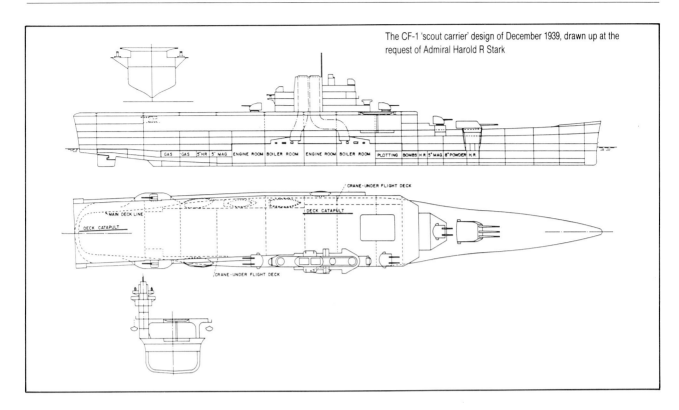

The CF-1 'scout carrier' design of December 1939, drawn up at the request of Admiral Harold R Stark

of a concentrated fleet. We have given thought largely to the ability to *establish command of the sea* rather than to the *exercise* of that command. By the *exercise* of command is meant the interruption of enemy trade routes, and sea communications, while protecting our own trade routes and sea communications (including air routes overseas)'. He then cited the difficulties Britain had experienced during the First World War in tracking down German surface raiders and in coping with the submarine even though 'the exercise of sea command, the denial of the use of the sea routes by Germany, was comparatively simple'. Ghormley considered US fleet strength sufficient to gain command of wide reaches of the Atlantic and Pacific, but 'the problem of *exercising* command of the sea will be a difficult one. Our superior strength . . . probably will cause the other fellow to spread out. We must be ready to spread out to get him'.

The US Navy could not spare the carrier-cruiser forces to counter a widely dispersed enemy without weakening the main fleet, perhaps fatally. 'For scouting', Ghormley continued, 'we need numbers of carriers in order to spread them out; we need to reduce their vulnerability (as regards the number of planes put out by a damaged flight deck or underwater damage); we need increased gun power in order to reduce their dependence on close and constant cruiser protection'.

The 'scouting carrier' was invoked as the answer to these requirements. It could track down raiders, defend convoys, even operate as an anti-submarine vessel. It could also function with the fleet: 'For an offensive movement of the *fleet* on a large scale, the "Scouting Carriers" will be in the advanced scouting groups where their reduced vulnerability in loss of plane strength, their increased gun power and the shorter time required to get planes into the air and back on board will permit them to operate efficiently'. A truly universal ship, the scouting carrier would locate targets for the big carriers and even provide spotters for the battleships.

Ghormley envisaged a vessel of 10,000 to 12,000 tons standard with a flight deck approximately 400ft long, two lifts, flush-deck catapults and protected hangar stowage for eighteen to twenty-four (preferably the larger number) of 'especially designed scout bombers'. It would be armed with eight dual-purpose 6in/47guns, presumably in the twin turrets advocated by the Bureau of Ordnance for the next generation of light cruisers, supplemented by 1.1in and smaller AA guns. Speed should be 32.5 knots ('great enough to operate with our cruisers'), radius from 10,000 to 12,000nm, and protection 'such as can be fitted in the tonnage'. He recommended that two such ships should be laid down as soon as possible, with an eventual total of perhaps six. He emphasised that '*The tonnage required for "Scouting Carriers" should not be related to any tonnage authorized'* but should instead come from an entirely new category of warship tonnage.

Rear Admiral Frederick J Horne, who, as commanding officer of *Saratoga* had some years earlier presided over the experiments to determine adequate flight-deck length for the original flying-deck cruiser, was now on the General Board and requested that Construction draw up plans for a small carrier to meet Ghormley's specifications. The result was an interesting little carrier of 10,000 tons standard displacement; unlike Ghormley's proposal, it was a full flight-deck vessel, able to operate thirty-six aircraft, and armed with eight 5in/38 guns. One particularly interesting feature was the location of the 5in battery, which was mounted in twin gunhouses on the flight deck, as in the later *Essex* class carriers.

It was an impressive achievement for such a small carrier, and in June 1939 it was mentioned as an alternative to the large carrier during the preliminary design process that led to the *Essex* class. A large carrier was preferred, however, and it was not until October that the 'scouting carrier' reappeared. In that month the board included four flying-deck cruisers in its recommendation for the coming fiscal year's construction programme, and specifications were issued for a new vessel in some ways akin to the small carrier of 1938. Displacement was to be in the same range, 'approximately 10,000 tons standard, but to be determined by essential characteristics', and a trials speed of 35 knots with an 'alternative fore-and-aft fireroom-engine room installation' were specified. Other features included an island structure and fixed funnels, a high-speed lift 'so located as to serve most advantageously the . . . recovery of aircraft', and two flush-deck catapults forward on the flight deck. The flight deck was to be at least 65ft wide and 'the minimum length required to accommodate the aircraft complement spotted for take-off'. This complement was to consist of a mere eighteen scout-bombers, albeit with stowage for at least nine more aeroplanes as spares.

The considerable reduction in aircraft capacity — half that of the 1938 small carrier — reflected changes in other areas of the design. The greatest of these was the specification of protection sufficient against 6in gunfire. Despite this level of protection, the main battery was limited to twelve 5in dual-purpose guns in twin mounts. Other armament was to consist of sixteen 1.1in AA guns in four quadruple mounts, eight .50 AA machine

guns, and a triple torpedo mount on each beam. This last was an odd requirement, considering that the US Navy had abandoned torpedo armament on cruisers in 1930.

A list of these characteristics was issued on 20 October 1939 and a copy sent to Rear Admiral John H Towers, a pioneer naval aviator who had become chief of the Bureau of Aeronautics in June 1939, with a handwritten note from Horne stating that 'Primary service of type is commerce protection and destruction'.

In November 1939 the General Board conducted another poll of senior commands afloat and ashore asking about future cruiser policy in the event that the treaty structure should collapse entirely. Of the types suggested, the CF drew a favourable vote only from the War Plans Division, which had also included it in its construction programme recommendation in October. Nevertheless, on 2 December 1939, Admiral Harold R Stark, CNO, asked Construction and Repair to study 'a flight deck cruiser, or scout carrier'. He specified a displacement of about 12,000 tons, a single triple 8in gun turret forward, a secondary battery of eight to ten 5in/38 dual-purpose guns and a speed of at least 32.5 knots. The request, Stark disclosed in later correspondence, was directly inspired by Ghormley's letter of 5 November 1938.

A tentative design was on Stark's desk on 20 December; its particulars are listed below.

Displacement:	12,000t standard, 14,220t trial
Dimensions:	640ft wl × 67ft wl × 21ft 8in
Machinery:	geared turbines, 100,000shp = 33kts. 10,000nm at 15kts
Armament:	three 8in/55 (1 × 3), eight 5in/38 DP (3 × 2, 2 × 1), eight .50 AAMGs
Aircraft:	24–36
Armour:	belt 5in, deck 2.25in, bomb (main) deck 1in, turret 8in face, 3.75–1.5in sides, 3in top

The flight deck was 420ft long, slightly angled like that of the 1931 CLV contract design, with two flush-deck catapults, one forward abaft the lift and one at the after end of the flight deck. At least a little of the 1938 small carrier survived in the placement of one twin 5in gunhouse forward and another abaft the island; a third twin mount was superimposed above the 8in turret, and there were two single 5in guns on sponsons on the quarters.

Stark forwarded a copy of the design to Secretary of the Navy Charles Edison on 9 January 1940. Edison had become secretary only seven days before, having served as acting secretary

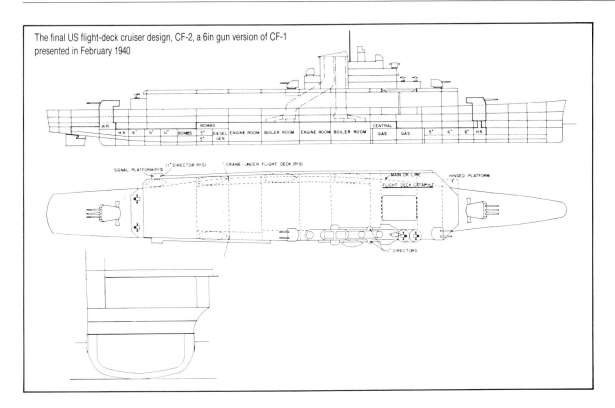

The final US flight-deck cruiser design, CF-2, a 6in gun version of CF-1 presented in February 1940

since Swanson's death the previous July. Edison had demonstrated an interest in hybrid vessels during the Gibbs and Cox affair (see Chapter 10); he lost no time in sending the design along to the General Board, as requested by Stark.

The result was the final US Navy flying-deck cruiser design. The tentative characteristics were set forth on 19 January. These specifications were broadly similar to the sketch already in hand, repeating the basic dimensions and characteristics of the ship, with one significant difference: in place of the single 8in turret there were to be two triple 6in turrets, one forward and one aft; only four 5in guns in two twin gunhouses were specified, but the light AA battery was now to include four 1.1in quad mounts.

The Bureau of Construction and Repair's sketch was sent to the General Board on 3 February. It was labelled Scheme CF-2, with the earlier study now retroactively designated Scheme CF-1. CF-2 was closely based on CF-1; in fact the CF-1 sketch in the General Board files shows the desired changes pencilled in. Unlike the rather attractive CF-1, CF-2 was an ungainly vessel, some 200 tons heavier, with the flight deck length reduced to 390ft because of the after turret. The flight deck was offset to port rather than angled, and the after catapult was eliminated.

A joint memorandum from the Bureaux of Engineering and Construction and Repair

accompanying the design sketch explained why some specified characteristics could not be attained. 'The flight deck', it noted, 'has been carried forward to a point where its width is considerably reduced in order to provide a margin of safety in take-off over the forward turret'. This was accomplished by cutting away the forward port corner of the deck. Consequently, 'a hinged platform is provided on the port side to extend the take-off area when the forward 6″ turret is not in use, and particularly to give a deck edge normal to the path of planes leaving the deck catapult'.

'The hangar and flight deck are as large as appear practicable with the general arrangement and size of the ship', the memo stated, but went on to lament, 'It is improbable that they will be sufficient to permit efficient operation of 36 VSB [scout-bomber] planes of current designs. . . . However, the plane carrying capacity depends on the size and type of plane assigned to the ship and other factors'. It was requested that the Bureau of Aeronautics study and comment 'on the aeronautical features and plane capacity of the design'.

Aeronautics obliged, and a most uncomplementary report on CF-2 was given to the General Board in a 15 February letter from Towers. The assessment was based on the projected use of the Vought SB2U-2 scout-bomber (later named Vindicator) and/or the Vought-Sikorsky OS2U-1 ob-

A Vought SB2U-2, with undercarriage and flaps down and carrying an auxiliary fuel tank, at Oakland, California, in November 1940. Later named Vindicator, it was the US Navy's first monoplane dive bomber and was considered for operation by the CF cruisers (*William T Larkins*)

servation aeroplane (later dubbed Kingfisher), the first monoplanes of their types in standard US Navy service. As it turned out, the lightly built, low-powered OS2U never saw carrier duty but it was widely used as a battleship and cruiser catapult seaplane, eventually replacing the biplane Curtiss SOC.

While Towers estimated that the flight deck was just barely adequate for take-off, he noted that 'for average carrier operation, it is usual to reserve 35% to 50% additional deck length for safe launching'. The longer take-off run required by the heavier VSB made it 'evident that only one . . . could be carried on deck and launched. Other planes would necessarily be carried in the hangar and transferred to the flight deck, singly, for take-off. The hangar could stow about 28 VSB's, wings folded, in a manner permitting warming up of the engines . . . In landing, due to the short deck length, it would be necessary to strike planes below as landed, presenting a clear deck, for safety, to each landing plane . . . Planes could be launched from the catapult, in which case . . . 28 VSB could be stowed on and launched directly from the flight deck'.

Rolling take-offs would be tricky because 'the island and 5 inch gun mounts present an unusual hazard extending to the end of the take-off run'. Towers calculated that a VSB pilot would have to 'maintain a take-off track with a tolerance of 5 feet

either side' of the aeroplane. 'This would require unusual piloting skill, particularly if the motion of a 12,000 ton ship in a seaway is considered.'

Landing would also be hazardous, the dangers 'increased because of short distance from the after ramp to the after 5 inch mount, 168 feet. The corresponding distance on carriers, which have a much greater deck width, averages 307 feet. The proximity of stack turbulence and smoke stack gases together with the after 6 inch turret would further aggravate landing conditions'.

Operation of the smaller VOS (observation) aircraft would be somewhat easier, both because of the shorter run required and a slightly greater wingtip clearance. Towers estimated that twelve of this type could be spotted on deck for take-off with thirty-two below in the hangar.

Altogether, Towers' view of CF-2 was a glum one; his concluding remark was, 'No promising rearrangements are apparent for improving the carrier features of the design without seriously curtailing existing cruiser characteristics'.

If the aviators were unhappy, so were the gunners. Rear Admiral William R Furlong, chief of the Bureau of Ordnance, considered the training arcs of the main battery unsatisfactory, the magazines dangerously located, the single fire-control director provided for the 6in battery inadequate, and protection insufficient. Furlong concluded, 'as far as armament is concerned, the proposed plan cannot be considered as embodying a satisfactory cruiser design'.

The colliding judgements of Towers and Furlong provide a classic example of the dilemma in which the hybrid designer was so often placed: the aviation features made for an unsatisfactory gunnery vessel, while the gunnery features made for an unsatisfactory aviation vessel.

Towers and Furlong did not quite hammer the final nail into the flying-deck cruiser's coffin. Some desultory work apparently continued during the summer of 1940, as indicated in a 20 August memo to Stark from Horne: 'While the Bureau of Ships [formed on 20 June 1940 by an amalgamation of the Bureaux of Engineering and Construction] has had under consideration a design for a flying-deck cruiser, low priority has been given to this type and it may well be some time before the design is submitted . . . It is still believed that such a type would not be as effective or advantageous as either one of pure types of light cruiser or aircraft carrier'.

The navy's final obituary was a terse note of 20 October 1940 headed, 'Subject: Proposed Flight

Deck Cruiser'. This document stated simply, 'This subject was removed from the calendar and placed in the files for later consideration by direction of the General Board at its meeting this date'.

Unofficially, too, the flying-deck cruiser was a thing of the past. In January 1941, the *Proceedings* published a short article advocating the type by then-Lieutenant William A Moffett Jr, son of the CLV's greatest proponent. 'There can be no doubt that our fleet will need enormous aircraft support in any major war. . . . Would not a flying-deck cruiser be a step forward? ' No one bothered to reply, and indeed the article has more the air of filial piety about it than the conviction of the true believer.

Thus, after a decade of off-and-on paper existence, the 'forerunner of future men-of-war' sank for the last time.

Some questions linger. How sincere was the US Navy's interest in the flying-deck cruiser? Why was the concept abandoned? How useful might such a ship have been?

As we have seen, the CLV was originally a 'political' ship conceived in a peculiar vortex of economic, social and diplomatic conditions. It was, even more than the 'treaty' cruiser, a creature of the naval limitation treaties; without them, and without an American government that was in the first instance parsimonious and pacifistic, and in the second financially straitened, the flying-deck cruiser would almost certainly never have attracted much official support.

It is also unlikely that the idea would have got as far as it did without the unceasing influence of Moffett, backed by the highly placed Pratt. What they wanted, of course, were both carriers and cruisers, but they turned to the compromise vessel when neither of these types was forthcoming in anything near adequate numbers. 'Admiral Moffett's aim', his son wrote many years later, 'was, by any means feasible under the handicapped conditions of the times, to get naval aviation at sea in strength at the maximum degree possible at the earliest date possible'. To this end, he often over-stated the merits of the hybrid, perhaps even in his own mind. Pratt's position seems more ambivalent; he agreed to the need for the new type, but treated it as much more of an experiment than Moffett did. Later, as we shall see, he repudiated the hybrid altogether.

The discarding of the flying-deck cruiser in 1934 has been attributed to a 'counterattack' by

The Vought-Sikorsky OS2U, the US Navy's first monoplane scout, was another type considered for operation by the CF cruisers. This Marine Corps example, with gunner's cockpit folded down and carrying a depth charge, wears early Second World War insignia (*US Marine Corps, courtesy of William T Larkins*)

the Gun Club, an amorphous group of moss-back, diehard 'battleship admirals' which air enthusiasts find convenient whenever there is blame to apportion for a setback in naval aviation. Yet in 1938 Captain Jonas H Ingram, USN, was able to write that 99-plus per cent of navy line officers 'feel that naval aviation is a great asset to our fleet and . . . are air-minded to a high degree'. This is undoubtedly an exaggeration, but not by much; in the hundreds of pages of correspondence and testimony generated by the CLV/CF debate, not one officer disparaged the value of aviation; all accorded it high importance even when they did not fully realise its potential. All were eager to increase its strength; critics of the hybrid ship opposed it not because of any antipathy to aviation but because pragmatic experience, often aboard carriers, had convinced them that 'pure' warships operating in cooperation were superior to an equal number of ships, each of which tried to serve two masters at once.

The demise of the flying-deck cruiser cannot be blamed on a clique of conservatives to whom aviation was anathema. It was scuttled for the first time because, as Ernest Andrade Jr puts it, the type was 'an expedient dictated by financial considerations which no longer applied after 1933'. It was vetoed again in 1940 for roughly the same reason; wars, and rumours of wars, threw treaty restrictions to the winds and loosened the national purse strings to an unprecedented degree. There was no necessity for compromise warships.

Light fleet carrier USS *Independence*, name ship of her class, in 1943 as originally fitted, built on a cruiser hull. Had any US flight-deck cruisers existed, they almost certainly would have been converted along CVL lines during the Second World War (*Naval Imaging Command*)

The final question is how useful such a ship might have been during the Second World War. Hindsight gives every reason to suppose that it would have displayed all the flaws and weaknesses its critics assigned to it. Its flight deck *would* have been highly vulnerable to aerial attack; it probably *would* have required support and protection by other ships during flight operations; thin-skinned and packed with inflammable fluids, it *would* have been a 'timid' cruiser in surface actions, especially in the close-range night gunnery/torpedo engagements typical of the South Pacific campaigns.

It was equally unthinkable that the vessel could have functioned in the Pacific in the perceived prewar role of commerce destroyer, for this would have required operations far too deep within Japanese-dominated waters. The reverse side of that coin, commerce protection against surface raiders, would also have been closed to the hybrid cruiser: the IJN never pursued trade warfare with any vigour, and the last German surface raiders were vanquished by early 1943. There was still ASW, either in direct defence of convoys or in hunter-killer groups, and here the CLV/CF might have been useful. Its high speed and gunpower, however, would have been wasted in such duties, which were performed ably by the inexpensive CVEs.

Of course, all this speculation is based on the assumption that the flying-deck cruiser could

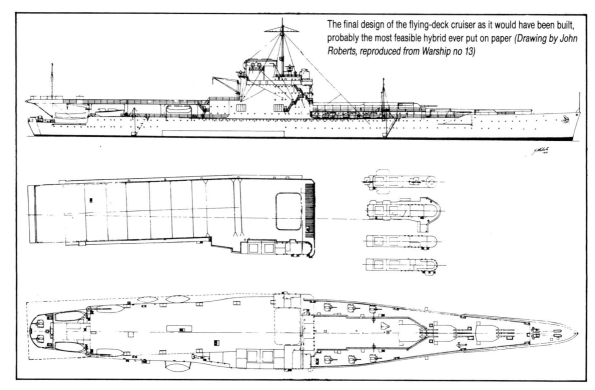

The final design of the flying-deck cruiser as it would have been built, probably the most feasible hybrid ever put on paper (*Drawing by John Roberts, reproduced from Warship no 13*)

have operated the aircraft coming into service after 1941, an uncertain assumption at best. The short length of the CLV/CF's flight deck had been criticised from its inception as barely sufficient for take-off, and lacking the reserve length desired for reasons of safety. It was realised from the start that the flying-deck cruiser would be unable to operate torpedo planes (the 'large bombers' mentioned in some critiques); this restriction would eventually have encompassed other types as aircraft increased in weight, size and speed. As Admiral King pointed out as early as 1934, such advances could outmode a flight deck very quickly.

The crucial factor here was not so much the increase in aircraft weight *per se*, but in weight expressed in terms of wing loading. This is calculated by dividing the aircraft weight by the wing surface area; as wing loading increases, higher horsepower and longer take-off runs become necessary. Taking US dive bombers as an example, the wing loading of the Curtiss F8C of 1929–30 (the original 'Helldiver') was roughly 13lb per square foot of wing surface; the Curtiss SBC of 1936–39 supported 24lb per square foot, and the 1942 Douglas SBD, 33lb (these figures are rounded off and would differ slightly according to the different variants of the aircraft cited).

This problem was solved in the case of the CVEs by use of catapults for launching; perhaps the same solution would have allowed the CLV/CF to operate bigger, faster aircraft also. It seems more likely, however, that any flying-deck cruisers afloat in 1942 would have been re-modelled — not by yanking off the flight deck as suggested by Pratt, but by removing the guns and extending the flight deck over the length of the ship, as Land suggested in 1934. Thus the CLV/CF would have ended up resembling the light carriers of the *Independence* (CVL-22) class, built on cruiser hulls to do almost precisely what the CLV was originally intended to do: make more flight decks available for the great trans-Pacific campaign.

CHAPTER 10

'A SHIP OF LARGE SIZE AND UNIQUE CHARACTERISTICS'

Now begins a convoluted tale of hybrid battleships that bounces back and forth between Moscow, Washington and New York, involving a cast of characters as diverse as a Soviet dictator, a Russian-American entrepreneur, the head of the world's largest naval architectural firm, and the President of the United States, as well as sundry naval officers, cabinet officials, bureaucrats and ambassadors.

The story has its beginning in the low ebb to which the Soviet Navy had fallen in the 1920s and '30s. The revolution and ensuing civil war had aborted a vast building programme intended to bring the Tsarist navy up to date, so its Soviet successor inherited only a miscellany of obsolescent vessels: three old battleships in poor condition, a few cruisers, some destroyers and submarines. Faced with ruined shipyards and an industrial plant laid waste, the Soviet Navy had little hope of bolstering its strength by new construction, while the impoverished economy and the hostility of most foreign governments meant that it would receive no help from other nations. In response to these conditions, the 'young school' of strategy came to the fore; like their predecessors in France's *jeune école*, these young officers believed that the use of light forces — in this case, torpedo boats, submarines and aircraft — could provide an adequate defence of the Soviet coasts.

The 'young school' held sway well into the 1930s. Then, in the middle of the decade, there was a sudden shift to the concept of a balanced 'oceanic' fleet built around battleships. This shift was due in part to the Soviet Union's improved industrial and economic situation; building big ships was becoming possible once again. A greater factor, however, was Josef Stalin's desire to build a navy that would command the respect of other nations.

In spite of increasing industrial capacity, the ability to design and build a complex warship such as a battleship was beyond Soviet means in the mid-1930s. Foreign help was required, and the

Soviets first turned to fascist Italy. Contacts between the Italian firm Ansaldo and the Soviet Union had started in 1933; this unlikely partnership had resulted in the construction of several Soviet warships in Italian shipyards and extensive Italian technical assistance in the construction of the *Kirov* class cruisers in Soviet yards. In late 1935, the Soviets broached the subject of battleship schemes; Ansaldo responded in July 1936 with the 'U.P. 41' design. This was a slightly enlarged version of the *Vittorio Veneto* class, displacing 42,000 tons, well protected and armed with nine 16in guns. There is no certain evidence as to whether these plans were ever delivered to the Soviets, although it seems likely that they were.

In July 1936 the Spanish Civil War broke out, and Rome and Moscow soon found themselves supporting opposite sides; this brought an end to Soviet hopes of acquiring a battleship with Italian help. Of the other powers with the requisite technical skill, Germany and Japan were hostile, and British and French shipyards were working to capacity on their own rearmament programmes; this left only the United States as a possible source for battleships.

The Soviets began their campaign for American assistance in battleship construction modestly enough; in May 1936 Amtorg, the official Soviet trading agency, made enquiries about purchasing battleship armour from American firms. The State Department decided there was no legal obstacle to such a deal as long as no military secrets were involved.

Enter Sam Carp, a Russian-born American citizen. Carp somehow managed to obtain Soviet support for the establishment of Carp Export and Import Company in New York in September 1936; his task was to obtain warships, especially battleships, or the plans and matériel required to build them in Soviet shipyards. Carp's sister was married to Soviet Premier Vyacheslav Molotov, one of Stalin's closest supporters, which probably explains why he was selected for the job; it is hard to imagine why else the Soviets would have chosen him to manage their efforts to get a battleship, as he had not proved an outstanding success in his previous enterprises and knew nothing about warships. In spite of Carp's inexperience, his firm began business with a $200 million credit line in banks in New York and Philadelphia, certainly an indication of the seriousness of Soviet hopes. Carp not only had financial backing, but diplomatic support as well;

at one point during the protracted negotiations, the Soviet ambassador approached Admiral William D Leahy, CNO, at a dinner party and informed him that any Soviet battleship built in the United States would be based in Vladivostok to help contain Japanese ambitions. Stalin went so far as to involve himself in the affair by having an unprecedented meeting with the US ambassador solely on the battleship question. Stalin had never before met any foreign diplomatic representative, as he maintained the fiction that he was only a party, rather than a government, official.

The major thrust of Carp's efforts was to get a complete battleship built in the United States for the Soviet Union. Although he failed, it was not for want of effort; Carp worked hard at the job, and apparently with good reason. One of his American employees told a State Department official that Carp and some of his associates feared there was some danger to their relatives in the Soviet Union should the effort fail, and a note of desperation creeps into some of his negotiations. Even with this incentive, however, he was not an ideal choice for a middleman. By all accounts he was a clumsy negotiator and a poor manager, and often exasperated both government officials and many of his own employees. Several of the businessmen he came in contact with felt that the Soviets would have had far less trouble in obtaining a battleship if only someone else were doing the negotiating.

In spite of Carp's faults, however, the main reason for his failure was the resistance of the US Navy. At every turn, Carp's firm met with unofficial navy interference, even though the State Department, and eventually the President, regarded the Soviet hopes in a more or less friendly light. Admiral Leahy, who often served as Acting Secretary of the Navy due to Secretary Swanson's chronic illness, repeatedly assured the State Department that the navy was not blocking contracts with the Soviets, but at the same time navy officers were privately expressing their determination to prevent any naval assistance to the Communist nation. Senior officers frequently worked behind the scenes to thwart the Soviet plans, leaking news of them to the press, which generated unfavourable publicity that put off some companies, or telling companies approached by Carp's firm that any deal with the Soviet Union would have an unhappy effect on future navy contracts. Since the navy was a major customer for many of these companies, this was a serious threat to their livelihood. From beginning to end, the US Navy did its best to undermine Carp's

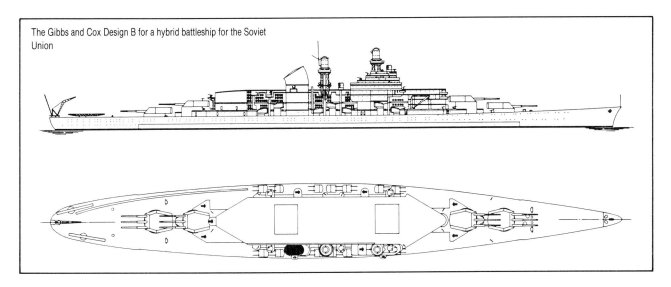

The Gibbs and Cox Design B for a hybrid battleship for the Soviet Union

efforts, and in the end succeeded.

Naval influence aside, the shipbuilders Carp had first contacted were simply unable to design a battleship from the keel. There was only one firm that might have had the requisite skills: Gibbs and Cox, then the world's largest naval architectural company. So in August 1937, after negative responses from most of the other major shipbuilding concerns, Carp approached William Francis Gibbs, president and founder of Gibbs and Cox. Even Gibbs was unsure if he could do it; although his firm had worked on numerous navy contracts, he had never designed a battleship. Gibbs told Carp that he would investigate it, then checked with the navy and the State Department about the Soviet offer. When no official objection was raised, he went to work.

The Soviets were thinking along the lines of an up-to-date 35,000 ton vessel, as this was the maximum limit on displacement at the time. However, they had vaguely specified 'a ship of large size and unique characteristics', and Carp gave Gibbs no specific guidelines to follow. Gibbs could certainly have designed a perfectly adequate 35,000 ton ship, but he did not. As Carp later said, the ship that eventually emerged 'was not what I asked them for. They drew something else'. The design can only be explained by the character of Gibbs himself: he was a man with a passion for the superlative. Sam Carp put it this way: 'Gibbs is a very peculiar man . . . I mean, he is like an artist. He likes his work'.

Gibbs did more than simply like his work; he lived it and breathed it; it animated his every waking moment. Fascinated by ships since boyhood, he never studied naval architecture formally — his father believed engineers were poor businessmen — earning a degree in law instead. But he spent every spare moment studying ships and their design, and with his brother, Frederic, he set about designing a transatlantic liner intended to earn a place beside the great Cunarders. America's entry into the First World War aborted the project, but the sense of the superlative never deserted Gibbs; obsessed by his work, he often put in ten-hour days, seven days a week. He brooked no compromise in his designs or the ships built to them — which earned him few friends in the shipbuilding industry — but his ships had unrivalled records for safety and quality, so the firm stayed solvent even during the lean years of the depression. Between the wars, he played a prominent role in persuading the US Navy to adopt high-temperature, high-pressure boilers in its engineering plants, a decision often cited as vital to the navy's success in the Second World War. His prewar masterpiece was the passenger liner *America*, at the time the largest commercial vessel ever built in the United States. Completed in 1940, she entered service as the troop transport USS *West Point*.

Gibbs accepted Carp's offer for the sheer challenge of it, later telling Carp that he had drawn the plans for himself. He also refused payment for his work, and told Carp that he would sell the plans only if he himself was satisfied with the design. Gibbs insisted on complete secrecy, allowing neither Carp nor his Soviet advisers to see the work as it progressed. By November 1937 the preliminary sketches were completed; Gibbs, unable to content himself with a modest 35,000 tonner, had drawn a ship of nearly 62,000 tons. That no dock in the United States could accommodate it did not matter; that the vessel be the superlative capital ship was the only important thing.

In later discussing this ship, Gibbs said that the Soviets 'were going to build a Navy, so they told us, to compete with any Navy, and of course particularly with the Japanese. The problem that I had was, if you were going to compete with the Japanese, what was the best way to spend your money to accomplish it. . . . It seemed to me that the proper method was to build such an extraordinary ship that in one step you had caused an extraordinary obsolescence of the Japanese fleet'.

The resulting designs were as extraordinary as anyone could have wished. The drawings were ready by January 1938. Two designs were actually prepared, one armed with eight 18in guns, the other with twelve 16in guns. Their characteristics are given below.

	Design A	Design B
Displacement:	66,074t normal	61,840t standard
		71,850t normal
		74,000t full load
Dimensions:	1000ft oa, 975 wl ×	1005ft oa, 980 wl ×
	126ft × 34ft 4in normal	128ft × 34ft 4in normal
Flight deck:	430ft long	402ft long
Machinery:	both designs: 6 sets geared turbines,	
	13 boilers, 6 shafts, 300,000shp = 34kts.	
	3750nm at 34kts, 17,800nm at 20kts,	
	29,000nm at 12 kts	
Armament:	eight 18in (4 × 2)	twelve 16in (4 × 3)
	twenty-eight 5in (14 × 2)	twenty-eight 5in (14 × 2)
	twenty-four 1.1in	thirty-two 1.1in
	ten .50MG	twelve .50MG
Aircraft:	both designs: 36 aeroplanes,4 floatplanes, 2 catapults	
Armour:	?	13in main belt sloped
		at 15°; 4.75+1.25in
		2nd deck (magazines);
		3.75+1.25in
		(machinery); 1.75in
		3rd deck (magazines);
		1.25 (machinery); 15in
		barbettes; 16in turret
		faces, 10in sides,
		7-8in turret roofs,
		15in CT sides, 8in
		roof
Complement:	?	2706

The sketches of Design A were unfortunately discarded some years ago; Design B, selected for further development, is the only one in the series for which drawings survive. They show a ship in which the main battery is arranged in the con-

ventional fashion, two turrets forward and aft, the only feature of the design that can be called conventional. Its tall superstructure contained two hangar decks: an upper, larger one with a clear height of about 18ft, and a lower 'small plane hangar' with about 12ft of clearance. This hangar was serviced only by the after lift. The 5in guns are ranged on each beam, while the superstructure — bridgeworks, two tall fire-control towers and a low, massive funnel — are to starboard, as on most carriers. The sides of the superstructure are pierced by many apertures, presumably to ventilate the hangars.

Some published sources assert that the flight deck was intended solely for landing, and that aeroplanes would have been launched from the two catapults at the stern. This seems a needlessly awkward arrangement, and requires the existence of a crane, not shown on any of the drawings, to lower the aircraft from the flight deck to trolleys that would wheel them aft to the catapults. This description of the intended flight operations was evidently inspired by the lack of catapults on the flight deck, and the rails that lead from the after end of the superstructure to the catapults along the port side of the quarterdeck, but Gibbs stated in a 22 April 1938 letter to the Secretary of State that the

> ship is equipped with 36 fighting and observation land planes for use in connection with the Flight Deck, and four sea planes for use in connection with the two catapults.

It seems clear from this that aeroplane launches were usually to be conducted on the flight deck, while the catapults aft would be used for launching the seaplanes. Gibbs apparently considered that the catapults could also be used as 'a matter of convenience, that you should be able to launch planes by catapult without changing course. And also if the central part was damaged and the planes were not you could use the planes as a normal battleship would'. This leaves unanswered the question of just how the aircraft would get from the hangar to the quarterdeck, although the rails on the quarterdeck would allow their quick transfer once they were on the deck.

Although catapult launches and arresting gear would certainly have been necessary to operate aircraft of reasonable performance from the short flight deck, the only features shown on this deck are two large lifts, each 50ft by 40ft. Gibbs may have thought that the deck, somewhat longer than that in earlier American flight-deck cruiser designs, would be long enough for rolling take-offs and unarrested landings; the slight uphill angle of the after portion of the deck may be a result of such thinking. Or perhaps flight-deck details were omitted because more study was considered necessary to devise the proper arrangements. There are certainly indications that Gibbs and his staff were unfamiliar with carrier operations. For example, the corners of the flight deck were cut away to give the main battery adequate fields of fire, a dangerous feature shared with so many hybrid designs. Adding to a pilot's perils were the low funnel and the mass of the turrets aft of the flight deck, which would have made for unpredictable air currents during landings. And, as in earlier battleship hybrid designs, flight operations would have been impossible during a gunnery engagement due to the blast of the guns, while a few shell hits would have quickly demolished the immense hangar. The hangar itself would have been a fire hazard because of its aircraft and their fuelling lines.

The design featured a novel engineering plant, intended to be the most powerful in the world. There were to be six sets of geared turbines driving six shafts. The machinery was laid out on the unit system, as in contemporary US battleship designs. Each machinery room, except for the aftermost, contained a turbine and two boilers. The run of the shafting through the after machinery space ruled out two big boilers, so three smaller ones were substituted.

Gibbs' design came complete with a strategy for its employment. In addition to the giant battleship-carrier, Gibbs was designing large destroyers and fast supply ships to accompany the hybrid. If this force 'got loose on the ocean you would probably cause the Japanese untold worry until they could locate that ship and bring it to action'. Even then, the battleship-carrier 'would be so powerful that only a mischance could stop its operations'. Its speed and range would allow it to roam at will, making it 'almost impossible for the enemy to count on any overseas commerce . . . until such a ship was either brought to an action or returned to port again'.

Design B generated a good deal of interest in political circles, where it became known rather dramatically as 'Ship X'. In early 1938 Gibbs submitted an outline of the design to Assistant Secretary of the Navy Charles A Edison, who was so excited by the idea that he arranged a lunch with the President for Gibbs in late February. Edison wanted to build Ship X for the US Navy.

Franklin Roosevelt was probably intrigued by the design; he had earlier favoured Scheme F, the combination aircraft carrier-battleship idea proposed by the Bureau of Construction and Repair in 1935, and had himself proposed an aircraft-carrying auxiliary cruiser (see Chapter 9). Whatever his personal feelings for this gigantic hybrid, however, Roosevelt managed to convey almost diametrically opposed impressions to Edison and Gibbs; Edison came away from the luncheon convinced that the President wanted such a ship built in the United States for the Soviets, while Gibbs was just as convinced that the President wanted to build the ship for the United States, and so he hesitated to show the plans to Carp.

Meanwhile, Stalin once again demonstrated his strong interest in the battleship negotiations by personally recalling Carp to the Soviet Union to explain why he had made so little progress. Carp survived whatever interview he had in Moscow and returned to New York in late March 1938, still in charge of the project. Soon after Carp's return, Gibbs submitted his finished plans to the government for approval; he was very concerned about doing business with the Soviets, and wanted to be sure that his actions had the approval of the administration — as large as his firm was, Gibbs was still feeling the pressure of the navy officers opposed to the project. He wanted it definitely established for the record that the government had given its blessing to the project. Among his selling points was that the ship would take five years or so to build, during which time it could be seized by the United States if any emergency arose. This argument seems to have won over even Admiral Leahy, who was another one of the government leaders impressed by Ship X.

Soon after Roosevelt approved the project, the State Department quashed it. The ship was well over the 45,000 ton displacement limit established by the escalator clause of the Second London Naval Conference, invoked in March 1938. Although the Soviet Union was not a party to any naval limitation treaty, the Washington Treaty, still the cornerstone of the treaty system, expressly stated that no capital ship exceeding the established maximum tonnage would be 'constructed by, for, or within the jurisdiction of' any of the signatories. It was also argued by Acting Secretary of State Sumner Welles that building Ship X would render all existing battleships, including those of the US Navy, obsolete. At the end of April, it was decided that no battleship of more than 45,000 tons would be built in the United

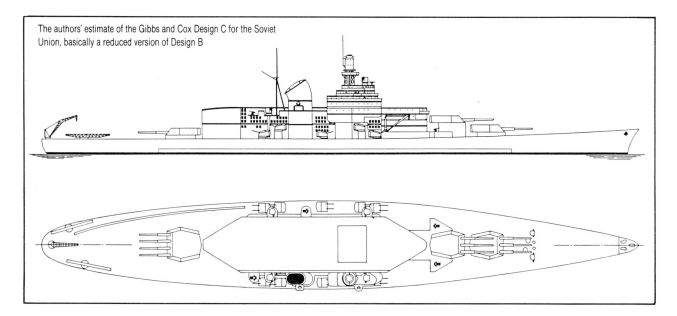

The authors' estimate of the Gibbs and Cox Design C for the Soviet Union, basically a reduced version of Design B

States for the Soviet Union.

The Soviets, when they finally saw the design, were not pleased. Their first real glimpse of the plans came in late 1938; the US government had approved their sale, on the theory that the Soviets could not build such a ship for some time to come. So in November Gibbs sent a representative with the drawings to Moscow; the Soviets were allowed to study the sketches during the day, but at night they were placed in the safe at the US Embassy to prevent any reproduction prior to their purchase. After reviewing the drawings for about a week, the Soviet naval authorities decided against purchasing them.

When the administration made its decision against building a ship in excess of the 45,000 ton limit for the Soviets, Gibbs set about designing a 45,000 ton version of Ship X. Design C emerged in July 1938, still slightly over the limit. It had the following characteristics.

Displacement:	46,520t standard; 55,200t normal
Dimensions:	845ft oa, 820ft wl × 118ft max, 115ft wl × 33ft 4in normal
Flight deck:	320ft long
Machinery:	4 sets geared turbines, 8 boilers, 200,000shp = 31kts. 2900nm at 31kts; 12,000nm at 20kts; 16,000nm at 15kts
Armament:	ten 16in (2 × 3, 1 × 4); twenty 5in (10 × 2); ? × 1.1in; ? × .50MG
Aircraft:	24 aeroplanes, 4 floatplanes, 2 catapults
Armour:	?
Complement:	?

No sketches of Design C survive. It is known that the main battery was to be arranged in two triple turrets forward and one quadruple turret aft, an arrangement considered for several US battleship designs at about this time.

Design C was the last hybrid design prepared for the Soviets; one further battleship design, designated D, was prepared by Gibbs and Cox by March 1939. This was a conventional battleship of 45,000 tons armed, like Design C, with ten 16in, and was the last battleship design prepared in the United States for the Soviet Union. On 17 September 1939 the Soviets invaded eastern Poland in accordance with the secret clauses of the Russo-German Non-Aggression Pact, and Gibbs refused to undertake any further work for them.

Edison still wanted to build the giant hybrid for the US Navy, but the navy was not thrilled with the idea. In a General Board memorandum of 24 October 1939, Admiral W R Sexton, senior member of the board, expressed thoughts undoubtedly shared by other senior officers. Calling the design 'the Big Ship', he pointed out that

The blast effect of 16″ guns is such that no planes could be kept on deck during 16″ gun firing . . . The question of location of funnels and disposal of gases, the problem of an offset island structure heavily protected and carrying conning tower and fire control stations, require construction features that may interfere seriously with the fighting qualities of the ship.

. . . The real need for Big Ship combining battleship and carrier characteristics is not apparent . . . In a capital ship combining heavy battery and considerable air strength, the complications of organization, training, and operation may be distinctly disadvantageous to the extent that the full effect of either battery or planes is seriously compromised. The design and use of the ship as outlined is not looked on with favor.

Edison was still interested in the design. On 20 November, he sent a memo to the General Board asking for a report on whether Ship X 'has sufficient merit as a military weapon to warrant inclusion in the scheme of National Defense for the United States, either as part of or in addition to the Fleet'. He also invited Gibbs to describe the design at a General Board hearing on 5 December 1939. The members of the board and the experts from the various bureaux went over the ship's features in some detail, then asked Gibbs to leave them the drawings so that they could study them at length. They finally passed judgement in a memo to Edison dated 27 December. While 'Examination of the proposed plans for this vessel does not disclose any feature in her design which the Board considers impracticable', there were still reservations about some features of the ship and its usefulness.

> . . . The armor provided is slightly lighter than armor now being provided in our latest capital ships under construction . . . Security against underwater damage is somewhat adversely affected by the additional number of large spaces necessary for machinery, magazines, and handling rooms . . .
> . . .The availability of 36 planes under many conditions would be advantageous. However, as in aircraft carriers, the operations required for the proper handling of planes will in many situations detract from freedom of action . . . necessary to the most effective use of gunpower.

The General Board concluded with a direct response to Edison's question, which could also be taken as a fair assessment of many of the hybrid schemes considered between the wars.

> Ship X, as designed, does not have sufficient merit as a military weapon to warrant inclusion in any scheme of national defense at this time.

If the Soviets had little to show for their two and a half years of negotiation for a battleship in the United States, it was by this time of little concern to them. In August 1938, the *Sovetskii Soyuz* was laid down in Leningrad; apparently Stalin had grown impatient with the drawn-out American negotiations and had decided to go his own way in the matter of battleship building. At 59,000 tons, the design approached that of Ship X in size, although its characteristics were considerably more modest and its configuration entirely conventional. Work on this class of four ships was suspended in October 1940, perhaps due to difficulties in producing the 16in guns and their mountings. None was finished; by the time of the German invasion of June 1941 no further work had been done on them, and there were far more urgent tasks facing Soviet industry than the completion of 'prestige' battleships.

If Ship X had been laid down, it almost certainly would never have been delivered to the Soviets. It might have been nearing completion in 1942, and by that time the US Navy would surely have commandeered it to boost its own strength. Even if the United States was not at war as the ship neared completion, the American neutrality laws forbade supplying weapons to belligerent nations, and the invasions first of Poland and then of Finland would have made the Soviet Union a belligerent in the eyes of the State Department. In a sense, then, the US Navy's efforts to prevent the Soviet Union from getting a battleship with American aid succeeded only in denying the United States the use of a fast battleship at a time when battleships were in very short supply.

As for William Francis Gibbs, any disappointment he may have felt was no doubt ameliorated by the flood of business created by the outbreak of the Second World War. After the war, he finally got his chance to build the superlative liner he had dreamed of for three decades: SS *United States*, the fastest and probably the safest liner ever to sail. Gibbs' passion for this culmination of his dreams was shown by the fact that he greeted her at the pier every time she steamed into New York — only doctor's orders could keep him away. He died in 1967, to all appearances a happy man.

There was a bizarre postwar echo of these big hybrid designs. In the 17 December 1945 issue of *Life* magazine there appeared an article on the Soviet Navy featuring a two-page illustration of some very peculiar ships. Asserting that 'Russians Like Odd Designs', the article pointed out the difficult naval position of the Soviet Union. Faced with widely scattered outlets to the sea, some of them nearly land-locked, and with the importance of naval aviation clearly demonstrated by the Pacific war, the 'American Naval Architects' working for *Life* conjured up a series of very strange aircraft-carrying vessels for the Soviet Navy: there was a 'floating base', essentially an aircraft carrier, but lacking that

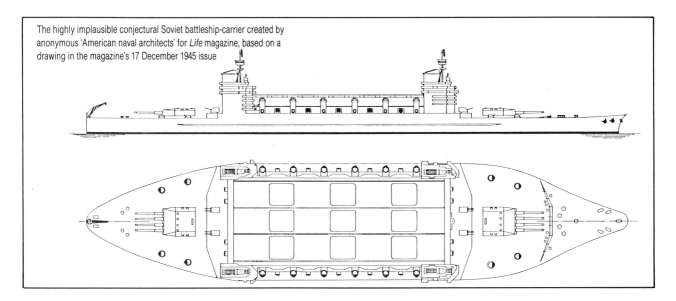

The highly implausible conjectural Soviet battleship-carrier created by anonymous 'American naval architects' for *Life* magazine, based on a drawing in the magazine's 17 December 1945 issue

type's high speed, 'designed to remedy Russia's lack of island bases'; there was a funny little 'dock for a seaplane'; and then there were the hybrids.

The centre of the drawing is dominated by an enormous battleship-carrier, 120,000 tons and armed with eight 18in guns in two quadruple turrets, one forward, one aft. These turrets, huge as they would have been, are dwarfed in the drawing by the ship's tremendous beam — by the look of it, 200ft or more. She has a bluff, block-like hull that even the most powerful engines could have driven at only a few knots. Between the turrets is a huge flight deck, complete with *nine* lifts, and rimmed by AA guns. Along all four sides of this tremendous structure are eighteen 'rocket projectors', blunt tubes that look like old-fashioned mortars. There are five of these strange devices on each beam, and four directed forward and aft. At each corner of the flight deck is an island incorporating numerous bridge levels, radar scanners, and a funnel. There are many typically American touches to this 'Soviet' design: the crane right aft, the shape of the directors atop the islands (duplicates of the Mk 37 directors fitted aboard most American warships during the war), and even the shape of the funnels, which mirror those of the then recently completed *Midway* class carriers.

Accompanying this monstrous battleship-carrier is a 'battle cruiser'. Armed with more of the rocket projectors (three can be seen facing forward; there may be others lost in the shadows of the drawing) and four small triple gun turrets on each beam (5in? 6in?), she also has a flight deck, more conventionally sized, with twin islands at its after corners; the shape of these islands, and the

other details of the sketch, are very similar to the battleship.

Both ships are bizarre, but the battleship is truly astounding in concept and execution. Putting aside the difficulties the Soviets would have faced in building a 120,000 ton ship, the combination of guns and rocket projectors and aircraft would make for a strange craft to handle in a battle — if handling such an unwieldy vessel would have been possible at all. Nine lifts seem excessive, and surely would have taken up valuable hangar space better devoted to aircraft stowage. No catapults or arresting gear are shown, although the aircraft shown on deck may be jets, their tiny size making it difficult to tell. All those islands, with their funnels, would have made for some interesting air currents over the flight deck. As an aviation platform, the battlecruiser is even worse, with pilots facing a tricky landing between the two close-set islands right at the after end of the flight deck. Otherwise, however, she is not too unreasonable, and is in many ways similar to *Kiev*.

Looking at these designs, one has to wonder if there is some connection with the Gibbs and Cox project of the 1930s. That they are hybrids is a strong link for a start, and for sheer size the battleship outdoes even Ship X; it is, in fact, the largest hybrid design to come to light. It is possible that the 'American naval architects' who dreamed up these pseudo-Soviet ships worked on the Battleship X design — *Life* may have consulted Gibbs and Cox in preparing its article. Or the anonymous naval architects may have read something about the Gibbs and Cox design in the press, where scattered details of Battleship X had been

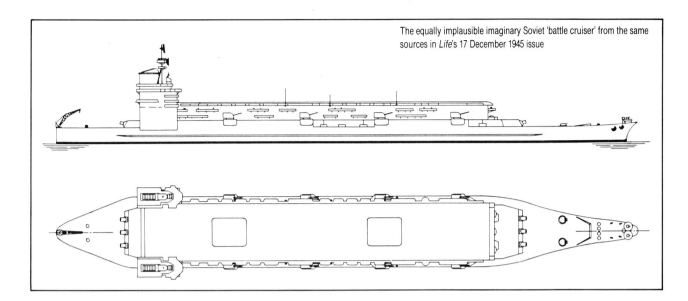

The equally implausible imaginary Soviet 'battle cruiser' from the same sources in *Life*'s 17 December 1945 issue

appearing for some time. These reports varied in their accuracy. For example, while the *New York Times* correctly reported in April 1938 that Gibbs and Cox were working on a 1000ft long design for the Soviets, *Time* magazine in September 1942 exaggerated it into an 85,000 ton 'one-ship navy, a battleship with a flight deck for some 60 planes, a behemoth which would dominate any naval engagement as easily as a shark dominates a school of mackerel'. If *Life*'s advisers knew or believed that plans for such a ship had been delivered to Moscow, they may have tried to predict what the Soviets would do with those plans — the 'next generation' of Ship X, with a few postwar exotica added.

Whatever the origins of these intriguing designs, they form an appropriate coda to the Soviet hopes of acquiring a battleship with US help, and for Ship X as well.

'THE RESULTS OF A PSYCHOLOGICAL MALADJUSTMENT'

The world war that began with the German invasion of Poland on 1 September 1939 had soon not only changed the political outlines of Europe, but the shape of war at sea as well. One of the most dramatic changes, evident both on land and at sea, was the growing power of aircraft; this inescapable fact led the navies of Britain, France and Germany to consider hybrid designs. Each had a different rationale for these investigations, yet in each the intersection of prewar doctrines and the new realities of aerial offence influenced the types of hybrid vessels examined.

The Royal Navy's investigations of the hybrid were directed to a very specific purpose: defence against air attack. Operations during the first year of war, especially in support of the Norwegian campaign, had demonstrated that even the most powerful battleships needed protection from land-based aircraft. AA guns had not proved as effective as prewar exercises had indicated, and there were not enough carriers to provide the coverage the fleet needed. The situation was so critical that the Home Fleet suggested a return to the prewar practice of carrying fighters aboard battleships. This was an idea with a long history in the Royal Navy, dating back to the fitting of turret-top flying-off platforms for aeroplanes on the capital ships of the Grand Fleet during the First World War. Intended to counter the German airships, this *ad hoc* practice was abandoned after the war, but was soon revived for two reasons: it reduced the number of fighters that carriers needed to embark, allowing them to carry more strike aircraft, and provided the battleship or cruiser with some degree of aerial protection when operating independently.

The Royal Navy's first specialised shipboard fighter, the Fairey Flycatcher, was operating from capital ships soon after its introduction in 1923, but because of the lack of suitable catapults, it at first flew from turret-top or revolving platforms, as had its First World War predecessors. HMS *Hood*, for example, carried a Flycatcher for some time on her 'B' turret. Later, when satisfactory catapults finally became available, the Flycatchers were fitted with floats; when they were phased out of this role in June 1934 they were replaced by the Hawker Osprey two-seat float reconnaissance-fighter. By this time, however, the increasing inferiority of the floatplane fighter in comparison to its wheeled counterpart was becoming ever more evident; the weight and drag penalties imposed by the floats affected both the aircraft's speed and manoeuvrability (see Chapter 14). The Royal Navy reportedly planned to overcome this handicap in wartime by converting its catapult floatplanes to their wheeled versions (nearly all were designed to accept both types of undercarriage), an impractical and wasteful policy reverting to the one-shot shipboard flights of the First World War. In the event, this was never carried out except in the case of the catapult merchant (CAM) ships and the RN catapult fighter ships, which employed not converted floatplanes but Hawker Hurricanes and Fairey Fulmars.

It was a mark of the urgency of the air defence problem that the Home Fleet resurrected the idea, but it was an unsatisfactory solution at best, and the Director of Air Materiel, M S Slattery, therefore came up with an alternative. On 17 October 1940 he minuted his colleagues on the Naval Staff: 'It is clear . . . that the Fleet feel a need for fighter protection; a need which they do not feel can be entirely satisfied either by carrier borne or shore based aircraft. Inevitably, therefore, one is tempted to return to the idea of the Carrier Battleship or Carrier Cruiser'.

Slattery gave in to temptation and proposed such a ship; he hoped that 'departments better qualified . . . will forgive him for inviting their attention to the sketch plan which appears to show that (without any exhaustive enquiry into such important questions as top weight, structural feasibility) it would be possible to superimpose on the K. G. V. Class or similar heavy ship, without, it would seem, impairing the efficiency of the heavy armament, a short landing deck of similar characteristics to the ILLUSTRIOUS Class, an Assisted Take Off Gear and a hangar for 18 Fleet fighters of our latest projected design'.

Slattery's sketch shows a ship whose general proportions match those of *Hood*, with four main battery turrets in superimposed pairs fore and aft. In place of the usual superstructure, there is a hangar structure topped by a flight deck, with a starboard island complete with tripod mast. The

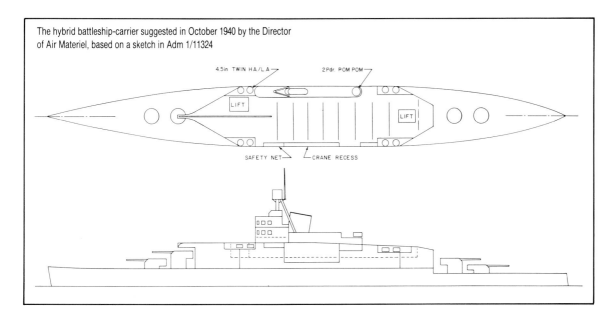

The hybrid battleship-carrier suggested in October 1940 by the Director of Air Materiel, based on a sketch in Adm 1/11324

flight deck has a pronounced slope up from its after end to a point abreast the island, while the 'Assisted Take Off Gear' (catapult) extends forward over 'B' turret. The estimate of eighteen fighters was based on folding-wing aircraft; specification N.5/40, which eventually resulted in the Fairey Firefly, figured in the discussions that followed. Failing a suitable folding-wing aircraft, Slattery estimated that his battleship-carrier could accommodate twelve Spitfires, an aircraft which was not adapted for carrier service as the Seafire until late 1941.

The D of P, Captain Charles L Daniel, agreed with Slattery. He 'strongly' recommended that the idea be examined, seeing the provision of aircraft as similar in theory to anti-torpedo bulges and degaussing gear — a defence against a new form of attack; he did not think that it should be regarded as 'some compromise between the capital ship and the aircraft carrier but as a battleship to which a defensive fighter equipment has been added'.

There was certainly some historical basis for this point of view. The battleship had survived the quick-firing gun, the torpedo boat, the mine and the submarine, all of which had been touted as Davids to the battleship's Goliath. In each instance, the battleship had adopted something of the threat — gaining its own batteries of quick-firing guns, turning the torpedo boat against itself in the form of the destroyer, developing complex and effective systems of underwater protection — and kept its place as the centrepiece of naval power. In that scheme of things, a complement of fighters was nothing more than a new type of long-range AA battery.

However, aircraft could act as an AA battery only because of a new development: radar. This sets Slattery's proposal apart from all earlier hybrids; previously, without knowing the course and altitude of incoming raids, fighters could not intercept enemy aircraft effectively. Indeed, early in the war even the Royal Navy's carriers relied on their guns for AA defence; in the first air attack on *Ark Royal* 'no attempt was made to meet the . . . German bombers with our own ship-borne fighters. All aircraft were recalled, struck down into the hangars and their petrol tanks drained, to reduce fire risk if the ship was hit. It was the policy to rely on the anti-aircraft gun'.

Radar changed all that; for the first time, defending aircraft could be efficiently directed to interception positions well before the enemy could attack. This new factor was recognised by the members of the Naval Staff, and 'RDF' (radio direction finding) played a prominent part throughout the discussion of the hybrid proposal.

Despite this radical change in the intended purpose of the hybrid's aviation complement, there is a familiar ring to some of the operational limitations of Slattery's hybrid battleship. When the Director of the Naval Air Division (DNAD), the Director of Tactical and Staff Duties (DTSD) and the D of P jointly suggested that the hangar need only be large enough to accommodate two aircraft for maintenance, Slattery replied that 'in an attempt to simplify the staff requirements the signatories to the joint minute have made the scheme impracticable'. He pointed out that, should the catapult break down, the short flight

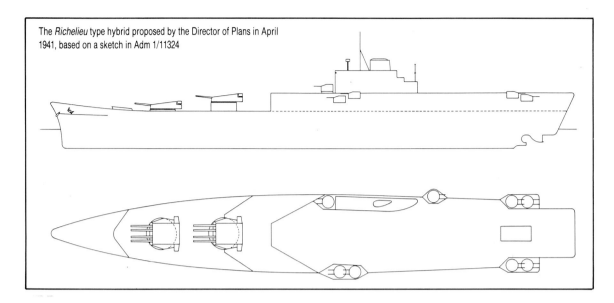

The *Richelieu* type hybrid proposed by the Director of Plans in April 1941, based on a sketch in Adm 1/11324

deck would allow only one aircraft at a time to take off — there was no room for a deck park. In a similar fashion, only a couple of aircraft could be spotted forward of the safety barrier during landings. The hangar, and lifts fore and aft, were therefore necessary either to bring up more aircraft for launching or to strike them down to get them out of the way during landings. He also noted that aircraft stowed on deck would be subject to blast from the big guns. All these problems had come up time and again during the history of the hybrid.

Slattery's points were accepted, and on 8 January 1941 the Controller, Rear Admiral Bruce A Fraser (later Admiral of the Fleet Lord Fraser of North Cape), asked Sir Stanley Goodall, Director of Naval Construction (DNC), to 'give me your impressions of this [the hybrid features] as applied to Lion'. The *Lion* class battleships, 40,000 tons and armed with nine 16in guns in three triple turrets, had been suspended in the early stages of construction soon after the outbreak of the war and so formed a convenient basis for the hybrid scheme. In the same minute, the Controller rejected a suggestion that *Vanguard*, then in the design stage, might make a suitable candidate for a hybrid. *Vanguard*, designed around the 15in turrets removed from *Courageous* and *Glorious* when they were converted into aircraft carriers, was urgently needed and Fraser probably feared that any alterations to the design would delay her completion.

DNC's department worked out a hybrid version of the *Lion* design and presented it to the Controller at a meeting on 12 March 1941; all the interested parties were present. After the meeting,

DNC observed that 'The arrangements shown on the drawing were not liked' by the participants. The sketch, now apparently lost, retained all the main battery turrets, and the flight deck was too short to be useful. It was suggested that a *Nelson*-style main battery arrangement might be better, although it was feared that this would lead to a 50,000 to 55,000 ton ship.

D of P suggested an alternative on 3 April 1941. Reducing the number of main battery turrets to two, perhaps using quadruple turrets, would allow a ship of more reasonable displacement. To illustrate his idea, he submitted a sketch based on the French *Richelieu* class; the sketch looks as if it were traced from *Jane's* or some other recognition manual, and as Daniel himself pointed out, it was 'in no sense a design'. It was, in fact, intended only to show the advantages of grouping the main battery forward and the aviation facilities aft. Daniel further noted that 'In view of our new relationship with the U.S.A. it might perhaps be concluded that we have no need to build 16″ ships in addition to theirs and that we could confine ourselves to 14″, which would render our future battlefleet homogeneous as regards ammunition, or to 15″ which would enable us to employ our largest ammunition reserves to advantage'. This is certainly a reference to the first Anglo-American staff talks, which ended on 27 March; if the United States was now to act as a counterweight to Japanese ambitions in the Pacific, then the American 16in gunned battleships would balance the rumoured construction of similarly armed battleships in Japan. Since the German and Italian capital ships carried 15in guns, the Royal Navy could afford to build ships with similar

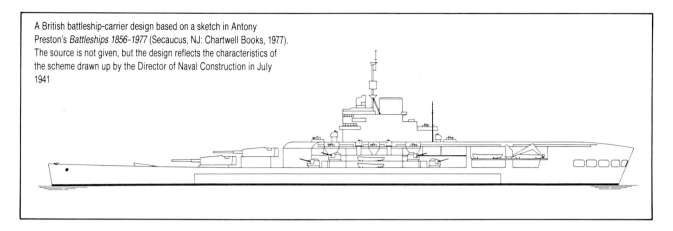

A British battleship-carrier design based on a sketch in Antony
Preston's *Battleships 1856–1977* (Secaucus, NJ: Chartwell Books, 1977).
The source is not given, but the design reflects the characteristics of
the scheme drawn up by the Director of Naval Construction in July
1941

Displacement:	44,750t standard, 51,000t deep
Dimensions:	800ft wl × 112ft max × 29ft 10in
Flight deck:	500ft × 73ft; 1 catapult
Machinery:	130,000shp = 28–29kts; 4350t oil; 14,750nm at 10 kts
Armament:	six 16in (2 × 3), sixteen 5.25in (8 × 2), eight 8-barrelled pom-poms
Aircraft:	12 fighters, 2 Torpedo/Bomber/Reconnaissance (TBR)
Armour:	13in belt abreast magazines; 6in deck over magazines, 5in over machinery; 15in barbettes, 15in turret face plates, 10–7in sides, 6in roof

armament, which would make for hybrids of a
reasonable size.

The hybrid battleship found another supporter
in the seemingly unlikely person of Rear Admiral
Sir Tom S V Phillips, Vice Chief of the Naval Staff
(VCNS). It has been said that Phillips 'had no
great opinion of the effectiveness of the modern
aeroplane or the danger it posed to warships', and
this is perhaps the mildest criticism aimed at him;
he has often been portrayed as the archetypal
'battleship admiral', contemptuous of aviation
and placing all his trust in the big gun. However,
recent research has shown that Phillips began to
show a greater appreciation for aviation following
the Norwegian campaign, and this view is borne
out by his position on the hybrid: on 20 April 1941
he minuted, 'Aircraft have come to stay and unless
there is hope of the gun alone dealing with them
(which I do not see at present) I think there are
many points in this design [the hybrid] if it proves
practicable'.

The Assistant Chief of the Naval Staff (Home)
(ACNS[H]), Rear Admiral Arthur Power, on the
other hand, was sceptical of the idea. On 4 April
1941, he pointed out that the battleship-aircraft
carrier's movements would be dictated by the
wind during flight operations, and that 'The
carrier as a target is considered to be the Gunnery
Officer's dream. Are our new 40,000 ton ships to
present such spectacles?'

Despite such criticism, there was still interest
in the hybrid, and DNC was asked to draw up a
new battleship-carrier, with only two main
battery turrets, as D of P had suggested. The
sketch was ready by July 1941, and had the
following characteristics.

There is some disagreement in published sources
regarding the calibre of the main battery guns;
both 15in and 16in have been mentioned. The
latter seems more likely in view of the fact that the
triple 16in turret had already been designed, while
a 15in triple turret would have been an entirely
new mounting.

The ship had clearly ceased to be simply the
'battleship to which a defensive fighter equipment
has been added' that Daniel had envisaged; aviation was very clearly forcing a severe reduction in
the gunnery features of the design. Not surprisingly, DNC regarded it as 'very inferior' to a pure
battleship, pointing out that the hangar was
unarmoured and the uptakes difficult to arrange.
The Director of the Gunnery Division (DGD)
expressed himself more forcefully, observing that
'the functions and requirements of carriers and of
surface gun platforms are entirely incompatable
. . . the conception of these designs . . . is evidently
the result of an unresolved contest between a
conscious acceptance of aircraft and a sub-
conscious desire for a 1914 Fleet . . . these abor-
tions are the results of a psychological maladjustment. The necessary readjustments should
result from a proper re-analysis of the whole
question, what would be a balanced fleet in 1945,
1950 or 1955? '

DGD's observation was apt; a battleship carrying defensive aircraft made sense in face of the

immediate crisis of 1941, but only if it was available immediately. A hybrid battleship could not be ready for sea before 1945, and so it would be far better to design vessels that would contribute to the efficiency of the future fleet. DGD may also have been hinting at the battleship's decline from its role as the main element in a fleet's striking power, as it had been in 1914; if aircraft could threaten and perhaps sink battleships (although no battleship had been sunk at sea by aircraft as of mid-1941), then perhaps it was time to replace the battleship with the aircraft carrier.

Two flying-deck cruiser designs were also prepared at this time.

	Cruiser-carrier A	Cruiser-carrier B
Displacement:	18,900t standard; 23,000t deep	20,000t standard; 24,500t deep
Dimensions:	670ft wl × 83ft	690ft wl × 83ft
Flight deck:	380ft × 80ft	340ft × 80ft
Machinery:	both designs: 120,000 shp = 30.75-32.25kts	
	3600t oil; 11,000nm at 16kts	3750t oil; 11,500nm at 16kts
Armament:	six 8in (2 × 3)	nine 8in (3 × 3)
	twelve 4in (6 × 2)	twelve 4in (6 × 2)
	three 4-barrelled pom-poms	three 4-barrelled pom-poms
	ten 20mm	eight 20mm
	six 21in TT (2 × 3)	six 21in TT (2 × 3)
Aircraft:	10 fighters	10 fighters
	4 TBR	2 TBR
Armour:	both designs: 4.5in belt; 4in deck over magazines, 2in over machinery	

No sketches of these ships have survived, and nothing is known about their intended configurations. Given the shorter flight deck of the larger design B, it may be that this ship had a conventional turret arrangement, two turrets forward and one aft; design A probably had its main battery concentrated forward.

By this time there was little support for any of the hybrid ships; Daniel had gone to sea and the new D of P, Captain Charles E Lambe, did not favour the idea. The final minute in the file dates from September 1941 and notes that 'Action on this paper is deferred'.

The idea came up again briefly in early 1942. By this time the need of surface ships for air cover had been irrefutably demonstrated by the destruction of Tom Phillips' Force Z — the modern battleship *Prince of Wales* and the old battlecruiser *Repulse* — at the hands of Japanese aircraft flying from bases in Indochina. Denis W Boyd, Rear Admiral, Mediterranean Aircraft Carriers, undoubtedly had this tragedy in mind when he sent a paper to Admiral Andrew Browne Cunningham, C-in-C,

Mediterranean. Boyd's topic was 'Capital Ship Design', and he began by pointing out that 'War experience creates a grave doubt whether existing battleships and large cruisers are of suitable design to fulfil their functions'.

Boyd went on to outline virtually all the issues that had been raised by Slattery in 1940, but added a new point, based no doubt on his own experiences in the Mediterranean: if battleships and cruisers carried their own defensive aircraft, the carrier squadrons would be free to carry out offensive operations. To this end, he proposed equipping capital ships with a 300ft flight deck, hangar and island superstructure; this would allow the ship to carry nine to twelve aircraft. Cruisers might be able to carry six aircraft.

Boyd included a sketch of a 45,000 ton ship, 800ft by 100ft, armed with nine 15in or 16in guns. The heavy AA battery would consist of sixteen dual-purpose guns, '5.25" or smaller'. The flight deck was 80ft wide, but it was noted that increasing the beam to 110ft would allow the deck to be widened.

Cunningham forwarded Boyd's paper to the Admiralty on 19 March 1942; in his cover letter, he said

I am in general agreement with this paper, but the practicability of designing a ship to fulfil these requirements is problematical . . .

It may well be that the future will show that the carrier pure and simple is the proper capital ship and that naval actions will be fought at ranges of 200 miles by waves of carrier-borne aircraft: but that time is not yet. It is, however, plain that, until fleets can maintain their own air protection, the war cannot be carried to the enemy's coasts nor can the sea be used for traffic within a distance of the enemy's shore-based air . . .

The Admiralty did not expend much effort reviewing this subject, as it had already been considered in detail. Instead, a simple reply was sent, based on a note drafted by Goodall. The message was dated 18 May 1942 and informed Boyd and Cunningham that

In 1941 three designs were prepared, two being Carrier-Cruisers and one a Carrier-Battleship. These dual purpose ships did not commend themselves to the Board, and the conclusion was reached that fighter protection for warships, is best provided by separate ships built in the main for that purpose.

By this time, Boyd was commanding the carriers in the Eastern Fleet, and no one else seemed very interested in hybrids. So ended the Admiralty's investigations of the hybrid warship

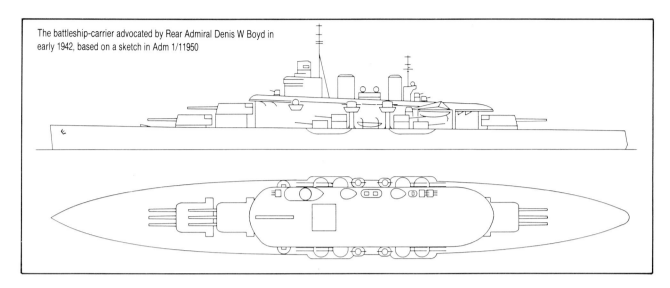

The battleship-carrier advocated by Rear Admiral Denis W Boyd in early 1942, based on a sketch in Adm 1/11950

during the Second World War.

★　　★　　★

Although official interest in hybrids had ended, there was an unofficial spurt of interest a month after the Admiralty's reply to Cunningham. In the 20 June 1942 issue of *The Illustrated London News* there appeared one of the most imaginative hybrid battleships of all time — imaginative, but completely impractical.

The vessel was dubbed the 'B.A.C. Ship', for 'Battleship-Aircraft-Carrier', and was depicted with a rather convincing two-page illustration by one of the *ILN*'s regular nautical artists, G H Davis. The design of the ship was worked out by Davis and anonymous 'naval experts' and provided for the following particulars.

Displacement:	45,000t
Dimensions:	890ft (oa) × 108ft (hull)
Machinery:	geared turbines, 3 shafts; 30kts
Armament:	nine 16in (3 × 3)
	eighteen 5.25in (6 × 3)
	numerous 2pdr pom-poms, machine guns
Aircraft:	15 fighters, 2-3 torpedo/reconnaissance

The drawing shows many novel features, and throughout demonstrates a curious mixture of the feasible and the fanciful. For example, Davis recognised that the ship would be very cramped — while the aviation facilities would increase the size of the crew, the hangar eliminated much superstructure space and this was in no way compensated for by the small island — and so a 'mother ship' would house part of the ship's crew when it was in port, rather like a submarine tender. Less reasonable, however, was the way the

forward main battery turret was recessed into the hull; this allowed the height of 'B' turret to be reduced, which in turn reduced the height of the hangar structure. The tub for 'A' turret would be 'constantly pumped clear of water in a seaway', but it is not difficult to imagine the problems resulting from a breakdown of these pumps. Davis had the turret so low that the breakwater forward of it shows notches to receive the guns when trained fore and aft.

Part of the rationale for reducing the height of the turrets lay in the flight-deck arrangements. Folding flight decks were nothing new, but Davis' design gave the idea a new twist. His short flight deck could be lengthened by means of long extensions; these would be stowed flat on the permanent portion of the flight deck when not required. When aircraft operations were wanted, columns on each beam forward and aft of the main battery turrets would be raised; each of these would receive a horizontal girder that would swing out over the turrets from stowed positions against the forward and after bulkheads of the hangar structure, and the flight deck extensions would then be slid out along these horizontal supports.

The whole system is quite ingenious, and quite impractical. A single small bomb or shell could hopelessly jam one of these extensions open or closed; in the former case, the main battery guns would be trapped by the extended structure, and in the latter, launch and recovery of aircraft would be impossible.

In addition to its fragility, Davis' system would seriously hamper the use of the 16in guns. His drawings show the hangar structure very close to the turrets; in fact 'B' turret's after end fits into a recess in the forward face of the hangar when

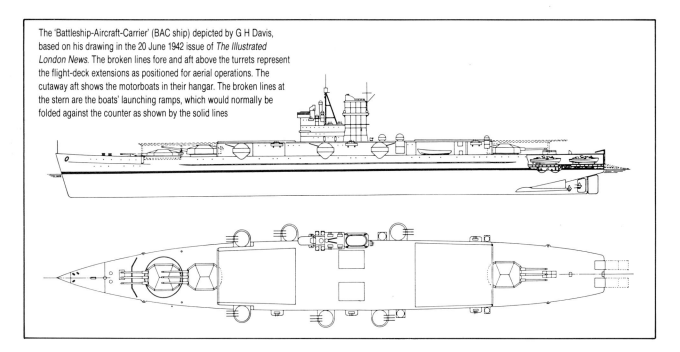

The 'Battleship-Aircraft-Carrier' (BAC ship) depicted by G H Davis, based on his drawing in the 20 June 1942 issue of *The Illustrated London News*. The broken lines fore and aft above the turrets represent the flight-deck extensions as positioned for aerial operations. The cutaway aft shows the motorboats in their hangar. The broken lines at the stern are the boats' launching ramps, which would normally be folded against the counter as shown by the solid lines

trained fore and aft. This would restrict the arc of fire of 'B' and 'X' turrets, limiting them to a maximum of about 90 degrees on each beam, allowing all nine guns to bear only when an enemy was directly abeam.

Davis took his 'B.A.C. Ship' one step further in the next issue of the *ILN* by adding four 'attack-boats' to her armoury. These 40 to 50ft long motorboats would be carried in a hangar aft and launched through a pair of doors in the broad transom stern. Each four-man, 40 knot boat would be armed with 'four large-calibre machine-guns' and torpedo tubes or depth charges, allowing the boats to attack either enemy surface craft or submarines. This is an idea that had not been seen since Strother's 1921 super battleship-carrier (see Chapter 2).

Despite its ingenious features and convincing details, the 'B.A.C. Ship' was no more feasible than the earlier Admiralty hybrid designs. As in Slattery's proposal, its aircraft were intended almost exclusively for defence, but by 1942 it was clear that the best way to fill that need was more 'ships built in the main for that purpose' — aircraft carriers.

This fact did not completely kill the hybrid idea in the press. The 12 March 1943 issue of the journal *Engineer* raised the possibility of the 'Fusion of Warship Types'. One type of fusion foreseen was that of the capital ship and the aircraft carrier; the writer believed that this hybridisation would probably come into being eventually, but doubted 'if one could design an efficient combination at the present time upon a tonnage which would allow of the passage of the Panama Canal and the use of existing docking facilities'.

The writer was apparently inspired by reports from the United States, where the idea was being 'fairly widely canvassed'. Oddly, a review of American periodical literature has turned up only one hybrid scheme, in *Collier's Magazine* (13 March 1943 issue), so it is unlikely that this crude drawing inspired the *Engineer's* article. Among the futuristic warships illustrated by Logan U Reavis (who, *Collier's* proudly noted, was a member of the United States Naval Institute) was a 'carrier-cruiser', a 'one-ship task force' that was supposed to combine six 11in guns and a flight deck in a 12,000 ton, 650ft by 75ft hull. Among its more unusual features were a small retractable island, a whale-back fo'c's'le, a cleaver bow and a 'treadmill accelerator' for launching aircraft (a device discussed in Appendix B).

This scarcely amounts to the sort of campaign on the hybrid's behalf hinted at by the *Engineer*; perhaps the writer was remembering the flying-deck cruiser of the 1930s, or perhaps it is just another example of the sort of transatlantic confusion that had dogged the hybrid since *Nelson* had been laid down; in both Britain and the United States, the alleged interest of the other nation had been cited on several occasions as support for the hybrid warship, often on only the thinnest of evidence.

★   ★   ★

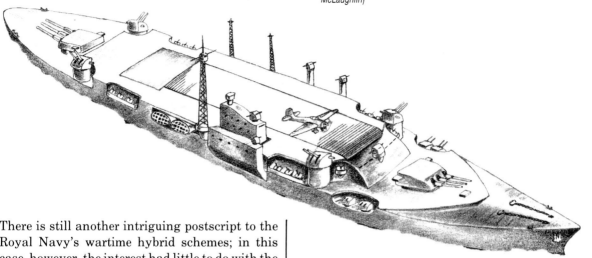

The futuristic 'carrier-cruiser' projected by Logan U Reavis, based on his sketch in the 13 March 1943 *Collier's* (*drawing by John P McLaughlin*)

There is still another intriguing postscript to the Royal Navy's wartime hybrid schemes; in this case, however, the interest had little to do with the design of such ships. It was instead a product of the murky realm of intelligence deception. This odd tale has its origins in the 'Twenty' (XX, ie, double-cross) Committee, which was concerned with methods of deceiving the Germans by sending false intelligence reports via Abwehr agents who had been captured. Ewen Montagu was the representative of the Naval Intelligence Division on this Committee; he is most famous as the instigator of the 'man who never was' ploy to deceive German intelligence about the Allied invasion of Sicily. In a 1977 book, *Beyond Top Secret U*, Montague discusses other deception operations, among them an alleged plan to dupe the Japanese into believing that the Allies were investing time and effort in the design of hybrid battleships. Montagu's chronology is vague; he says the operation was mounted after the end of the war in Europe, but he also ascribes the idea to the D of P, Captain Lambe, who had left the Admiralty a year before VE day, taking command of the carrier *Illustrious* in April 1944. It may be that Lambe, remembering the consideration given to hybrid battleships in 1940-41, suggested it to Montagu some time before he left the Plans Division, and Montagu pursued it only after Germany's defeat.

According to Montagu, Lambe suggested two potential lines of deception intended to waste the energies and material resources of the 'Japanese technologists'. One was to leak information about Habbakkuk, the fantastic and abortive 1942 plan to make giant aircraft carriers out of 'pykrete' (a mixture of ice and wood pulp); the other scheme centred on battleship-carriers.

Lambe reportedly provided the requisite background material to Montagu's unit, which set about preparing snippets of information that, released by double agents in carefully arranged driblets, would seemingly prove the reality of the schemes and eventually induce Japan to emulate them. Montagu states it was considered that the Japanese belief in the existence of such 'efficient ships' as the battle-carrier could have 'an effect on their naval tactics and strategy beneficial to the Allies'. Perhaps, but we shall never know — Japan capitulated just as the deception was set to start.

By the time the operation described by Montagu was being prepared, Japan had already hybridised two battleships into quasi-carriers, wasting a good deal of shipyard time and material in the process (see Chapter 12). Montagu indicates the intelligence planners were aware of this fact — and no wonder, since the existence of the Japanese hybrids had been known to the Allies since October 1944 — so perhaps it was thought that deceiving the IJN into a belief in enemy vessels of the same type would prod it into squandering still more manpower and metal.

It is difficult now to know how seriously Allied intelligence planners regarded the whole affair, and just what they hoped to accomplish. Whatever the truth of the matter, the odd discrepancies in this story are somehow appropriate for the hybrid concept's strange voyage into the realm of cloak, dagger and decyphering machine.

The Admiralty's interest in hybrids was quite specific; the purpose behind the several French schemes for such warships during the war is more obscure. Before the war, the *Service Technique Constructions* of the French Navy had demonstrated a style all its own, and its excellent designs — the battlecruisers *Dunkerque* and *Strasbourg*, the fine heavy cruiser *Algérie* and the series of large and powerful *contre-torpilleurs* — were all much admired by foreign observers. The collapse of the Third Republic in 1940 halted a large shipbuilding programme, but not before the impressive battleship *Richelieu* had been virtually completed. This ship was fully a match for the German *Bismarck* and the Italian *Littorio* in firepower, protection and speed despite a standard displacement some 5000 tons less than either of the Axis ships.

In one area, however, the *Service Technique* showed a definite lack of inspiration. The design for the aircraft carrier *Joffre* was archaic, showing little appreciation of efficient aviation operations — and it was ugly. In a large measure the failings of this design can be attributed to the French Navy's lack of experience with this type of ship; this lack was not made good in the course of the war, since the construction of *Joffre* and her sister *Painlevé* was stopped by the French defeat. However, some useful information may have been gathered from observing British carriers before the surrender; for example, the use of a 'hurricane' bow in at least one of the hybrid schemes (and perhaps in others as well) may have been based on contemporary British carriers.

The *Service Technique* continued studying warship designs during the occupation. There was no intention of actually building these ships; the object was probably to keep the staff in practice and to study the lessons of the war so that they could be put to use when major construction again became possible. Among these studies was a series of carrier designs that included several hybrid variants. Unfortunately, the published information on these designs lacks certain details, such as the year of their origin, and the surviving documents are apparently not yet available for publication.

Three basic lines of carrier design were explored: one was the pure carrier, which falls outside the scope of our study; the other two were hybrids. One series featured complete armour protection, even for the hangar; the other also had extensive protection but it did not encompass the hangar. Both types carried heavy gun batteries,

and both show a concern for underwater protection, especially of the propellers and rudders, strongly indicating that they were done after the loss of *Bismarck* in May 1941. The fact that *Bismarck* had been lost after a torpedo hit rendered her unmanoeuvrable was well known at the time. It is likely that it was this event that led the French designers to place the screws and rudders in a tunnel-like hollow flanked by downward extensions of the hull; German designers also adopted a similar method of protection in the 'H' series of battleship designs in response to *Bismarck*'s loss. The turbo-electric propulsion used in the French hybrid designs may also have been intended to increase protection against underwater hits; electric transmission of power allowed greater subdivision of the machinery plant and shorter shaft runs. This type of powerplant had been used with considerable success in the liner *Normandie*, so the French constructors were familiar with it. These designs may therefore be dated to the period following *Bismarck*'s loss in May 1941. They were probably completed by 1943; the PA 19 design for a pure carrier was sketched in that year.

The first group began with design PA-PC (perhaps an abbreviation of *Porte-Avions Partout Cuirassé*?). This called for a ship of about 47,000 tons; length between perpendiculars was a surprisingly short 656ft and waterline beam was 113ft 6in. Given this rather stubby hull, the 110,000shp propulsion plant could not have driven it to very high speeds. It was armed with a single quadruple 12in turret, with part of the flight deck extending over it; whether the turret was forward or aft is not clear but the latter location seems more likely as all the subsequent designs had their gun batteries aft. Horizontal protection consisted of a 7.5in flight deck and the hangar sides were 9.8in.

PA-PC was not satisfactory; among other things, the uptakes apparently took a big bite out of the hangar. It was therefore superceded by PA1-PC, another large ship (50,000 tons full load, 780ft 11in on the waterline by 105ft), armed with a quadruple 13in turret (of the type fitted in the *Dunkerque* class battlecruisers) located aft of the flight deck. The AA battery consisted of twenty-four 4.5in guns (12 × 2) and twenty quadruple 25mm mounts. With 120,000shp and finer lines, it would have been considerably faster than PA-PC. PA1-PC was followed by PA1-PC2, slightly longer at 794ft (wl), with slightly reduced protection.

The armoured hangar and flight deck in these

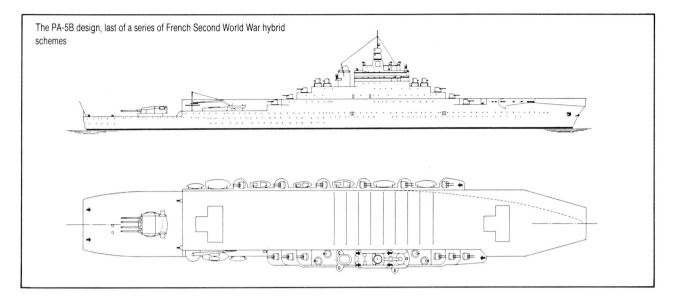

The PA-5B design, last of a series of French Second World War hybrid schemes

designs may have owed something to information about the British *Illustrious* class obtained early in the war, but the level of protection envisaged was far beyond anything the Royal Navy had ever considered. The weight of protection in PA1-PC2 amounted to 22,000 tons; these ships could have withstood 8in gunfire at virtually any range, and their armoured flight decks were thicker than the armoured deck of the battleship *Richelieu*.

The other series of designs was outwardly similar, but lacked heavy protection for the hangar. It began with PA1, a 30,000 tonner with a quadruple 12in turret aft and a 60,000shp two-shaft powerplant. This design trimmed by the stern; the heavy turret right aft was certainly the culprit. In the designs with protected hangars the weight of armour forward probably balanced the turret's mass; throughout this second series of designs, trim would be a major problem.

Next came PA2, also of about 30,000 tons. This design was 754ft 8in long, with a 623ft 5in flight deck. Even though the main battery was reduced to a quadruple 11in turret aft, it still trimmed by the stern, requiring 1500 tons of permanent ballast forward. The designers therefore went on to the intermediate PA3, which quickly evolved into PA4. This ship displaced 35,000 tons and was 780ft 11in long. The trim problems were apparently overcome in this version; it was modified into PA-5A, in which the hangar height was increased from 15ft 9in to 19ft 8in. PA-5A in turn evolved into PA-5B, the ultimate vessel in the series.

PA-5B had a trials displacement of 42,000 tons, almost as much as the PA1-PC2. Like the other designs in the series, it featured a quadruple turret

aft, in this case for 11in guns; this location would have made for unpredictable currents at that most delicate point of aviation operations, just as the aircraft approached for landing. On the other hand, the provision of turbo-electric propulsion would have allowed the ship to steam at full power astern, which would have made recovery of aircraft over the bow quite feasible; certainly this technique was occasionally practised by American carriers. This possibility gains some support from the fact that the arresting gear is located at almost the exact midpoint of the flight deck, rather than in the after section.

All the French designs show an appreciation for the need for AA defence, and PA-5B was no exception, with twelve twin 4.5in turrets and thirty quadruple 25mm mounts. It was well protected, with a 9.8in belt and a 5.1in deck, and had a 110,000shp powerplant.

Although the aircraft complements are not given for any of these designs, they probably would have carried about forty aircraft, like *Joffre*, since the flight decks (and presumably the hangars) were of similar dimensions. Such a small number of aircraft would scarcely be an effective air arm for such large ships, but this shortcoming was not unique to the French designs. In fact, the contemporary German hybrid designs were far worse in this respect.

The German Navy had taken a step toward the hybrid during the design of the carrier *Graf Zeppelin*. Because Germany was forbidden by the Treaty of Versailles from building aircraft

Graf Zeppelin at her launching on 8 December 1938, showing the casemates that, had she been completed, would have made her the last of the heavily armed carriers (Naval Imaging Command)

carriers or military aircraft during the 1920s, German designs of the early 1930s were affected by the same factors that had influenced the carrier designs of other navies a decade earlier: fundamental inexperience in carrier operations and a belief that the vessel should be able to defend itself against surface ships. In 1933, when the carrier design process was initiated, it was thought that the ship would have to fight its way through a North Sea blockade; later, it was theorised that a carrier might serve as a surface raider, either accompanied by cruisers and battleships or alone. In the latter case it would function as a sort of super-Wolf, the aircraft-equipped mercantile menace of the First World War. To these ends, the early characteristics for Germany's first carrier, issued in March 1934, called for a 15,000 ton ship armed with either six 8in or nine 6in guns. Speed was to be 33 knots, and aircraft capacity was set at about 60.

Admiral Erich Raeder, Commander-in-Chief of the Kriegsmarine, was especially interested in providing these ships with firepower astern; he believed they would need guns aft to deter a pursuer. He probably saw the ship as a lone commerce raider; however, this battery proved impossible on the desired tonnage. Instead, eight 5.9in guns in armoured casemates were substituted; eventually, this battery grew to sixteen guns in twin casemates. These guns, useless against aircraft, were supplemented by a strong AA battery of 4.1in guns. Since such weapons could have shot up unprotected merchantmen almost as well as the 5.9in guns, the heavier guns

must have been intended to defend the ship against small warships. Nevertheless, it is difficult to understand why the single-purpose batteries were not merged into a uniform dual-purpose armament.

At this point, Adolf Hitler enters the story. The German dictator had shown a lifelong interest in big ships and their technology, sometimes drawing improbable battleship designs in his sketchbooks. As in so many other areas, his interest was sporadic and his comprehension of the topic incomplete; it often showed that peculiar combination of penetrating insight and impossible fantasising that characterised so much of his military thinking. So, shortly before Graf Zeppelin was launched, Hitler remarked that a well armed aircraft carrier would make an excellent commerce raider; he did not pursue this line of thought at the time, but he would return to it occasionally in the years ahead.

Graf Zeppelin was still incomplete when the Second World War broke out. The German Navy soon found itself in the uncomfortable position of having neither a substantial surface fleet nor an adequate submarine force; Hitler had promised Raeder that war with Britain would not come until the mid-1940s, so the navy had initiated a massive construction programme, the famous 'Z Plan', centred on powerful battleships. All this went into the scrap heap on 3 September 1939 when Britain declared war. Only those ships nearing completion were to be worked on; efforts would otherwise be concentrated on the construction of U-boats. By May 1940, work on Graf Zeppelin had come to a halt, even though the ship was more than 85 per cent complete. It was felt that the war would be brought to a successful conclusion before the end of the year, well before the carrier could be finished. When the hope of a quick victory passed, there were always other, more pressing concerns, and the carrier languished in a variety of Baltic ports until she was finally scuttled at Stettin to avoid her capture by the Soviets. Salvaged, she was taken under tow to Leningrad, but apparently foundered during the voyage, perhaps after striking a mine.

While *Graf Zeppelin* was towed from harbour to harbour, the German constructors, like their counterparts in the *Service Technique*, continued designing warships even though there was an ever-diminishing possibility of such ships ever being built. Most famous of these paper projects were the enlarged versions of the 'H' class battleships studied at Hitler's orders, which resulted in the giant H-42, H-43 and H-44 designs. Hitler's interests were not confined to battleships, however. In July 1940, he once again mentioned the commerce-raiding potential of 'cruisers equipped with flight decks' during a naval affairs conference with Raeder. In response, the navy's construction office suggested the conversion of one of the incomplete 'M' class light cruisers to carry about fourteen aircraft with some reduction in armament and speed. However, at 7800 tons standard displacement, these ships would clearly have made inadequate flight-deck cruisers.

Hitler probably expressed interest in hybrid ships on subsequent occasions, for in 1942 the Naval War Staff prepared a paper which specifically concluded that battleship-carrier hybrids were not feasible, since the aviation facilities would interfere with gunnery. A hybrid cruiser, on the other hand, was considered a much sounder proposition. The roles envisaged for such a vessel were exactly those advanced by American advocates of the flying-deck cruiser some twelve years earlier: scouting, air defence, convoy protection and commerce raiding. Admiral Raeder liked the idea sufficiently to order further study.

In the end, two series of hybrid designs emerged: small flight-deck cruisers (*Flugdeckkreuzer*), and much larger ships (*Grossflugzeugkreuzer*). The smaller designs were completed by 1943; all showed modest characteristics, as a glance at the table will show. Armed with four or eight 5.9in guns and carrying ten to twenty-five aircraft, they are in some ways less impressive than the American flying-deck cruiser designs of the 1930s. As in other German designs for aviation ships, the aircraft capacity seems relatively small compared with the size of the ships; this was probably the result of a tendency on the part of

German designers to avoid sponsons and other projections from a ship's side, which meant that the AA guns and directors cut into the hull width available for the hangar; workshops and crew quarters surrounding the hangar may have reduced its potential volume as well. In all these flight-deck cruiser designs, the use of diesel or combined diesel/steam propulsion would have given the ships a considerable cruising radius — valuable for commerce raiding — at the cost of a heavier machinery plant.

These flight-deck cruisers, perhaps better classed as well armed carriers, might have functioned well as merchant raiders; the same cannot be said of the *Grossflugzeugkreuzer* designs. These enormous ships showed little appreciation for the operational needs of aircraft; moreover, their aircraft capacities were remarkably small for their size. They have been characterised by Wilhelm Hadeler, who had been in charge of the design of *Graf Zeppelin*, as 'sham assignments which were worked out to protect a small circle of younger employees from conscription'. However, Hadeler was not in the design office when these hybrids were sketched, and the surviving documentation on the projects is incomplete, so their exact origins remain obscure.

The series began with Design A II of 9 April 1942. This ship had a full load displacement of 40,000 tons, yet carried only twenty-three aircraft. Forward, there was a quadruple turret for 8in guns, a battery that seems very light both in number and calibre; the drawing shows a turret similar in size to the quadruple 11in turret of the later A IV design, so it may be that the calibre given with this drawing was in error. This supposition gains some support from the fact that an undated variation on this design, A II*, apparently was to be armed with six 11in guns in two triple turrets on about the same displacement as A II; it seems unlikely that a greater number of guns far larger than 8in could have been substituted without considerably increasing the displacement. The quadruple turret may have been inspired by a review of the French design materials that had fallen into German hands in the summer of 1940. In other respects, A II shows features that would be shared by the subsequent designs in the series: a heavy 5.9in battery in twin casemates, a 4.1in AA battery located along the sidedecks, a narrow hangar, AA directors projecting dangerously above the level of the flight deck for no apparent reason, and a portside island. This last feature has no explanation. Propulsion

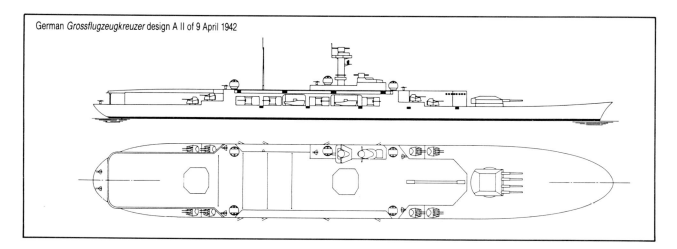

German *Grossflugzeugkreuzer* design A II of 9 April 1942

was to be pure diesel, with the exhaust to be vented via outlets along the ship's side; as in the subsequent designs, a speed of 34 knots was anticipated. The most unusual feature of this sketch is the extreme flare of the bows, which surely would have subjected the ship's structure to severe pounding in any sort of a seaway.

A II was followed by A III; this called for a ship of no less than 70,000 tons, yet it carried only thirty-two aircraft and had a battery of six 11in guns in two triple turrets forward. Its tremendous displacement is explained in part by the heavy protection specified; side armour consisted of a 9.8in belt, while the flight deck was almost 2in thick and an armoured deck was 5.9in. This design was to be driven by a combined steam/diesel plant and so shows a funnel, which seems rather short; most carrier funnels were high to get the hot gases as far above the flight deck as possible. The forward end of the flight deck, as Hadeler says, 'appears to have been laid out specifically to cause turbulence'. Worse still, the height of the second 11in turret was such that the catapults had to be angled off the centreline so that aircraft could clear it, which would have made rapid launching of aircraft impossible. The ship would have had to zig-zag wildly to get first one, then the other, catapult into the wind. Combined with all its other faults and weaknesses, it seems a very poor effort indeed, and demonstrates a lack of understanding of even the most basic requirements of shipboard aviation.

A IV offered some improvements. Again, the ship was 70,000 tons, with protection somewhat reduced from that of A III. The battery was concentrated in a single quadruple 11in turret forward, which allowed a reduction in the height of the hangar; more importantly, the two catapults could now be placed parallel to the axis of the

ship, greatly facilitating aviation operations. Propulsion was pure diesel, the increased weight of which may account in part for the reduced level of protection. Aircraft capacity was again a paltry thirty-two machines.

The final design in the series, Project A IIa, was the worst of a bad lot. Another 70,000 tonner, it showed all the worst features of its predecessors and added the final lunacy of a centreline superstructure. The draughtsman tried to ameliorate this retrograde ediface with a half-hearted attempt at streamlining, but the typical German tower-mast structure with its attendant platforms and directors would surely have created almost as much turbulence as had *Furious'* upperworks. The catapults are once again angled outboard, the periphery of the flight deck cluttered with AA directors.

No drawings seem to have survived for a final undated design, designated C. This is unfortunate, for it shows a completely different mix of features from the other designs. It was armed with six 11in guns and featured protection as heavy as that of the other designs, and a diesel/steam propulsion plant good for 34 knots. Unlike the other designs, however, it was to carry no fewer than eighty aircraft, a complement befitting its 56,000 ton size. How this was to be accomplished is not known; perhaps the AA battery was finally sponsored out from the hull proper, allowing an increase in hangar width; or perhaps a permanent deck park was employed. Whatever its arrangements may have been, it is the only design in the series that seems anywhere near adequate.

★   ★   ★

All the wartime hybrid schemes show a concentration on defensive qualities. In the case of the

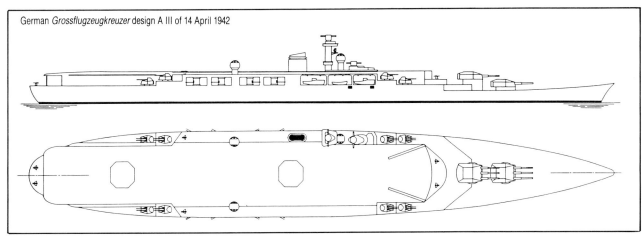

German *Grossflugzeugkreuzer* design A III of 14 April 1942

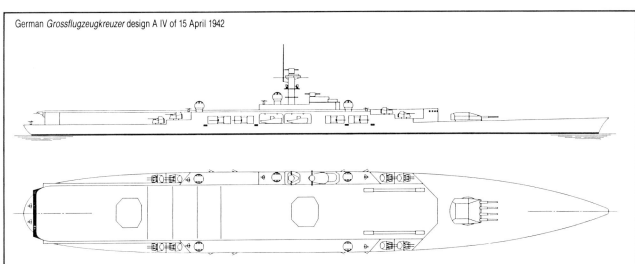

German *Grossflugzeugkreuzer* design A IV of 15 April 1942

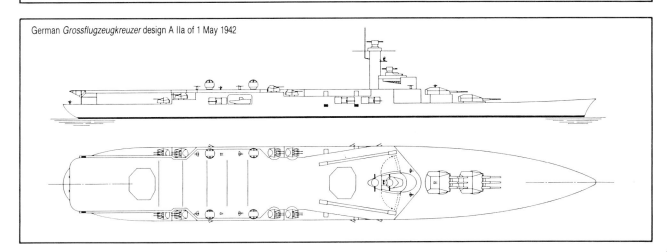

German *Grossflugzeugkreuzer* design A IIa of 1 May 1942

British schemes, the question was how to protect the fleet against shore-based aircraft. The ultimate answer to this question was to build more aircraft carriers, but the emotional baggage of battleship supremacy obscured this solution for some time. And in all fairness it must be remembered that aircraft had yet to sink a capital ship at sea when Slattery made his proposal. There was still reason to believe that battleships were needed to deal with an enemy's battleships, a situation which held true in the Atlantic until well after the sinking of *Bismarck*. In such an environment, the idea of aircraft serving as a long-range AA battery for capital ships was quite plausible,

GERMAN FLUGDECKKREUZER DESIGNS

	Entwurf EIV	Entwurf EV	Entwurf EVI
Displacement:	10,500t standard 12,750t full load	15,550t standard 19,150t full load	19,500t standard 23,100t full load
Dimensions:	623ft 5in × 62ft 4in	695ft 7in × 69ft 11in	787ft 5in × 86ft 11in
Machinery:	steam/diesel; 120,000shp = 34kts	steam/diesel; 180,000shp = 35.5kts	diesel; 180,000shp = 34kts
Armament:	four 5.9in (2 × 2) eight 88mm (4 × 2) twelve 37mm (6 × 2) eight 20mm (2 × 4)	eight 5.9in (4 × 2) ten 88mm (5 × 2) twelve 37mm (6 × 2) twelve 20mm (3 × 4)	eight 5.9in (4 × 2) twelve 88mm (6 × 2) twelve 37mm (6 × 2) twelve 20mm (3 × 4)
Aircraft:	10	18	25
Armour:	1.97in belt	2.36in belt; 0.79in deck	(heavy cruiser scale)

and in many ways developed logically from the earlier practice of carrying float fighters on battleships and cruisers.

The belief in the battleship as the 'backbone of the fleet' was eventually erased by events in the Pacific, but even then the new realities required difficult adjustments. In support of the 'B.A.C. Ship', the *ILN* quoted Vice Admiral Conrad Helfrich, former commander of the Netherlands East Indies naval forces: 'A combination of aeroplanes and big guns on capital ships will bring the most effective success'. Helfrich had had the misfortune to preside over the Allied débâcles in the Java Sea and Sunda Straits, and so had experience of the unhappy effects resulting from a lack of air cover. But, as the Admiralty had determined almost a year before, hybrid warships were not the best way to remedy this lack; the real answer was to

GERMAN GROSSFLUGZEUGKREUZER DESIGNS

	Project A II 9 April 1942	Project A III 14 April 1942	Project A IV 15 April 1942
Displacement:	40,000t full load	70,000t full load	70,000t full load
Dimensions:**	803ft 10in × 105ft × 28ft 9in (245m × 32m × 8.75m)	918ft 8in × 124ft 8in × 37ft 9in (280m × 38m × 11.5m)	918ft 8in × 124ft 8in × 37ft 9in (280m × 38m × 11.5m)
Machinery:	diesel; 3 shafts 210,000shp = 34kts; 18,000nm at 19kts	diesel/steam; 4 shafts; 280,000shp = 34kts; 20,000nm at 19kts	diesel; 4 shafts 280,000 shp = 34kts; 20,000nm at 19kts
Armament:	four 8in (1 × 4) sixteen 5.9in (8 × 2) sixteen 4.1in (8 × 2) fourteen 37mm (7 × 2)	six 11in (2 × 3) sixteen 5.9in (8 × 2) sixteen 4.1in (8 × 2) twelve 37mm (6 × 2) six 21in TT	four 11in (1 × 4) sixteen 5.9in (8 × 2) sixteen 4.1in (8 × 2) fourteen 37mm (7 × 2) six 21in TT
Aircraft:	24	32	32
Armour:	5.9in belt; 3.9in deck; 0.79in flight deck; 7.9in barbettes	9.8in belt; 5.9in deck; 2in flight deck	9.8in belt (?); 1.6in flight deck

build more carriers.

The logic behind the French schemes was also defensive, although here it is protection against gunfire that seems to have weighed most heavily. This concentration on ballistic protection may have been inspired by the loss of *Glorious* to gunfire from *Scharnhorst* and *Gneisenau* off Norway in 1940. Consideration of that action may also have led to the aft location of the turret, since it would allow firing on a pursuing enemy. This would force the pursuer to zig-zag, thereby losing speed; such an armament might have saved *Glorious*. This seems the only reasonable explanation of the turret's placement, as the squared-off after end of the hangar structure severely limits the turret's firing arcs.

The German mania for protection definitely played a part in the disappointing offensive qualities of the *Grossflugzeugkreuzer* schemes. They are inadequate both in terms of aircraft capacity and artillery. Insofar as they were intended for commerce raiding, their hybrid nature made sense; but in every other aspect they are so bad that mere inexperience with shipboard aviation seems an inadequate explanation; one has to wonder if the architects of these unlikely vessels were perhaps consciously trying to produce bad designs. Perhaps they were drawn up specifically to demonstrate the undesirability of such hybrids to Hitler. It should be remembered that the Naval War Staff had recommended against battleship-carriers; these ships, although dubbed 'large flight-deck cruisers', were clearly more akin to battleships than cruisers. It may be that Hitler's interest in hybrid warships was sufficiently annoying to the construction staff as to drive them to draw up deliberately dreadful designs in an attempt to dissuade him. If this is the case, they surely were, more than any other hybrid ships, the 'results of a psychological maladjustment'.

** Length and beam are on the waterline

	Project A IIa 1 May 1942	Project A II* ?	Project C ?
Displacement:	40,000t full load	37,500t full load	56,000t full load
Dimensions**	820ft 3in × 105ft × 28ft 9in (250m × 32m × 8.75m)	803ft 10in × 105ft × 28ft 9in (245m × 32m × 8.75m)	918ft 8in × 121ft 5in × 32ft 10in (280m × 37m × 10m)
Machinery:	diesel; 3 shafts 210,000shp = 34kts; 18,000nm at 19kts	diesel; 3 shafts 180,000shp = 33kts; 18,000nm at 19kts	diesel/steam; 4 shafts; 260,000shp = 34kts; 20,000nm at 19kts
Armament:	six 11in (2 × 3) twelve 5.9in (8 × 2) sixteen 4.1in (8 × 2) twelve 37mm (6 × 2) twenty 20mm (5 × 4)	six 11in (2 × 3) sixteen 5.9in (8 × 2) sixteen 4.1in (8 × 2) twenty 37mm (10 × 2)	six 11in (2 × 3) sixteen 5.9in (8 × 2) sixteen 4.1in (8 × 2) twenty-four 37mm (12 × 2)
Aircraft:	23	32	80
Armour:	7.9in belt; 3.9in deck; 0.8in flight deck; 2in barbettes	5.9in belt; 3.9in deck; 0.8in flight deck; 7.9in barbettes	9.8in belt; 4.7in deck; 2in flight deck; 9.8in barbettes

CHAPTER 12

PHANTOMS OF THE PACIFIC

The stunning loss at Midway of four carriers, two-thirds of the First Air Fleet, shocked Japanese naval authorities into a radical change in construction policy. The battle had not only proved positively that the carrier was the new prime weapon of sea warfare, it had also left Japan sadly bereft of that same crucial weapon. New carriers were authorised to join those already building, but it would be months or years before any of these appeared. Shipyards were already overcrowded with vessels needing repairs, and soon the pinch of material and labour shortages would make itself felt. One stopgap expedient that could offer aircraft platforms relatively quickly was the conversion of vessels already afloat or on the stocks, and such proposals were advanced even before the end of June 1942.

The desperation with which the *IJN* strove to rebuild its carrier force after the Midway disaster is demonstrated by how hastily the conversion programme was conceived. By the end of August 1942, the Naval Technical Department (*Kaigun Kanseihonbu*), vigorously prodded by the Naval Aviation Department (*Kaigun Kokuhonbu*), had drawn up plans for the conversion of the incomplete super-battleship *Shinano*, third unit of the *Yamato* class, into a flight-deck carrier. Other ships targeted for conversion included the incomplete cruiser *Ibuki*, two of the big seaplane tenders, seven merchant ships and three existing warships that would become hybrids: the cruiser *Mogami* and battleships *Ise* and *Hyuga*.

★ ★ ★

Mogami was the first of the post-Midway hybrids. She and *Mikuma* had been the first two light cruisers of the *Mogami* class to be completed, but had been found during their trials to be both lacking in stability and structurally unsound. This led to extensive modifications for all four ships in the class; the hulls were strengthened and the beams increased by the addition of bulges, which increased displacements to 12,500 tons standard and cut speed from 37 to 34.9 knots. The 6.1in guns were replaced with 8in weapons during these extensive refits.

Mogami was badly damaged at Midway, first by collision with *Mikuma*, then by five bomb hits during the air attacks that sank her sister. Temporary repairs at Truk enabled her to reach Sasebo, where she was reconstructed between 1 September 1942 and 30 April 1943. The purpose was to turn her into what was officially termed an 'aircraft cruiser' capable of operating a large number of scouting seaplanes, in order to remedy

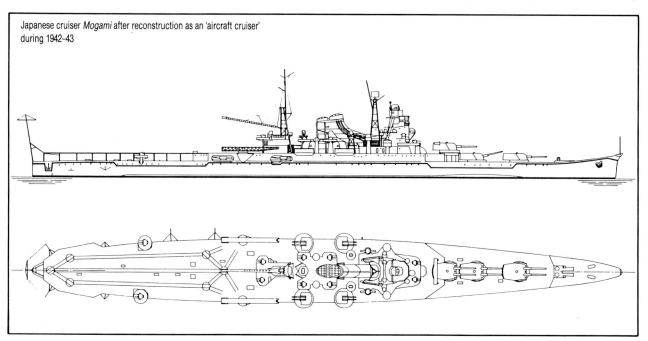

Japanese cruiser *Mogami* after reconstruction as an 'aircraft cruiser' during 1942–43

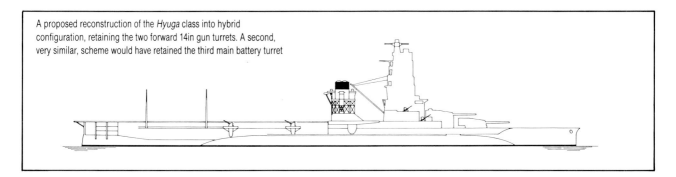

A proposed reconstruction of the *Hyuga* class into hybrid configuration, retaining the two forward 14in gun turrets. A second, very similar, scheme would have retained the third main battery turret

the defects in aerial reconnaissance demonstrated so disastrously by the cruisers at Midway.

The first step was the removal of X and Y turrets; Y turret had already been wrecked by an aircraft bomb. The turrets were replaced by an aircraft handling deck extending from the former seaplane carriage deck between the catapults right aft to the stern; it was supported over the quarterdeck by stanchions, ten on each side. This deck was equipped with a series of rails and eleven tiedown spots for floatplanes. Aircraft could be quickly shunted about on these rails, and launched from the original two catapults. It was anticipated that all eleven aircraft could be launched in 30 minutes, but this timetable was never put to the test. The original seaplane derrick on the mainmast was retained. Belowdecks, the magazine spaces for the 8in turrets were adapted for stowage of aircraft fuel and bombs.

Other modifications included replacement of the former light AA armament with ten triple 25mm mounts, installation of radar and an AA control platform, and plating over a number of scuttles to improve watertightness.

This reconstruction reduced *Mogami*'s displacement slightly, increased her endurance, and restored a quarter of a knot to her speed. Her principal particulars as an 'aircraft cruiser' were

Displacement:	12,206t standard
Dimensions:	661ft 6in oa × 63ft (over bulges) × 19ft 9in
Machinery:	4 sets geared turbines, 10 boilers, 152,000shp (154,266shp on trials) = 35kts. Oil 2411t; 7700nm at 18kts
Armament:	six 8in (3 × 2); eight 5in (4 × 2); thirty 25mm AA (10 × 3); twelve 24in TT (4 × 3)
Aircraft:	11
Armour:	4in main belt, 1.5in deck, 1in turrets, 5in magazine
Complement:	930 incl aviation personnel

Mogami saw no real action again until 5 November 1943, when she was severely damaged at Rabaul by a single bomb from a US carrier aircraft. She was again temporarily patched up at Truk and fully repaired at Kure from late December until 17 February 1944.

During her first major operation after returning to service, the Battle of the Philippine Sea on 19–20 June 1944, *Mogami* was attached to B Force of Vice-Admiral Jisaburo Ozawa's First Mobile Fleet, helping battleship *Nagato* and eight destroyers to screen the force's three carriers. She contributed two seaplanes to a reconnaissance on the 19th and the next day escaped damage during the American attacks that sank carrier *Hiyo*.

In the Battle of Leyte Gulf, *Mogami* was a unit of Vice-Admiral Shoji Nishimura's ill-fated C, or Southern, Force, the first of two squadrons assigned to enter the gulf by way of the Surigao Strait. On 24 October she launched a seaplane, reportedly the only operable one in Nishimura's force, for a reconnaissance that found and reported fairly accurately the American vessels in and beyond the gulf. In the ensuing night action, *Mogami* was badly battered by US gunfire and then collided with cruiser *Nachi* of the second force attempting to enter the strait. Adrift the next morning, *Mogami* was hit twice by carrier aircraft and finally put out of her misery by a torpedo from destroyer *Akebono*.

In addition to conversion of the incomplete battleship *Shinano* into a carrier, the IJN studied conversion schemes for all ten of the older battleships: the four ex-battlecruisers of the *Kongo* class, and the two-ship *Fuso, Ise* and *Nagato* classes. All had been completed between 1913 and 1921, and all had undergone at least one major reconstruction and several extensive refits. None except the *Kongos* had fired a shot in anger since the beginning of the war, and with the sudden new dominance of the carrier some officers doubted that they ever would.

The battleship conversions would have been radical: all superstructure, main batteries and casemated secondary guns would be replaced by full-length flight decks, island superstructures, offset funnels and a battery composed exclusively of AA guns. Aircraft capacity of each was estimated at about fifty-four.

The *Kongos*, with their 30.5 knot speed, would have been the best bet for such remodelling. They were the only battleship hulls that could keep pace with existing or future carriers. However, that speed made them valuable as the only big-gun carrier escorts, a role they had played since the Pearl Harbor operation, and it was probably that unique quality that eliminated them from consideration.

Speed, or the lack of it, was the Achilles' heel of the other battleships. Although their modernisations had raised their average speed to about 25 knots, this was still too slow for carrier operations. And in the case of the *Nagatos*, there was reluctance to deprive the fleet of their 16in guns, second only to the 18.1in guns of the *Yamatos* in range and hitting power. There was still a lingering, if remote, chance that a battleline action could come about.

After considerable discussion, conversion of *Shinano* was authorised but the rest of the project foundered, principally on the factors of time and resources. It was estimated that full conversion of the older ships could take up to twenty-four months, and the navy needed carriers sooner than that. Moreover, the enormous scope of the work would divert labour and material from completion of carriers already building and postpone the laying down of others.

Thoughts then turned to the idea of fitting some of the old battleships as quasi-carriers, retaining some of their big-gun armament while also fitting them with limited aircraft facilities. Such modifications could be carried out far more quickly than full conversion and would require less manpower and material. This plan was approved by June 1943 but again the *Kongos* and *Nagatos* were out of the running; the same objections voiced to their full conversion applied to any partial conversion. Hence only the two *Fusos* and two *Ises* would undergo the remodelling. By the time this decision had been made, however, shipyard congestion and the urgent need to concentrate on other types of warship resulted in the *Fusos* being dropped from the project.

Why they and not the more modern *Ises* were eliminated does not seem clear, but there are some plausible reasons. For one thing, *Ise* and her sister *Hyuga*, with a speed of 25.4 knots, were marginally faster. Probably more important was a certain deficiency in their firepower stemming from a problem encountered during their 1934–37

modernisations.

Among the improvements was an increase in the elevation, and thereby the range, of their main batteries. Other navies achieved this by raising the guns' trunnions, necessitating an increase in the size of the gunport and a consequent reduction in the turret protection. The Japanese chose the more laborious and costlier method of deepening the wells beneath the turrets so the guns would have sufficient room to recoil when the muzzles were at extreme elevation. This allowed great increases in elevation, from a maximum of 25 degrees to a new maximum of 43 degrees. But the *Ises* lacked sufficient depth of hull aft to allow this treatment to be applied to X and Y turrets. Thus in a long-range action these four guns would have been ineffective, depriving the ships of one-third of their firepower.

In retrospect we know this was of no consequence; by 1943 a daylight battleship gunnery engagement, the only kind in which long-range fire would have been important, was a thing of the past. This was far from clear at the time, however, and if a reduction of firepower had to be accepted on any of the battleships the *Ises* were the logical choice. Moreover, *Hyuga* had already lost two of her 14in guns when an internal explosion wrecked her X turret during gunnery practice on 5 May 1942. Fifty-one men were killed and eleven wounded, and the turret had yet to be replaced.

Three alternative plans for the *Ises'* conversion were drawn up. The most thorough-going would have retained only the two forward turrets and eliminated all superstructure aft of the funnel. In its place would be an aircraft deck about 360ft long. It was estimated that forty to forty-five aircraft could be carried, and two trainable catapults were sited abreast the funnel to launch them. To get them all into the air in reasonable time, however, would have required at least four catapults, and this, combined with the long conversion period and the drastic reduction of main battery firepower, led to this scheme being rejected.

Six guns were considered the minimum needed for effective surface action, so one proposal retained both forward turrets and the no 3 turret. This shortened the aircraft deck to approximately 280ft. While this design retained the six-gun minimum battery, it offered no appreciable increase in aircraft capacity over the plan finally chosen, in which both midship turrets were retained. Their retention shortened the aircraft deck still more, but in compensation it was raised two levels above

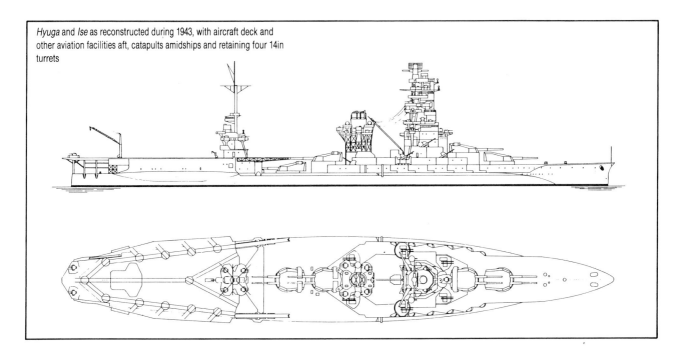

Hyuga and *Ise* as reconstructed during 1943, with aircraft deck and other aviation facilities aft, catapults amidships and retaining four 14in turrets

the former quarterdeck, thus creating a hangar space below it. A roughly T-shaped lift connected hangar and deck. An aircraft-handling crane was fitted aft.

The after superstructure and mainmast were retained. Parallel to them were two 85ft catapults, one on each beam, raised on tall pedestals to the level of the aircraft deck. The catapults overlapped no 4 turret and the muzzles of the no 3 turret's guns, thus severely restricting the training arcs of both.

Secondary aramament was radically revised by removal of all sixteen 5.5in casemate guns (a number already reduced from the original twenty during reconstruction in the 1930s) and their replacement by eight more 5in AA guns in twin mounts, bringing the heavy AA battery up to a respectable sixteen barrels. Light AA armament was increased to fifty-seven 25mm guns in triple mounts.

Conversion of *Ise* began at Kure on 15 March 1943 and was completed on 8 October; *Hyuga* was converted at Sasebo between 1 August and 30 November 1943. They emerged with these particulars.

Displacement:	35,350t standard (*Hyuga* 35,200t); 38,676t full load
Dimensions:	720ft oa × 111ft × 29ft 6in
Machinery:	4 sets geared turbines, 8 boilers, 80,000shp = 25.4kts. Oil 4182t; 9449nm at 16kts
Armament:	eight 14in (4 × 2); sixteen 5in AA (8 × 2), fifty-seven 25mm AA (19 × 3)
Aircraft:	22
Armour:	12in belt thinning to 3in at the ends; 6.75in deck over vitals; 12in barbettes; 6-12in conning tower (it is unclear whether the original 6in casemate armour was retained)
Complement:	1463

The redesign of the *Ises* involved the removal of considerable topweight; the two after turrets weighed 864 tons each, and their barbettes represented a reduction of an additional 800 tons or so. Japanese naval architects had become particularly skittish about stability as a result of prewar problems, which had culminated in the capsizing of the torpedo boat *Tomodzuru* in 1934; they were consequently worried that the loss of so much topweight on the *Ises* would increase the metacentric height to a point where rolling would become too rapid, an undesirable quality both for aircraft operations and good gunnery. Consequently, an 8in layer of concrete was added to the aircraft deck. This apparently had the desired effect, for the total displacement of the ships was reduced by only about 600 tons and draught by 6in.

Ise and *Hyuga* have often been referred to as 'seaplane carriers', but this was not the designers' intention. The twenty-two machines were originally to be Yokosuka D4Y *Suisei* (Comet) dive bomber aeroplanes (Allied code name Judy). The aircraft's design was based on a German Heinkel He 118V4 imported in 1938. It began life as a high-speed carrier-based reconnaissance aeroplane, as the IJN had finally come to the conclusion that its carriers needed a few aerial scouts of their own. It was developed, with several variants, into a dive

Ise, probably running sea trials, after reconstruction to hybrid configuration. The US Navy dates this photo as 24 August 1943, but Japanese sources state the conversion was not completed until 8 October 1943 (*Naval Imaging Command*)

bomber to replace the increasingly obsolescent Aichi D3A, the mainstay dive bomber since the start of the war.

The D4Y began to succeed the D3A in 1943; it was a much superior craft, with a longer range and heavier bomb load. A two-place single-engine mid-wing monoplane with retractable landing gear, it could attain a maximum speed of 360mph, making it the fastest carrier bomber operated by any navy during the Second World War. It was also one of the few to be powered by an in-line, liquid-cooled engine. With a span nearly 10ft shorter than the D3A, it could fit on carrier lifts without the need for a wing-folding mechanism. Its big defect was that, like so many Japanese aircraft, it lacked any crew protection in the form of armour and self-sealing fuel tanks, and D4Ys were slaughtered in great numbers during their first major test in combat, the Battle of the Philippine Sea.

These aeroplanes could not, of course, take off from or land on the hybrid battleships' small aircraft decks; they were to be launched by the catapults and either alight on accompanying carriers or fly to land bases. In this respect, *Ise* and *Hyuga* were no better off than *Furious* in 1917–18. The decks were for aircraft handling, and were fitted with a system of rails, turntables, tie-down spots and trolleys similar to the arrangements on

Mogami. It was calculated that this would permit an aircraft launching every two minutes on each catapult. Under ideal conditions, therefore, with both catapults functioning simultaneously, the entire complement could be in the air in somewhat less than thirty minutes. However, Rear Admiral Chiaki Matsuda, who commanded the two hybrids, noted that the aeroplanes were launched 'broad on the bow into the wind', so both catapults could *not* be used at the same time. Theoretically, the ship could zigzag back and forth across a base course into the wind, using first one catapult, then coming about nearly 90 degrees to use the other; but it seems unlikely that she could have done so in the nominal sixty seconds between launches. One way or another, launching would probably have taken at least forty-five minutes, and under operational conditions — engine failures, improper seating on catapults requiring readjustment, etc — it probably would have taken an hour or more. The matter is moot, since no such mass launchings were ever attempted.

Somewhere along the line it was decided that the ships should have some more easily recoverable and reusable aircraft, so the complement was altered to provide a number of seaplanes. The type chosen was the Aichi E16A *Zuiun* (Auspicious Cloud, Allied code name Paul), a powerful two-place single-engine twin-float low-wing monoplane just coming into production. It was designed as a shipboard reconnaissance type, as the E code designation shows, but was also fitted out as a dive bomber. Its respectable bomb load could have

Ise or Hyuga under attack by US aircraft during the engagement off Cape Engaño, 25 October 1944, with her AA guns and rockets producing a large cloud of smoke. The catapults appear to be in place, trained outboard to open arcs of fire for the 14in guns (*Naval Imaging Command*)

augmented greatly the already hefty punch of the *Suiseis* and, unlike so many Japanese seaplanes, it had a good defensive armament: two 20mm guns mounted in the wings. The wings folded upward for shipboard stowage.

Most references give the complements of the hybrid battleships as twelve *Suiseis* and ten *Zuiuns*, but Admiral Matsuda told American questioners during a postwar interrogation that there were eleven of each type per ship, half carried in the hangar and half on deck, with a mix of types in both places.

Ise began working up in November 1943 and *Hyuga* in December, but it would be months before they received any aircraft. The IJN was still staggering under the horrendous loss of aircraft and pilots suffered in the Battle of the Philippine Sea. In May 1944 the two hybrids and the carriers *Junyo* and *Ryuho* were formed into the Fourth Air Squadron (or Carrier Division) under the command of Admiral Matsuda. When asked in his US interrogation what *Ise* and *Hyuga* had been doing before and after formation of this unit, Matsuda's reply was that they did 'nothing but hide because of the deficiency of aircraft'.

They did, however, have their light AA armament augmented during this period. In June 1944 the AA battery was increased to the astonishing total of 108 25mm guns, in thirty-one triple and fifteen single mounts. Eleven of the latter were placed on the aircraft deck and could be dismounted for flight operations. Air defence was further augmented in September 1944 with the

installation of six 30-tube 5in rocket launchers mounted in sponsons on each beam far aft.

By mid-August 1944 the 634th Air Group had been formed to provide Matsuda's command with a total of 130 aircraft, but most of the aviators were inexperienced and required lengthy training in deck flying. This was still in progress when in October the American invasion of the Philippines began, setting in train Operation *Sho* (Victory) that resulted in the series of engagements now collectively known as the Battle of Leyte Gulf. Under the *Sho* plan, Matsuda's ships were to be grouped with the four carriers of the Third Air Squadron as the First Mobile Fleet, commanded by Admiral Ozawa. But because the fliers of both units were judged unqualified for shipboard operations, all of Matsuda's aeroplanes and half of those from the other carriers were flown off to Formosa. Consequently, carriers *Junyo* and *Ryuho* were left behind when the First Mobile Fleet sortied on 20 October for its sacrificial mission of luring the main enemy carrier force north and thereby opening the way for surface and air attacks on the American shipping in Leyte Gulf.

On the way, almost all of the fleet's remaining 108 aircraft were launched to land in the Philippines, attacking anything they might encounter *en route*. This left only a handful of fighters for air defence. The hybrid battleships, devoid of aircraft, acted purely as surface escorts, *Ise* screening carriers *Zuikaku* and *Zuiho*, *Hyuga* guarding carriers *Chyoda* and *Chitose*.

The decoy mission succeeded only too well, drawing Admiral William Halsey's Task Force 38 north and thereby allowing a powerful battleship/cruiser force under Vice Admiral Takeo Kurita to enter Leyte Gulf. In what became known as the Battle Off Cape Engaño, Halsey's aircraft swarmed by the hundreds over Ozawa's ships. Of the Japanese carriers, only a badly damaged *Chitose* escaped destruction. Ozawa's sacrifice, however, was in vain; despite an enormous superiority in firepower, Kurita failed to destroy the American escort carriers and destroyers — and, more importantly, the transports — in the gulf.

Ise and *Hyuga* were not spared the attentions of the American fliers during the action off Cape Engaño. The hybrid battleships zigzagged through torrents of near misses that ruptured hull plates and sprayed upperworks with splinters. Both took on some water and *Hyuga* developed a slight list that was quickly corrected. The only direct hit on either seems to have been a bomb that struck *Ise* outboard of the port catapult, inflicting, according to Matsuda, forty to fifty casualties.

A factor in the hybrid ships' survival may have been their rocket launchers. Although these weapons failed to down or even damage a single enemy aircraft, the tremendous volume of barrage-like fire they churned out may have deterred the American aviators from closer approaches; according to one American report the battleships put up an 'exceedingly intense anti-aircraft fire'.

After the last US aeroplanes roared away, *Ise* and *Hyuga*, together with cruiser *Oyodo*, to which *Ozawa* had transferred his flag after *Zuikaku* was damaged, and a few destroyers, sailed south for a few hours in an attempt to deliver a night attack on enemy vessels. Nothing was found, and at about 9pm the Japanese force turned north for home.

Some Western books indicate that the catapults had been removed from the ships before Leyte, in order to improve training arcs of the midship turrets. However, American aerial photos taken during the battle seem to show the catapults still in place, trained outboard to get them out of the way of the big guns. The catapults were probably removed from the battleships soon after their return to Japan, thus ending their career — if it

could be said they ever had one — as hybrids. After serving as glorified munitions transports to Manila, they spent the rest of 1944 wandering around Indochinese and Mayalan waters. The first day of 1945 found them at Lingga Roads, near Singapore. On 10 February, after taking on a cargo of petrol and other materials scarce in Japan, they sailed for Kure, arriving on 20 February after narrowly escaping attack by British and American submarines *en route*. Matsuda's command was officially dissolved on 1 March, and *Ise* and *Hyuga* were sunk in shallow water by US carrier aircraft at Kure during August.

Although Japan from first to last possessed only four surface warships that can be classified as hybrids — six if the 'almost-hybrids' of the *Tone* class are included — there was belief in the United States that others existed. Two classes of 'flying deck cruisers' totalling seven ships were attributed to the IJN, largely but perhaps not entirely due to the speculations of naval analyst Jay Launer. Launer, who wrote for *Sea Power*, the publication of the Navy League of the United States and in 1944 produced a book, *The Enemies' Fighting Ships*, devoted to the Japanese and German navies, based his extrapolations on known trends in Japanese warship design. Although he heavily qualified his projections, noting that the existence of such vessels could not be verified and that their supposed particulars were merely estimates, the idea that these ships were afloat gained fairly wide credence through descriptions and drawings in *Sea Power*, Launer's own book *Our Navy* (a semi-official magazine with a large readership among enlisted personnel) and *Fighting Fleets*, a sort of poor man's *Jane's Fighting Ships* published in three editions during the war.

One type of imaginary vessel, called the *Tsushima* class, made its debut in the 1943 edition of *Fighting Fleets*. The 1944 edition elaborated on it and also illustrated the second type, the so-called *Tugaru* or *Tukaku* class, which had first appeared in *Sea Power*. More details of the *Tsushimas*, with some variations, appeared the same year in *The Enemies' Fighting Ships*. The *Tsushima* design, the volume states, was developed from the *Tikuma*, this being a widely used alternative transliteration of *Chikuma*.

The vessels were given the names *Tsushima*, *Yahagi*, *Hirado* and *Aso*. The first two were purportedly laid down in 1937, the second pair in

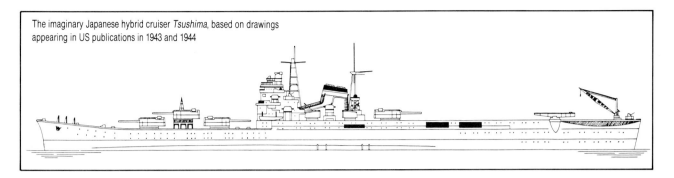

The imaginary Japanese hybrid cruiser *Tsushima*, based on drawings appearing in US publications in 1943 and 1944

1938, and all completed in 1941.

Putting together details from the two books, we arrive at a ship with the following partial particulars.

Displacement:	9000t approx
Dimensions:	650ft oa approx × 63ft × ?
Machinery:	unspecified; 96,000shp = 34kts
Armament:	eight 8in (4 × 2); eight 5.1in (4 × 2); 'numerous small AA'; eight 24in TT (2 × 4)
Aircraft:	11-13 seaplanes; 2 catapults
Armour:	'better protected than *Tikuma* class'
Complement:	1100

The same drawing of the ship appeared in both books. It shows a vessel with a normal centreline superstructure and single funnel forward of a lengthy aircraft deck with hangar deck below; two rotating catapults and a handling crane aft complete the aviation arrangements. The 8in guns are in three twin turrets forward of the superstructure and one aft of the funnel. The 5.1in AA guns are in twin turrets on each beam abreast the superstructure. The overall impression is of *Gotland* writ large, as Launer pointed out.

Fighting Fleets gives less detail on the other hybrid class, which closely resembles the *Tsushima* design. The forward centreline superstructure is similar, but this vessel is envisaged as a flight-deck ship, so the aft turret is omitted and the single funnel is offset to starboard, supposedly allowing deck landing. Three triple turrets are forward, mounting either 8in or 6.1in guns. Twelve AA guns of unspecified calibre are mounted aft in three sponsons on each beam. Two catapults are fitted flush with the flight deck to launch aircraft over the stern, and an opening in the hull below the flight deck seems to show a rotating catapult on each side. There is an aircraft crane immediately aft of the funnel. Names of the supposed three-ship class were given as *Tugaru* (or *Tukaku*), *Soya* and *Kasino*.

The *Tsushima* design is quite reasonable for a hybrid seaplane carrier (save for the after 8in guns, whose blast would have damaged any aircraft on deck); that of the *Tugaru* is preposterous, for deck landing on a ship of its configuration would have been impossible.

There are several pointers as to why Japan was thought to be leaning toward the hybrid, although not all of them could have been known to Launer. First is the appearance of the *Tone* class. Although no photos of these vessels appeared anywhere until after the war, drawings of them had appeared in foreign naval publications. Fairly accurate depictions of them, erring only in ascribing to them the original 6.1in guns, were contained in an official US identification manual dated for distribution just twenty-two days after the Pearl Harbor attack. Aerial photographs taken during the Battle of the Santa Cruz Islands even cleared up the armament calibre, and an April 1943 ONI recognition manual credited the ships with their correct battery of 8in guns.

Then came the spotting at Rabaul in November 1943 of *Mogami* in her new guise as a seaplane cruiser. From the appearance of what seemed an entirely new and unknown ship, it was logical to suppose that Japan had taken the *Tone* design one step farther. The sighting of the transformed *Ise* and *Hyuga* in October 1944 must have appeared the final confirmation that Japan had created a considerable number of hybrid warships. This would not have seemed unlikely to those who remembered the agitation for hybrids in the US Navy only a decade before.

The discovery of the *Ise* and *Hyuga* conversions came too late for illustration in the two popular books cited above, but did attract comment later in 1944. One of the commentators was, curiously enough, retired Admiral William V Pratt, whose role as hybrid proponent when CNO was noted in earlier chapters. He now condemned the type roundly in a *Newsweek* magazine article entitled 'The Japanese Mistake: Hybrid Men-of-War', smugly defending the infinite wisdom of the US Navy in rejecting the type. The reader without

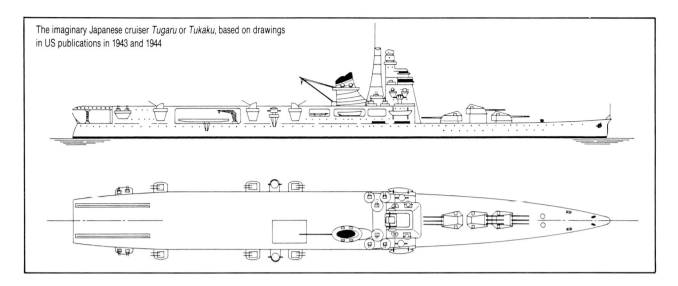

The imaginary Japanese cruiser *Tugaru* or *Tukaku*, based on drawings in US publications in 1943 and 1944

prior knowledge would have had no idea that Pratt and other US Navy officers were once prepared to take hybrids very seriously indeed. 'We have adhered firmly to the principle that the pure-type craft', he wrote, 'is better than the one which incorporates in its design the characteristics pertaining to others'. Referring specifically to *Ise* and *Hyuga*, which he identified by name, he declared, 'The idea of a battleship-carrier was no novelty to us, but it violated the function implicit in type, for she could operate with full efficiency neither as a battleship nor as a carrier'.

'No novelty', indeed. His condemnation aside, the tone of Pratt's article seems to indicate that he believed in the existence of more Japanese hybrids than were really afloat.

He was, of course, far from the only one deceived. Part of the credibility may well have stemmed from the very plausible drawings of the imaginary *Tsushimas* by Bruno Gruenwald, a prolific naval illustrator. By blending together known features of other ships — bow shape, funnel configuration, turret arrangement, masting, etc — he created a reasonable and even to some eyes aesthetically pleasing piece of naval *Japonaiserie*.

With two exceptions the names attached to the phantom vessels were those of actual Japanese ships. *Tsushima*, *Yahagi* and *Hirado* were old cruisers dating from near the turn of the century, totally or largely disarmed and used for training. More recently, two war-constructed escort vessels were named *Tsushima* and *Hirado* and an *Agano* class light cruiser had been dubbed *Yahagi*. *Aso* was the name of a never-completed *Unryu* class carrier, and *Soya* was an ammunition ship. There were never vessels named *Tuguru*, *Tukaku* or

Kasino, but these names closely resemble those of real ships named *Tsugaru*, *Tsukushi* and *Kashino*.

The surprising correspondence in the names of imaginary and real ships has led to speculation that Launer might have received information from official sources. One writer has theorised that because the three old cruisers may have carried out training exercises in the Kure area, where *Aso* was under construction, the names of all four ships could somehow have been connected by US intelligence and then applied to the fictitious vessels. This would imply that Launer was privy to secrets gleaned through Ultra/Magic intercepts. Accordng to Bruno Gruenwald, Launer never received any official information but arrived at the ship names by studying Japanese naval nomenclature and geographical names, thus making some remarkably inspired guesses.

★   ★   ★

The Japanese experience in the Second World War is the only example so far in history of an attempt to employ hybrids in a real, sustained naval conflict, the British operations of 1917–18 being too brief to provide a model. The attempt, as we have seen, was a failure in all respects.

The ships themselves cannot be held accountable for this failure. If the *Tones* are accepted as hybrids, they and *Oyodo* were well designed and well equipped for their functions. The functions themselves, however, were less well conceived, and quickly outmoded by changes in strategy, tactics and technology. *Mogami* as a hybrid was an expedient created before the consequences of these changes were completely understood. She might have been perfect for her purpose in the early 1930s, but was as much an anchronism as *Gotland* by 1943.

Often regarded as freaks, the *Ises* were even more desperate expedients, and illustrate the classic paradox inherent in hybrid design. To a great extent they were a paradigm of the type as envisaged between the world wars, with a big-gun armament not terribly inferior to several contemporary foreign battleships and with an aerial complement that would have been a formidable addition to a carrier force. On the other hand, their aircraft facilities restricted full employment of their artillery and weakened their survivability in a surface action, and their inability to recover their aeroplanes meant they could shoot their aerial bolt only once.

Even so, the *Ises* might have been successful in their intended role as stopgap carrier substitutes had Japan been able to produce the personnel needed to man their high-performance aircraft. It was the lack of pilots, not their hybrid configuration, that made the ingenuity, labour and material expended on them a total waste.

The Japanese experience certainly tarnished the image of the hybrid warship, but really only proved again that the finest of technology is useless if the time is out of joint.

CHAPTER 13

EXTINCTION?

The decades since the end of the Second World War have witnessed changes in naval warfare as fundamental as those following the introduction of the ironclad warship. If those changes somehow seem less revolutionary, it is only because the external appearance of warships has not changed as radically. However, weaponry, sensors, propulsion, and the intended roles of warship types have altered dramatically.

One of the most basic changes was the battleship's demotion from the 'backbone of the fleet' to an auxiliary. Aircraft were the greatest factor in this process; they could strike hundreds of miles beyond the range of the biggest gun, and the introduction of the jet engine increased speed to such a degree that traditional AA guns were virtually useless as a defence. But there were other considerations involved in the passing of the battleship. It was in essence a gun platform, but this platform had to be propelled and protected, and these secondary requirements had come to dominate the battleship design process; the actual guns seem in some cases an afterthought to a battleship's design.

More and more of the battleship's weight was being given over to protection in one form or another. The threat of long-range gunfire necessitated ever greater horizontal protection, while underwater protection, once a negligible factor, had become vitally important. Torpedo warheads were always growing larger, and the Second World War saw the introduction of explosives such as Torpex, used in US torpedoes, which was twice as powerful, pound for pound, as the TNT warheads of earlier types. Influence fuses for torpedoes and mines meant that these weapons could attack a ship in the one place that could not be effectively defended: directly under the bottom.

The greatest threat of all was the new air-launched guided weapons. The German FX-1400 glider bomb was the first such weapon, and in spite of its rudimentary nature it demonstrated its effectiveness all too clearly by the destruction of the Italian battleship *Roma* on 9 September 1943, followed in quick succession by serious damage to the American cruiser *Savannah*, the British battleship *Warspite* and cruiser *Uganda*. More powerful versions, with rocket propulsion, were on the draughting boards at the war's end.

As the battleship faded in importance, the roles of other ships altered as well. The cruiser had lost its independent offensive role with the increasing dominance of aircraft; in the latter part of the Pacific war, cruisers provided AA escort to carrier task groups, acted as command ships and conducted shore bombardment during amphibious landings. 'Cruising', either for commerce protection or commerce raiding, was a thing of the past, as was the cruiser's duty as the 'eyes of the fleet'. By 1960 the designation 'cruiser' really was no more than an indication of a ship's size.

That size, however, was not without its virtues. The threat posed by the new guided weapons could be met only by destroying an attacking aircraft before it could get within launch range — far beyond the effective range of any AA gun. This led to the development of AA homing missiles, but these missiles were large and required a great deal of electronic control and guidance equipment. Cruisers were good platforms for such missile systems, since they could carry enough of them to make the effort worthwhile, and they had the speed to keep up with the fleet. They also had room for the communications gear required for fleet command, an increasingly vital role.

While guided weapons of various types were replacing guns as the main batteries on surface ships, jet aircraft were working a revolution in carrier design and operation. Jets greatly accelerated the trend toward larger and heavier aircraft that had been evident since the 1930s; the growth of US Navy aircraft weights is given below as an example of this process.

Aircraft	Year	Gross weight (lb)
Grumman F3F-1	1935	4,543
Grumman F4F-4 Wildcat	1941	7,975
Grumman F6F-5 Hellcat	1944	12,740
Grumman F9F Panther	1949	17,766
Douglas F4D-1 Skyray	1951	27,000
LTV F-8C Crusader	1958	37,938
McDonnell F-4B Phantom	1961	54,600
Grumman F-14A Tomcat	1970	65,000

As take-off weights increased, take-off runs increased also. Catapult launches first became standard practice on the escort carriers of the Second World War, and eventually on all aircraft carriers. The F3F-1 of 1935 could get airborne in 183ft with a 25 knot wind over deck, but the F4 Phantom required 1230ft (longer than any flight deck in existence) with the same wind over deck; other naval aircraft require even longer runs. Increasing aircraft size did mean increased capabilities; the development of night flying and airborne radar devices eliminated a long-standing gap in a carrier's striking power. And as aircraft grew, so did carriers; a corollary to this was improved seakeeping qualities, so that the number of occasions when bad weather would restrict flight operations was reduced.

The explosive growth in aircraft size made any attempt at hybrid warships virtually impossible; other weapons systems were simply squeezed out by the vast flight decks and hangars. Another factor in the postwar eclipse of the hybrid was the extreme vulnerability of carriers, amply demonstrated during the course of the war. This vulnerability was one strong reason why both sides in the Pacific war took pains to avoid exposing carriers to enemy surface units, and the constraints this policy put on manoeuvring may have shaped the tactical conduct of that conflict as much as the growing power of the aircraft they carried. To put carriers at risk by giving them short-range anti-ship weapons was clearly a mistake.

The distressing fragility of carriers had been most effectively shown on the two occasions in the Second World War when they were exposed to surface gunfire. In 1940 HMS *Glorious* was quickly destroyed by long-range shellfire from the German battleships *Scharnhorst* and *Gneisenau* despite the extreme gallantry of her two escorting destroyers. Equal heroism on the part of escorts and aircrew could not save the American escort carrier *Gambier Bay*, which was destroyed by a Japanese battleship-cruiser force off Samar. It may be noted in passing that this last incident was one of probably only two actions in which carriers fired guns at major surface units; the other was the Battle of Cape Matapan in 1941, when HMS *Formidable* fired one salvo against the Italian cruisers.

Still another factor in the eclipse of the hybrid was the fact that there was no one navy possessing the combination of weapons systems necessary to create a useful hybrid; in the West there were no anti-ship weapons to compete with aircraft, and the Soviets, who had developed powerful anti-ship missiles in the face of a massive Western naval superiority, long derided shipboard aviation for ideological and economic reasons.

★ ★ ★

In a book published in 1947, *Fundamentals of Naval Warfare*, there appeared what might be termed the last of the traditional hybrids. This book was written by Lee J Levert, a man of many accomplishments, according to the dust jacket blurb.

> He was graduated from the University of Michigan as a Naval Architect and Marine Engineer, and later earned the degree of Doctor of Jurisprudence at New York University. He is both a Licensed Professional Engineer and a member of the New York State Bar.
>
> Commander Levert served throughout the war as an officer in the Naval Reserve . . .

With these impressive credentials to back him up, Levert set out to describe the elements of naval power in the hope that this would make the need for a large permanent naval establishment plain to the public. His book includes descriptions of weapons, ships, logistics, naval bases, planning, staff organisation and operations — everything connected with war at sea. On the basis of this information, he then set about describing the future needs of the navy, including the sort of ships it would require. The ship he foresaw was the 'battle-carrier'.

In order to understand why a former naval officer, writing in the aftermath of the great carrier battles of the Pacific war, predicted the 'twilight of the aircraft carrier' and its replacement by ships armed with a combination of heavy guns and aircraft, it is necessary to examine one of the author's assumptions: that radar-controlled AA gunfire and the influence or variable time (VT) fuse had restored the defensive power of surface ships against aircraft. Levert mentions this many times throughout his book, and also gives a prominent place to the famous 'Battleship X' incident, in which USS *South Dakota*'s radar-controlled AA gunfire proved

> that plenty of life is still left in capital ships. The *South Dakota* was attacked by thirty-two Japanese aircraft off Savo Island, near Guadalcanal, and she shot down all but one of the attackers. . . .
>
> Here the air enthusiasts met with their first setback. The efficacy of counter measures taken against the aircraft menace was demonstrated . . .

This statement is demonstrably false. The official figure credited to *South Dakota* in that day's action is twenty-six aircraft, but this is probably an exaggeration. According to one source, *South Dakota*'s own air defence officer was sure of only seven aircraft, and her officer of the deck thought fourteen the true total. The problem was that the reports of downed aircraft came from 'individual gunners and mount captains. Obviously a lot of them were duplicate reports because the descriptions were so similar'.

Whatever her true total, *South Dakota*'s achievement had come before the introduction of VT fuses for AA shells. These small radar fuses, set to detonate the shell in the vicinity of an aircraft, increased the effectiveness of AA gunfire by a factor of four or so. Yet they did not grant immunity to surface ships against aircraft attack; it would be more accurate to say that they restored the prewar status quo. But aircraft were getting faster and carrying heavier weapon loads all the time, including stand-off weapons such as the German FX-1400 radio-controlled glide bomb. Levert took no account of these facts.

Levert felt that actions such as Surigao Strait showed that the battleship was still a vessel to be reckoned with, and of course he was correct. However the circumstances under which a battleship could bring its guns to bear were growing rarer all the time. The same radar that made naval gunfire so accurate also implied that ships wishing to avoid gunnery duals could do so more surely than ever before. There were simply fewer and fewer opportunities for a battleship to get close enough to an enemy to use its guns. Clearly, a ship that had to be so huge (and expensive) in order to survive, yet which was useful under such rare circumstances, was a bad investment.

Levert's battle-carrier is meant to be a combination of a 55,000 ton battleship and a 45,000 ton aircraft carrier. Her characteristics are given below.

Displacement:	100,000t oa
Dimensions:	1200ft oa? × 140ft (hull?)
Flight deck:	650ft × 150ft
Machinery:	4 turbines, 8 boilers in 4 engine rooms; ten 2000hp diesel engines in one engine room; electric drive, 7 shafts, total horsepower 420,000 = 37kts. 7500nm at 30kts
Armament:	twelve 16in (3 × 4); forty-two 5in (8 × 4 + ?); 'large number' of 3in; 'limited number' of 40mm
Aircraft:	200
Protection:	'heavily' protected citadel forward, incl main battery magazines and forward engine room (internal belt armour); 'a single heavy protective deck' extends to the stern

The rough sketches in Levert's book give some idea of how his battle-carrier was supposed to look. The main battery was to be concentrated in three quadruple turrets forward, *Nelson* style, with a

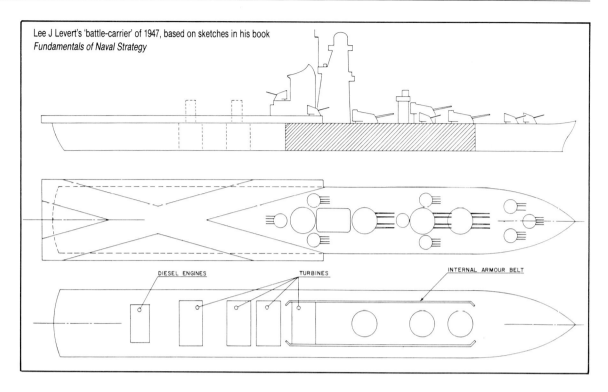

Lee J Levert's 'battle-carrier' of 1947, based on sketches in his book *Fundamentals of Naval Strategy*

DIESEL ENGINES   TURBINES   INTERNAL ARMOUR BELT

conning tower between the second and third turrets. These turrets were to be 'divided into two sections', presumably by a centreline bulkhead as in the quadruple turrets of the French *Dunkerque* and *Richelieu* class ships; they would not be fitted with optical rangefinders, to save weight and space. The secondary battery of dual-purpose 5in guns were to be 'of at least fifty-caliber length', and most of them would be mounted in heavily protected quadruple gunhouses, some on the fo'c's'le, others around the tower mast and funnel. The remaining 5in guns, ten in number, would be mounted in sponsons aft and would be protected only by splinter shields. The numerous 3in gun positions are not indicated in the sketches. The sketches do show an incredibly tall 'streamlined' tower mast, about 250ft high if the drawing is to scale — clearly the vertical dimension has been exaggerated somewhat. The armour belt would cover only the forward portion of the ship, leaving most of the machinery spaces without vertical protection. The heavy protective deck, on the other hand, would extend all the way to the stern. Underwater protection would be the liquid-loaded type.

The machinery was to be unique, a combined turbine/diesel plant with electric transmission to keep the shaft lengths within reason. The exhaust gases of the two forward engine rooms would apparently have been vented through a single large funnel, while the sketch shows each of the two aft engine rooms with its own stack. These funnels do not appear on the plan view, so it is impossible to determine just where they were to be — on one side of the hull, both, or on the centreline in some form of telescoping arrangement *à la* the 1925 Progetto Rota. The latter seems most likely, as they were drawn in broken lines; if this is the case, they would have consumed a great deal of valuable hangar space. As protection against torpedo hits, the inner propellers are forward of the outer shafts. The centre propeller 'is placed well below the others, and is protected by a tunnel'. It would be used only in emergencies because of its inefficient location. The total output of this plant was to be 420,000 'horsepower', presumably a combination of brake and shaft horsepower. There would be three rudders.

The aviation facilities were a remarkable combination of the prescient and the absurd. Levert proposes what amounts to an angled flight deck, actually an 'X' pattern. He gives two possible flight-deck layouts; the object of these alternatives is to allow simultaneous launching and recovery of aircraft. In both, aircraft would land straight-on; the arresting wires are perpendicular to the ship's axis, and Levert writes that an aircraft that misses the crash barrier would 'hit the base of the conning tower'. Take-offs, on the other hand, would be accomplished by catapults angled to avoid the funnel and tower mast. In one sketch, aircraft would land to one side of the flight deck while launchings would be conducted on the other side; in the other sketch, the entire width of the flight deck is used for landings and take-offs, with catapults angled on each beam. In either arrangement, 250ft is allowed for landing.

The space available for the hangar seems totally inadequate for the 200 aircraft the author projects, especially if the after funnels were led up through it, while the short (650ft) flight deck, with its peculiar arrangement, would make any sort of deck park very difficult. The aircraft complement would be composed largely of fighters, with only a few torpedo and bombing aircraft.

Levert's battle-carrier was to operate without escort; short-range destroyers would only be a handicap. Its high speed would provide some protection against submarines, and it would also carry a few helicopters equipped with sonobuoys. Levert considered cruisers too weak for modern warfare; only the battleship had the staying power he considered necessary, and only carriers could provide the air cover modern naval warfare required. Apart from its purely naval tasks, the Levert ship could be stationed in the vicinity of strategic targets to provide fighter escort for long-range land-based bombers. It was Levert's view (shared by many contemporary air power proponents) that effective bombing could be conducted only by big aircraft with heavy bomb loads. Such aircraft were necessarily land-based, but no fighter could match their range, so the best combination was short-range fighters based on battle-carriers escorting long-range land-based bombers. A similar role for naval air was actually considered in a 1947 US Navy study, although in this the carrier aircraft would have been responsible for suppressing the enemy aircraft in raids apart from the air force's strategic bombing missions rather than protecting them by close escort, as Levert proposed.

Levert dealt with the danger of exposing the vulnerable flight deck to damage in a gunnery duel with an argument that by now should be familiar: 'Gun duels are far more likely to follow and not precede air strikes [original emphasis], and usually take place after the carrier strength on either or both sides is partly depleted'. In other words, the aircraft were expendable once the initial strikes were made. Hazarding the flight deck in a gunnery duel would therefore be acceptable.

There are other similarities to hybrid ideas from the 1920s. Like earlier schemes, the battle-carrier was supposed to represent all the capabilities of a battleship and a carrier in one hull. In this case, Levert believed that his battle-carrier would have the full capabilities of a 55,000 ton battleship and a 45,000 ton carrier. Yet the flight deck is about 275ft shorter than that of the 45,000 ton *Midway* class carriers (650ft *vs* 924ft), and is smaller in area despite its greater width (150ft *vs* 113ft). The *Midways* had a 692ft by 95ft hangar and carried sixty-four F4U-4 Corsairs, sixty-four SB2C Helldivers, five night fighters (F6F-5N Hellcats) and five photo-reconnaissance aircraft (F6F-5P Hellcats), a total of 138. The battle-carrier was to carry 200 aircraft (whether piston-engined or jets is never specified) although her hangar would be much shorter and only marginally wider (at most 500ft by 130ft) for almost the same area. Although some space would be gained by carrying mostly fighters, it would not be enough to add sixty-two aircraft to the total; fighters were almost as big as carrier bombers by the end of the war. The aircraft group therefore could have been similar to *Midway*'s, but the flight deck would be smaller. Levert's sketches do not show any indication of lift locations, which would have consumed some hangar space.

The battle-carrier is also flawed as a battleship. Only one of its engine rooms is afforded the protection of belt armour; the other engine rooms are shielded only by the heavy deck. In a close-range night action — about the only type of big-gun duel one could reasonably expect in the late 1940s — this could quickly lead to the loss of three-quarters of the engineering spaces to relatively light, low-angle hits.

On close examination, therefore, the battle-carrier does not combine all the capabilities of a battleship and carrier. But Levert's semi-angled deck, designed to permit simultaneous launch and recovery of aircraft, presaged the fully angled deck that would become a standard feature on all modern carriers, and on many modern hybrid proposals.

There was another, far more realistic attempt at a hybrid-like ship designed to operate modern aircraft. This design was roughed out at about the same time as the characteristics of the nuclear-powered super-carrier USS *Enterprise* were being drawn up; it was never considered for construction, but was instead a sketch of future possibilities. Nevertheless, it gives some idea of the problems confronting a hybrid designer in a world of high-performance jets and guided weapons.

Sketched by the US Navy's Bureau of Ships in 1955, the ship was a nuclear-powered 'self-protecting' carrier. It had the following characteristics.

Displacement:	64,875t light; 81,150t full load
Dimensions:	990ft (wl), 1030ft (oa) × 132ft (wl) × 36ft
Machinery:	8 nuclear reactors, 4 shafts; 280,000shp = 32kts
Armament:	2 twin Talos AA missile launchers, 4 twin Terrier AA missile launchers
Aircraft:	24 VTOL interceptors
	4 night fighters (McDonnell F3H-1N Demons)
	8 attack bombers (of similar size to the A3D Skywarrior)
	16 ASW helicopters (Sikorsky HR2S)

The ship has an angled flight deck, with a large island sited on the forward portion of the deck rather than on a starboard sponson, as on other carriers. The Talos long range AA missile launchers were located fore and aft of the island, which carried the various guidance radars required by the big air-breathing missile. The four Terrier medium-range missile launchers and their less complex guidance radars were mounted on sponsons below the flight deck, one on each quarter. An astonishing total of 132 Talos and 242 Terrier missiles were to be carried. The underwater protection system was a conventional five-bulkhead type. Although the ship was intended to operate without escorts, its design shows no provision for sonar.

Despite its great size, the 'self-protecting CVAN' shows the reduced aviation facilities typical of hybrid warships when compared with 'pure' carrier designs. The ship would have had three catapults for launching conventional aircraft (one fewer than contemporary carriers) and six 'VTOL nets' for recovering the interceptors. There were three deck-edge lifts (again, one fewer than in the *Forrestal* and subsequent carrier classes). The location of the island, presumably dictated by the location of the Talos magazines, cuts into the deck area available for flight operations. Most significant is the reduced aircraft complement. Whereas the *Forrestal* class can operate more than eighty aircraft, the 'self-protecting CVAN' could handle only fifty-two.

The reduced number of catapults and the awkward location of the island may have been acceptable because of the expectation of more flexible VTOL aircraft operations. The Bell Company worked on several VTOL aircraft schemes in the 1950s, some of which were partially financed by the navy. These projects led eventually to the Bell XF-109, a joint air force/navy Mach 2+ inter-

ceptor with swivelling engine nacelles at the tips of its short wings. This design reached the mock-up stage in 1961, but no working aircraft was ever constructed. However, a very similar aircraft that used much of the Bell technology, the German VJ-101, was later built and flown. So the 'self-protecting CVAN', had it been built, might well have had its supersonic VTOL interceptors.

This heavily armed carrier would have been tremendously expensive; the costs were estimated at $375 million for the lead ship and $340 million for succeeding vessels. This price tag was almost certainly an underestimate. The cost of *Enterprise*, estimated at $314 million in 1957, actually soared to more than $450 million; a similar increase in the cost of the 'self-protecting CVAN' would have led to a $540 million lead ship, which would have been about two and a half times the cost of a *Forrestal* class carrier.

It is interesting to note that the Royal Navy considered a somewhat similar, but considerably smaller, ship in 1956. Designs for 30,000 ton carriers armed with long-range surface-to-air missiles were investigated in an attempt to economise by combining the carrier and escort functions in one hull. Although a missile-armed carrier figured in various proposals for construction in the late 1950s, it never got past the draughting board. The idea survived in the CVA-01 design, which was the centrepiece of the Royal Navy's carrier plans in the early 1960s and featured a Sea Dart missile launcher aft. CVA-01 was in no sense intended to be self-escorting, however, and in fact specially designed ships, showing many hybrid characteristics, were studied as escorts for this never-built carrier (see Chapters 14 and 16).

In Levert's 'battle-carrier' we can see the last gasp of the old technology of guns and piston-engined aircraft. In spite of a few prescient features, his conception is no more advanced than hybrid schemes of the 1920s and '30s. His arguments for the hybrid are essentially the same as those advanced twenty years earlier, and contain the same flaws. Levert underestimated the advantage of aircraft over AA guns and therefore overestimated the chances of his ship against aerial attacks. The idea that the aircraft were essentially expendable goes right back to the very beginnings of shipboard aviation and the earliest hybrids; it is predicated on the fundamental fallacy that a battle will be a one-shot affair. In the Pacific war naval battles usually involved continuous ope-

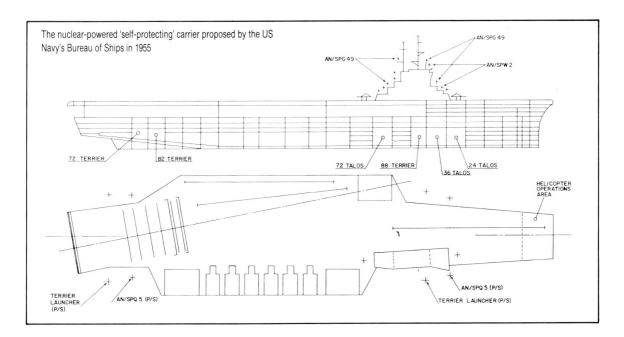

The nuclear-powered 'self-protecting' carrier proposed by the US Navy's Bureau of Ships in 1955

rations by fighters and multiple launchings of strike aircraft; in addition, carriers often had to undertake sustained operations against targets ashore, a role that has become one of the prime justifications for aircraft carriers in the postwar world. Under such conditions, the idea of an 'expendable' flight deck, or air group, is untenable. In a similar vein, the idea of using guns to 'finish off' a crippled enemy was equally outdated. Aircraft proved perfectly capable of 'finishing off' the enemies they had crippled.

The 'self-protecting CVAN', on the other hand, can be seen as the first of the new generation of missile-armed ships with high-performance jet aircraft. The question of whether it was a hybrid is a difficult one, and reflects some of the ambiguities of modern naval warfare. It would have carried no specific anti-ship weapons, the traditional role of the gun aboard the hybrids of the past. Although the Talos missile did have a limited anti-ship capability, the designers no doubt saw the aircraft as the ship's main weapon against enemy ships; its missile batteries were intended to defend against aircraft only. It can therefore be argued that the Talos and Terrier missiles are analogous to the 5in and 40mm AA guns of Second World War carriers. By this reasoning, the 'self-protecting CVAN' is really nothing more than an unusually well armed carrier.

There is another side to this issue, however; the Talos and Terrier missile systems are both classed as 'area defence' weapons today, which means that they have sufficient range to defend more

than just one ship against air attack. Shorter-range weapons that protect only the ship carrying them are designated 'point defence' missiles. If aircraft have taken over traditional destroyer roles such as torpedo attack, and such traditional cruiser roles as reconnaissance, then a ship armed with area defence weapons is in effect 'screening' a task force in the same way as the American flight-deck cruisers were intended to screen the fleet from light forces. Seen in this light, the 'self-protecting CVAN' is carrying the equivalents of 8in or 6in cruiser guns.

The argument seems almost exactly balanced, and the 'self-protecting CVAN' can be seen as either hybrid or heavily armed carrier. What cannot be denied is the fact that this roughly sketched design foresaw many of the features of a ship such as Kiev; the resemblance of the superstructure arrangement is almost uncanny. The 'self-protecting' ship's large size was in part a function of conventional aircraft operations; the demands of such operations were one of the major reasons why hybrid ships were nearly impossible in the postwar decade. Yet her design also showed an early appreciation for a new type of aircraft that would eventually make the hybrid a viable proposition once again — VTOLs.

VERTICAL MONOPOLY

The Bureau of Ships' giant 'self-protecting' nuclear-powered carrier clearly demonstrates how the demands of high-performance aircraft operation had driven carriers — and by extension, hybrids — to tremendous sizes. There was, however, an alternative to the ever-larger carrier: find aircraft that would make fewer demands on the ships that carried them. This was the logic behind the seaplane; from the beginning of naval aviation, it had seemed ideally suited to maritime operations. It needed no flight deck for recovery, just a crane, and most ships already had boat cranes. Catapults and a stowage area of some sort were all they required.

However these advantages were eventually outweighed by one simple fact: the seaplane could not keep up with the performance of wheeled aircraft. At a fundamental level, the seaplane is handicapped in the air by the very features required for waterborne operation, which impose penalties in aerodynamic drag, and usually in weight as well.

This fact had not always been evident; indeed, for several years the fastest aircraft in the world were the seaplanes designed for the revived Schneider Trophy races. Although these aircraft were militarily useless, they seemed to show that the disparity in performance between seaplanes and wheeled aircraft was inconsequential, but as aeronautical science advanced in the 1930s the gap began to grow; it was not that the seaplane failed to improve, but that the wheeled aeroplane had inherent advantages, such as its adaptability to retractable landing gear, that enabled it to improve at a quicker pace.

One result was the seaplane's growing vulnerability in aerial combat because of its relative inferiority in speed and manoeuvrability. This alone would not have doomed it; the decisive factor was its loss of utility. While catapult-launched floatplanes and flying boats performed quite usefully on many occasions during the early stages of the Second World War, their value was increasingly eroded by the proliferation of carrier aircraft and the increasing range of land-based aircraft. One of the seaplane's functions simply vanished, that of spotting for long-range gunfire in a battleline engagement, a role on which the prewar US Navy had placed great emphasis. Strike, reconnaissance and ASW functions could be performed more effectively by carrier aircraft, which were faster, could carry heavier payloads, were better able to defend themselves and were not dependent on favourable seas for return to their floating bases. In the close-range night gunnery actions that characterised the Solomons campaign, seaplanes and their highly inflammable stores of fuel and lubricants were positive dangers, and it became standard practice for US cruisers to jettison their aircraft before going into battle.

By the closing stages of the Second World War the shipboard seaplane's value resided almost entirely in spotting gunfire against shore targets and in short-range search and rescue at sea (and even the latter role was soon to be taken over by another type of aircraft entirely). Thus by the war's end nearly all navies, with the notable exception of the Japanese, were removing aircraft, catapults and associated equipment from battleships and cruisers, often replacing them with increased AA armament. In the form of the large, long-range flying boat, the seaplane has lingered on, sometimes adopting itself to jet power, but today only the Soviet Union, China and Japan are still operating this type.

The death of the seaplane did not end the search for an aircraft with a minimal impact on a ship. Even better than an aircraft that could alight on the water would be one that could arise and descend vertically; as the seaplane was fading in importance, just such a craft was developed. The helicopter was in many ways the ideal naval aircraft: it required no launching mechanism, no retrieval device, no take-off run and no more deck space than the diameter of its rotors, which could be folded for handy stowage.

The principle of the rotary wing was known as early as the fourth century AD in China, where it was used in flying toys that were eventually diffused to the West. Despite this early start, the road to the development of the powered, man-lifting helicopter was a long and hard one, littered with the wreckage of a wild and weird variety of craft that at best could sputter a very short distance a very few feet, or even inches, above ground.

The only successful rotary-wing predecessor of the helicopter was the Autogiro, developed in the 1920s by the Spaniard Juan de la Cievra y Cordonia and soon widely manufactured around the world under his patents. The Autogiro differs from the helicopter in that its horizontal blades are not powered — or in late models powered for take-off only — but, substituting for fixed wings, rotate freely in the airflow of a conventional propeller. In the Autogiro, lift, control and propulsion are essentially separate functions; in the helicopter, they are combined in a single system.

The American, Spanish, Italian and French navies all experimented with the Autogiro during the 1930s, and the Japanese Navy used it operationally during the Second World War, as will be noted in Chapter 15. The Autogiro was not, however, the answer to the naval aviator's prayers: it was 'difficult to build, too expensive, rather hard to fly and could not carry a suitable military payload'. The last liability was its greatest handicap.

The breakthrough in rotary-wing flight came in the late 1930s and early 1940s. 'Breakthrough', however, is perhaps too strong a word. In no case was there a sudden stroke of inspired genius but, rather, a gradual accumulation of experience and technological advances that overcame the basic stumbling blocks: lighter engines that achieved an acceptable ratio of weight to horsepower, the elimination of the problem of torque (the tendency of the rotor-engine combination to spin the fuselage) and the development of complex gearing that enabled the rotors to tilt forward and back or from side to side, allowing the craft to manoeuvre by changing the angle of attack of the blades. As so often in the history of invention, these developments were made independently and almost simultaneously by several men: Louis Breguet in France, Anton Flettner in Germany and Igor Sikorsky in the United States. Flettner was by a small margin first off the mark, and consequently the German Navy was the first to adopt the helicopter, the first to take it aboard ship and the first to employ it operationally during wartime.

On the other side of the Atlantic, Sikorsky's success led the US Navy to acquire its first helicopters in 1942; their shipboard use was pioneered in joint US Navy, US Coast Guard and British trials during 1942-44. The US Navy established its first all-helicopter squadron in 1946, the Royal Navy followed suit in 1950, and by

In a 1935 experiment, this British civilian Cierva C-30 Autogiro was flown from a special platform erected on the Italian heavy cruiser *Fiume* (sister cruiser *Gorizia* is in the background). An aft deck for six Autogiros was considered as a design feature of the Italian *Littorio* class battleships but was rejected in favour of a catapult for three conventional-wing aircraft (*Aldo Fraccaroli collection*)

1960 nearly every maritime force of any consequence had acquired the type. The trend has accelerated since then, as the helicopter's initial inability to carry truly useful payloads was overcome by advances in design and power.

By the late 1950s helicopters had proved their value by providing a much needed long-range ASW capability against even the fastest submarines, but there was a considerable problem in fitting their operating cycle into a strike carrier's routine: the steady but low-intensity ASW work did not accord well with the intensive but episodic strike operations. The obvious solution to this problem was to move the ASW aircraft to other ships, getting them out of the way of the ever bigger jets. The minimal demands of helicopter operations allowed them to fly from all manner of ships, and the Royal Navy pioneered the operation of ASW helicopters from small platforms on vessels such as frigates and destroyers. The US Navy operated special-purpose ASW carriers, using light fleet and escort carriers and eventually *Essex* class carriers for the job, while other navies built or converted cruisers to carry ASW helicopters. The helicopter also found a valuable role in landing troops during amphibious operations: both the US and Royal navies converted flight-deck carriers into assault helicopter carriers, and the US Navy eventually built a series of specially designed helicopter assault ships.

In such cases the helicopter was simply grafted onto an existing type of ship, but it also offered an opportunity to design a new type of aviation ship, considerably more modest in size and in its scope of operations than the super-carriers. Perhaps it is not surprising that these new helicopter ships bore a strong resemblance to an earlier generation of vessels designed to handle an earlier generation of minimum-impact aircraft, the seaplane cruisers of the 1930s.

The helicopter-carrying cruisers which have been built by several navies all follow a pattern set

A typical modern naval helicopter capable of shipboard operation is this Westland-Aérospatiale Sea Lynx of the West German Navy's *Marinefliegergeschwader* 3 *Graf Zeppelin* equipped with dipping sonar. Variants of this design are also employed by the British, Netherlands and French navies. Although primarily an ASW craft, it can be missile-armed, and two British shipboard Lynxes are credited with sinking an Argentine ship and damaging another with missiles during the 1982 Falklands conflict (*West German Navy, courtesy of Dr H U Oppermann*)

One of the first of the post-Second World War helicopter carriers, the French *Jeanne d'Arc*, which in peacetime doubles as a cadet training ship and has cruised extensively in that role (*L & L van Ginderen collection*)

Italian helicopter carrier *Caio Duilio*, originally designated with her sister, *Andrea Doria*, as an 'escort cruiser'. *Caio Duilio* is seen here after her conversion to a training ship, which reduced her aerial complement and armament (*L & L van Ginderen collection*)

by *Gotland* and *Tone*: armament forward, superstructure amidships and helicopter flight deck aft. However their aircraft are not intended to act as fleet scouts or undertake strike missions; in every case their major role is ASW, although some add a capacity for assault troop landing.

One of the first of these new ships was the French *Jeanne d'Arc*. Built to replace an aging training cruiser of the same name, her construction was first considered in the mid-1950s. Perhaps as a result of the 1956 Anglo-French assault on the Suez Canal, where helicopter-landed troops were used with considerable success, it was decided to build a combined cadet training and helicopter-carrying cruiser.

The result was design PH-57, which had a centreline superstructure incorporating the command facilities and funnel uptakes with the after half of the ship given over to a large, flat deck for helicopter operations. Below the flight deck was the hangar, large enough for four helicopters when acting as a training ship; in wartime, the quick removal of cadet accommodations would increase capacity to eight helicopters. High speed was not required, so the powerplant was relatively

modest and compactly arranged in two compartments, each with one turbine set and two boilers.

The design was approved in 1957, but limited budgets delayed her laying down until July 1960. The ship was launched on 30 September 1961 with the temporary name *La Résolue*. She began trials in July 1963, and finally entered service as *Jeanne d'Arc* in July 1964, at which time the old training cruiser was finally retired.

Characteristics of the ship as completed are given below.

Displacement:	10,000t standard; 12,365t full load
Dimensions:	597ft 2in oa × 72ft 2in wl (78ft 9in oa) × 21ft 8in (24ft full load) (182m oa × 22m [24m oa] × 6.6m [7.32m full load])
Flight deck:	203 ft 5in × 68ft 11in (62m × 21m)
Machinery:	4 boilers, 2 sets geared turbines, 40,000shp = 26.5kts. 6000nm at 15kts
Armament:	four 3.9in (100mm) guns (4 × 1)
Aircraft:	4 Super Frelon helicopters
Sensors:	Radars: 1 DRBV-22D air search; 1 DRBV-50 air/surface search; 1 DRBI-10 3-D surveillance; 3 DRBC-32A fire control. Sonar: SQS-503
Complement:	617 + 183 officer cadets

As completed, the ship had a low funnel; this was raised considerably after her trials in order to keep smoke off the flight deck. The armament was originally intended to include six 3.9in guns, but two single mounts abreast the superstructure were deleted during construction. It was also intended to fit a quadruple 375mm ASW mortar forward of the bridge, but this was never shipped. The mortar has the look of a stopgap; provision was probably made during the design for the installation forward of 'Masurca' (*MArine SUpersonique Ruelle Contre Avions* — 'naval supersonic AA missile', equivalent to the US Terrier), which also began development in the mid-1950s. As early as 1961 the intention to mount a twin-arm Masurca launcher was being reported in naval yearbooks, and throughout the 1960s the installation of the launcher seemed imminent, but it was never fitted. Instead, six Exocet MM38 anti-ship-missiles were added to the ship in 1974, the canisters mounted on the first superstructure deck just forward of the bridge.

The hangar is 108ft long, expanding to 197ft in wartime; it is served by a lift at the after end of the flight deck. *Jeanne d'Arc* is designed to handle the larger Super Frelon helicopter, which can act as troop carrier, minesweeper or ASW aircraft. When operating as a troop carrier, *Jeanne d'Arc* can carry a battalion of 700 men.

Jeanne d'Arc is clearly a very flexible ship, but is she a hybrid? Her basic configuration matches that of many earlier hybrid schemes, but she seems to lack the offensive role implicit in traditional hybrids. For much of her career she lacked any offensive shipboard armament at all, and although her Exocets now give her a credible anti-ship capability, their relatively short range (23nm) probably limits them to self-defence. The Masurca launcher, so long contemplated, combined with her ASW helicopters, would have made her a valuable fleet screening ship in the tradition of the American flight-deck cruisers of the 1930s, although her relatively low speed might have barred her from escorting fast carrier forces. In the end, she seems to fit into that same limbo of semi-hybrids as the Japanese *Tone* class ships.

The Italian Navy began design work on helicopter-cruisers at about the same time as the French Navy, and the resulting vessels present the same problems of classification as *Jeanne d'Arc*. The first pair of ships, *Andrea Doria* and *Caio Duilio,* were laid down as part of the 1957–58 construction programme. Half the size of their French contemporary, they carry only half her helicopter complement; their characteristics as completed were

Displacement:	5000t standard, 6500t full load
Dimensions:	489ft 9in oa × 56ft 5in × 16ft 5in (149.3m × 17.2m × 5m)
Flight deck:	98ft 5in × 52ft 6in (30m × 16m)
Machinery:	4 boilers, 2 sets geared turbines; 60,000shp = 31kts. 5000nm at 17 kts
Armament:	1 twin Terrier SAM launcher (40 missiles); eight 3in (76mm) (8 × 1); six 324mm ASW TT
Aircraft:	4 helicopters
Sensors:	Radars: 1 SPS-39 and 1 SPS-12 air search; 1 SPQ-2 air/surface search; 2 SPG-55 guidance for Terrier; 4 RTN 10X for 3in fire control. Sonar: SQS-23F
Complement:	485

The two ships differ somewhat in electronics suite; that given above is for *Andrea Doria*. Both ships were laid down in May 1958; *Andrea Doria* was commissioned in February 1964 and *Caio Duilio* in November 1964.

These ships are aptly designated 'escort cruisers' by the Italian Navy. The missile launcher forward gives them a valuable AA screening capability, while the helicopters and torpedo tubes contribute to an ASW screen. The 3in guns, mounted on pedestals on each side of the superstructure, are intended for close-range defence against aircraft.

The helicopters are hangared in the after end of the superstructure, and the ships are fitted with fin stabilisers to allow them to operate their aircraft in rough seas. In an interesting parallel to *Jeanne d'Arc*, *Caio Duilio* was converted in 1979–80 to a midshipmen's training ship, her original hangar being given over to classrooms and accommodation, and a new, smaller hangar added on, reducing the flight deck and allowing only two helicopters to be carried. Her 3in battery was also reduced by the removal of the two after mounts.

A third ship of the class had been planned, but the design was reworked and enlarged several times, and in the end the ship was not laid down until June 1965. She was commissioned in July 1969 and christened *Vittorio Veneto*. Her characteristics as completed were

Displacement:	7500t standard, 8850t full load
Dimensions:	589ft 3in oa × 63ft 8in × 19ft 8in (179.6m × 19.4m × 6m)
Flight deck:	131ft 3in × 61ft (40m × 18.6m)
Machinery:	4 boilers, 2 sets geared turbines; 73,000shp = 32kts. 5000nm at 17kts
Armament:	1 twin Terrier/ASROC launcher (40 or 60 missiles); eight 3in (76mm) (8 × 1); six 324mm TT
Aircraft:	9 ASW helicopters
Sensors:	Radar: 1 SPS-40 and 1 SPS-52 air search; SPQ-2B air/surface search; 2 SPG-55B guidance for Terrier; 3 RTN-10X for 3in fire control. Sonar: SQS-23
Complement:	550

Italian escort cruiser-helicopter carrier *Vittorio Veneto*, seen here with her original armament before its modification during 1981–84 (*L & L van Ginderen collection*)

A planned sistership, *Italia*, was never laid down. Unlike the two *Andrea Doria* class ships, *Vittorio Veneto* has a hangar in the hull, with a lift at the forward end of the flight deck. Like the *Dorias*, she has fin stabilisers.

Vittorio Veneto was refitted during 1981–84, receiving three twin 40mm Breda mounts, one superimposed above the missile launcher and two on each beam on the flight deck just abaft the superstructure. Four canisters for Otomat anti-ship missiles were fitted abreast the super-structure amidships. The electronics were also upgraded.

The *Dorias*, with their limited helicopter facilities, seem completely outside the hybrid category; *Vittorio Veneto*, like *Jeanne d'Arc*, pre-sents a less clear-cut case. She is a very capable 'escort cruiser', but whether she is a hybrid or not is largely a matter of opinion. Unlike *Jeanne d'Arc*, however, she has a considerable potential for offensive operations; not only can her heli-copters be armed with anti-ship missiles, but the Otomat surface-to-surface missiles (SSMs) have a range in excess of 80nm.

★   ★   ★

The next helicopter cruisers to appear were the Soviet Union's two *Moskvas*. The design of these

two ships was probably conceived in the early 1960s; two rationales for the design have been given in Western publications. The first, and by far the most common, is that they were intended to track down American submarines before they could get close enough to the Soviet Union to launch ballistic missiles; the first generation of Polaris SSBNs had a range of less than 1500nm, so the American submarines would have had to approach relatively close to the Soviet coasts to hit inland targets. The second possible design ration-ale is as ASW/AA escort cruisers for a cancelled class of large strategic missile-launching surface ships.

As many as twelve *Moskvas* may have been planned, but changing defence priorities reduced the number actually built to two units, *Moskva* and *Leningrad*. As completed, they had the follow-ing characteristics.

Displacement:	14,500t standard, 18,000t full load
Dimensions:	620ft 1in oa × 85ft 4in wl (111ft 7in oa) × 24ft 11in (27ft 11in max) (189m oa × 26m [34.1m] × 7.6m [8.5m max])
Flight deck:	265ft 9in × 111ft 11in (81m × 34.1m)
Machinery:	4 boilers, 2 sets geared turbines, 100,000shp = 30kts. 14,000nm at 12kts
Armament:	2 twin SA-N-3 SAM launchers, 44 missiles; four 57mm guns (2 × 2); 1 twin SUW-N-1 ASW launcher; 2 RBU-6000 12-tube ASW mortars; 2 quintuple 533mm TT
Aircraft:	14 Kamov Ka-25 'Hormone' helicopters
Sensors:	Radars: 1 Top Sail, 1 Head Net air search; 3 Don-2 surface search/navigation; 2 Head Light for SA-N-3 guidance; 2 Muff Cob for 57mm fire control Sonars: 1 hull mounted, 1 variable depth
Complement:	850

A bow view of the Soviet helicopter carrier *Leningrad* shows the impressive array of weaponry that has frequently caused her and her sister, *Moskva*, to be labelled hybrids (*US Navy*)

An overhead view of *Leningrad*, taken while she was engaged in manoeuvres off the Faroe Islands in 1970, displays her broad helicopter deck and its two lifts (*Ministry of Defence*)

Moskva was laid down in 1962 and completed in 1967; *Leningrad* was laid down in 1964 and completed in 1968. Both were built in the South Yard at Nikolayev. The torpedo tubes were removed from both ships in the mid-1970s and the hull embrasures were plated over, but otherwise the ships have undergone little change in their appearance. They generally trim by the bow and seem to have poor sea-keeping qualities.

Unlike most large Soviet ships, *Moskva* has no anti-ship missiles; her armament, while visually impressive, is either defensive or directed against submarines. The SA-N-3 AA missiles first appeared in these ships, and were probably included because the ships might have to operate outside the range of direct protection by land-based aircraft when hunting Polaris submarines. It has often been argued that the redundancy in *Moskva*'s armament, as well as that of other Soviet ships, is due either to the expectation of battle damage or because of the unreliability of the individual weapons; the latter explanation is perhaps supported by the unreliable performance of the first generation of US and British AA missiles.

Moskva's aviation facilities include a main hangar 219ft 10in by 82ft (67m by 25m), connected to the flight deck by two narrow lifts. There is also a small hangar at the base of the superstructure, large enough for two of the ship's fourteen ASW helicopters.

The two *Moskvas* are among the few modern ships frequently referred to as 'hybrids' or 'hermaphrodites' by observers, although they are no more (or less) hybrids than the French and Italian helicopter cruisers. This appellation can be attributed to their very visible armament; there

are so many weapons that it seems only reasonable to view these ships as offensive vessels, but on close examination they seem little more capable than *Vittorio Veneto* despite their much greater size.

In 1960 Britain had a number of flight-deck carriers and was in the process of converting the small fleet carrier *Bulwark* into a commando helicopter carrier, with her sister *Albion* soon to follow. However, the Royal Navy possessed no specialised ASW carriers, and the relatively small British strike carriers were increasingly strained and cramped by the demands of jet operations; carrying ASW aircraft reduced even further the number of fighters or attack aircraft they could carry. Consideration was therefore given to helicopter-equipped ASW escorts in the late 1950s, but, while many sketch designs were worked out, none was constructed. Instead of purpose-built helicopter cruisers, the 1964 Defence White Paper included plans to convert the three *Tiger* class cruisers into helicopter cruisers; they would serve as ASW escorts for the new CVA-01 strike carriers, which formed the basis of the Royal Navy planning during the early 1960s. *Tiger, Blake* and *Lion* had been laid down during the Second World War but were not completed until 1959-60 due to design changes and lack of funds. Armed with four 6in semi-automatic guns, by the late 1960s these ships were valued mostly for their good command facilities. Their conversion to ASW helicopter cruisers would give them a useful active role in the fleet and justify their large complements and expensive operating costs.

Blake was taken in hand for conversion in 1965 and emerged as a 'command helicopter cruiser' in 1969 with the following characteristics.

Displacement:	9975t standard, 12,080t full load
Dimensions:	566ft oa × 64ft × 23ft
Machinery:	4 boilers, 4 sets geared turbines, 80,000shp = 31.5kts. 6500nm at 13kts
Armament:	two 6in (1 × 2); two 3in (1 × 2); 2 quadruple Seacat SAM launchers
Aircraft:	4 Sea King helicopters
Armour:	belt 3.5-3.25in, decks 2in, turrets 2-1in
Sensors:	Radars: 1 Type 965, 1 Type 992Q air search; 1 Type 278 surface search; 4 Type 903 for fire control; 1 Type 978 navigation
Complement:	880

The conversion programme went ahead even after the cancellation in 1966 of the CVA-01 fleet carrier programme; helicopter cruisers could still be valu-

able as ASW ships escorting the American carriers in a NATO war, while their size made them excellent command ships for purely Royal Navy operations. *Blake*'s conversion cost £5.5 million; *Tiger*, converted between 1968-72, eventually cost an 'astonishing' £13,250,000. The conversion of *Lion* proved impossible due to inadequate funds and instead she was stricken in 1975.

The two ships had a rather clumsy look after their conversion, with the big hangar and flight deck tacked on aft. They first operated Westland Wessex helicopters, but later were equipped with the larger and more capable Sea King. *Tiger* and *Blake* had short lives as helicopter cruisers; with the light fleet carrier *Hermes* redesignated an ASW carrier in 1977 and *Invincible* nearing completion (see Chapter 16), there seemed little point to keeping these costly, limited ships in commission. In 1979 *Tiger* was put on the disposal list, and *Blake* was laid up in 1980 and sold for breaking up in 1982.

The patchword quality of these ships extended to their operational qualities; the ASW role of the helicopters had nothing whatsoever to do with the 6in guns, which were a hold-over from an earlier role. An early plan had called for conversion to assault helicopter carriers; their remaining guns would have provided gunfire support in such a role. As ASW vessels, however, it is unlikely in the extreme that both helicopters and guns would have come into play during any one operation; for that reason, they are perhaps more truly hybrids than any of the continental helicopter cruisers discussed above.

One last ship deserves mention in this disparate sisterhood of helicopter cruisers. Like *Blake*, she is a conversion from a conventional cruiser: the Peruvian *Aguirre*, formerly the Dutch cruiser *De Zeven Provinciën*. Laid down in 1939, her construction was interrupted by the war and she was not completed until 1953. As completed she had a battery of eight 6in guns, but during 1962-64 she was equipped with a twin Terrier launcher in place of the two after twin turrets. She was sold to Peru in 1976, but, in accordance with US stipulations, the Terrier system had to be removed before she was transferred. It was replaced with a small flight deck and a hangar for three helicopters. Commissioned in the Peruvian Navy in 1977 (after some confusing name changes), *Aguirre* has the following characteristics.

HMS *Blake* in her final configuration as a 'command helicopter cruiser'. Before her decommissioning in 1980 she conducted some of the earliest shipboard trials of the Sea Harrier (*Ministry of Defence*)

Another representative modern naval helicopter, a Sikorsky Sea King, over *Blake*'s flight deck. Similar craft took a prominent part in the Falklands conflict. Widely produced in more than a score of variants, the Sea King has equipped or is equipping the US Navy, Marine Corps and Coast Guard and the navies of at least seven other nations (*Ministry of Defence*)

Aguirre's conversion was aesthetically far more successful than *Blake*'s had been, as the aviation facilities do not seem quite as much an imposition on the ship's handsome and balanced profile. One interesting feature of this ship is the second helicopter landing pad atop the hangar; more interesting still are her helicopters themselves, which carry Exocet AM39 air-to-surface missiles (ASMs). Their principal role may well be anti-shipping strikes rather than ASW; none of the other navies on the west coast of South America has much in the way of naval aviation, so the helicopters could present a considerable threat to opposing ships. Her combination of 'strike air-craft' and relatively heavy guns puts *Aguirre* in a direct line of descent from the hybrids of an earlier era; whether her three helicopters represent a sufficient investment in aviation features to warrant classing her as a hybrid is, once again, largely a matter of opinion.

Displacement:	9850t standard, 12,250t full load
Dimensions:	609ft 3in oa × 56ft 7in × 22ft (185.7m oa × 17.25m × 6.7m)
Flight deck:	114ft 10in × 55ft 9in (35m × 17m)
Machinery:	4 boilers, 2 sets geared turbines, 85,000shp = 32kts. 6000nm at 17kts
Armament:	four 6in (2 × 2); six 57mm (3 × 2); four 40mm (4 × 1); 2 depth charge racks
Aircraft:	3 Sea King helicopters
Armour:	belt 3–4in, decks 0.8–1in
Sensors:	Radars: 1 LW-02, 1 DA-02 air search; 1 SGR-103, 1 ZW-03 surface search; 1 ZW-01 navigation; 1 WM25 for 6in fire control; 1 M45 for 57mm fire control Sonar: 1 hull mounted CWC-10N
Complement:	856

The helicopter cruiser has proved a useful type of warship, but the fundamental limitations of the helicopter, both in speed and range, have confined them, and the ships carrying them, to a relatively narrow range of roles: ASW, transportation of assault troops, search and rescue, and under-way replenishment. The helicopter can function as a strike aircraft only as long as it is not opposed by conventional aircraft, and its survival against even relatively simple shipborne AA weapons is problematic.

These limitations took no one by surprise, so the search for an aircraft that would have a minimal effect on a ship did not end with the helicopter. From the early 1950s another type of aircraft, one which better combined the virtues of VTOL and the performance of conventional aircraft, has been sought. The US Navy was financing VTOL research as early as 1951, and the 'self-protecting CVAN' sketch shows 'nets' for such aircraft. As early as 1953 a VTOL carrier was briefly discussed by the Royal Navy.

There are many ways of achieving vertical take-off and landing, and all were considered during the 1950s and early 1960s; many were eventually flown in prototype form. The United States seemed fond of tail-sitters such as the Lockheed XFV-1, the Ryan X-13 and the Convair XFY-1; another American favourite was tilt-rotor craft such as the Bell XV-3 and X22A. European projects, on the other hand, leaned toward lift engines, such as the Short SC.1 and Dassault Mirage III-001, while Germany's VJ-101C combined swivelling engine pods and lift jets like the earlier American Bell XF-109 mock-up. However, the first VTOL aircraft to achieve operational status was the vectored-thrust Harrier.

Vectoring the thrust of a single powerful jet engine grew out of an idea of Michel Wibault, a French aircraft designer. In 1956 he designed a small combat aircraft which, although impractical, used rotating nozzles so that the same engine could be used for vertical and horizontal flight. Engineers at Bristol Aero-Engines improved and simplified the basic idea in a series of turbojet designs; designers at Hawker Siddeley saw promise in these engines, and so began a series of engine and airframe developments that led directly to the P.1127 prototype. This aircraft first hovered on 21 October 1960 and led in turn to the Kestrel, which had a more powerful engine and first flew on 7 March 1964.

The Kestrel's extensive testing demonstrated both the potential of VTOL aircraft and the soundness of Hawker's basic design. However the Kestrel was not a warplane; to translate it into the VTOL tactical support aircraft the RAF wanted would require a new airframe, a new wing, landing gear, jet inlets, avionics and, most of all, a new and more powerful engine. All this was completed with remarkable speed, and on 31 August 1966 the first of the preproduction aircraft flew. The Harrier GR MK.1 entered service with the RAF in 1969.

There was naval interest in the Harrier almost from the beginning; a P.1127 had landed aboard the carrier *Ark Royal* in February 1963, and numerous other shipboard tests followed. British and American Harriers flew from a variety of vessels during evaluation exercises, and Harriers have flown from *Jeanne d'Arc*, *Andrea Doria* and *Blake*. The claim has been made that Harriers have 'operated from more ships, of more diverse types, than any other aircraft in history'.

Experience with the Harrier aircraft soon showed that even a short take-off run could considerably increase the payload. A vertical take-off is a brute force affair, with the engine supplying all the lift; therefore the combined weight of aircraft and payload cannot exceed the thrust of the engine — in fact, it must be considerably less. Even a short take-off run would, however, add aerodynamic lift, allowing the aircraft to get airborne with far greater loads. Short take-off, vertical landing (STOVL) has become the preferred pattern of operations. This principle was taken a step further by Lieutenant Commander Douglas Taylor, RN, who devised the 'ski-jump' ramp in 1973. As a Harrier zooms up the ramp, it is not yet travelling fast enough for wingborne flight; some of the lift comes from the engine, some from aerodynamics, but its path is still partly ballistic. The ramp launches it upward in an arc that gives the Harrier more time to accelerate to full wingborne flight, imitating the advantages of a longer take-off run. The ski-jump can be used either to shorten the take-off run or increase the launch weight of the aircraft; it is especially well suited to shipboard use.

Other novel launch and recovery schemes have been devised for VTOL aircraft; several of these are intended to overcome the lively motion of small ships in heavy seas. One of the most bizarre proposals along this line was put forward by Grumman in the mid-1970s. This scheme involved a VTOL aircraft dubbed the 'Nutcracker' that featured a hinged rear fuselage; the forward section, including small stub wings and cockpit,

would remain horizontal during take-offs and landings, but the rear section, with the engines, would hinge downward to provide vertical thrust. This configuration would have demanded a peculiar recovery operation: the Nutcracker would nose up to a crane fixed to the ship, a platform would rotate out and gradually scoop up the aircraft, then bring it inboard.

This unlikely idea was never pursued, but in the early 1980s British Aerospace began developing the somewhat similar, and far more feasible, SkyHook. In this system, a Harrier would be recovered by an articulated crane on the ship. The system is designed to allow aircraft recovery and launch even in severe bad weather by 'isolating' the head of the crane from ship motion. According to engineers who helped develop the device, this stabilisation of the SkyHook could be 'accomplished with high fidelity by using an active control system which detects excursions of the ship relative to its mean path and articulates the crane to counteract them in such a manner that the head moves smoothly along the ship's directed velocity vector with extraneous perturbations removed at the crane head'. In other words, despite the ship's rolling and pitching, the head of the crane would travel in a smooth, constant line. A Harrier would fly up underneath the crane head, which would automatically lock on to attachment points on top of the fuselage. Once captured, the aircraft is swung inboard, its motion gradually

A Hawker Siddeley Sea Harrier Mk 1, early version of the aircraft that has opened new vistas in shipboard aviation (*Courtesy of Hawker Siddeley*)

made to match that of the ship; it can then be safely set down on the deck. For launch, the Harrier would be swung clear of the ship, its vertical thrust taking over from the crane's support; once the crane senses the upward motion of the aircraft, it would disengage and swing clear, and the Harrier would be on its way.

As fantastic as it may sound, SkyHook has been tested ashore and shows every indication of successful shipboard operation. Moreover, its designers assert that SkyHook requires 'no significant developments . . . to a large extent, off-the-shelf components can be used'. Some proposals even suggest doing away with the Harrier's landing gear; SkyHook could set the aircraft down on a cradle that could be used to move it, and could even have already stocked rearming stations, so that munitions could be quickly put on the aircraft's underwing pylons even in heavy seas. The SkyHook would also have fuel lines, so aircraft would not even have to be brought aboard ship for refuelling; caught by SkyHook, they could be refuelled while suspended outboard of the ship.

If successful, SkyHook could have a tremendous impact on naval operations; small ships could operate high-performance aircraft in weather conditions that would make helicopter operations from those same ships impossible. Aircraft could be refuelled and rearmed while 'on station' at the outer edge of a task force, reducing the number of aircraft required for combat air patrol (CAP) coverage. Dispersal of the aviation element of a task force is another significant advantage. SkyHook would allow flexible flight operations from all sorts of ships, including hybrids.

Like the earlier seaplane cruisers, the helicopter cruisers do not seem to fit the mold of the hybrid warship. They are certainly a collateral line of development, however, and, combined with relatively high-performance VTOL aircraft, can easily lead to true hybrids. It is no coincidence that the Soviet, British and Italian navies have led the way in the development of VTOL ships; *Kiev, Invincible* and *Giuseppe Garibaldi* all have their roots in helicopter cruiser designs, and all exhibit hybrid characteristics to one degree or another. They, like many similar hybrid projects of recent years, rely on VTOL aircraft for their feasibility. Conventional high-performance aircraft simply make too many demands on an aviation vessel to allow any substantial shipboard weapons systems to be included in a design. Therefore, it can truly be said that modern hybrids are a 'vertical monopoly'.

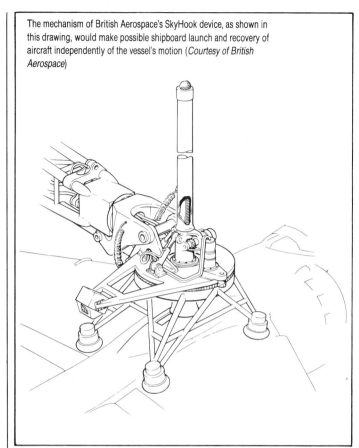

The mechanism of British Aerospace's SkyHook device, as shown in this drawing, would make possible shipboard launch and recovery of aircraft independently of the vessel's motion (*Courtesy of British Aerospace*)

CHAPTER 15

VARIATIONS ON A THEME

Since antiquity, ships have been specially built or modified to land troops, animals and weapons on hostile shores. Thucydides tells of the Athenian conversion of old warships into horse transports during the Peloponnesian War and indicates the Persians possessed such craft even earlier. Even the twentieth-century vehicle landing ship had its early-day antecedents in the form of special vessels built to transport elephants.

As such craft proliferated during the Second World War, it is probably not surprising that the Japanese, with their penchant for putting aircraft aboard nearly everything that could float, would carry the concept into a 'triphibious' mode by creating three unusual vessels that combined the functions of transport, landing ship and aircraft carrier.

They were not, however, creatures of the navy but of the *army*, which, suspicious of the IJN's logistic and convoy-protection competence, acquired just before and during the Pacific war quite a little fleet of its own, eventually including a couple of escort carriers and numbers of cargo-carrying submarines.

The three vessels in question were merchantmen converted on the stocks. The first two, *Akitsu Maru* and *Nigitsu Maru*, were laid down as passenger liners for Nippon Kaiun KK in 1939 and taken over by the army in June 1941. As completed, they boasted short flight decks with starboard islands amidships and a slightly canted vertical funnel. At 403ft 6in by 73ft 9in, the flight deck was too short to allow landing; aircraft were to be flown off it for service ashore. An open lift at the rear of the flight deck connected with a hangar deck that could accommodate either aeroplanes or landing craft.

Particulars of these vessels were

Displacement:	11,000t, 9186grt (*Akitsu Maru*); 11,800t, 9574grt (*Nigitsu Maru*)
Dimensions:	488ft 6in wl × 64ft 3in × 29ft 9in to 37ft 9in
Machinery:	2 sets geared turbines, 4 boilers, 2 shafts; 7500–13,000shp = 20–21kts
Armament:	two 3in AA, ten 3in army pattern field guns; unknown number of 20mm AA

Radius, bunkerage and complement unknown

The field guns were to provide support for the troops during the first stages of a landing. The ships could carry twenty to thirty aircraft or alternately twenty *Daihatsu* landing craft in the hangar and eight aircraft on deck. The landing boats were handled by tall derricks right aft and to starboard abreast the island. There may have been a hinged door at the stern for direct launch-

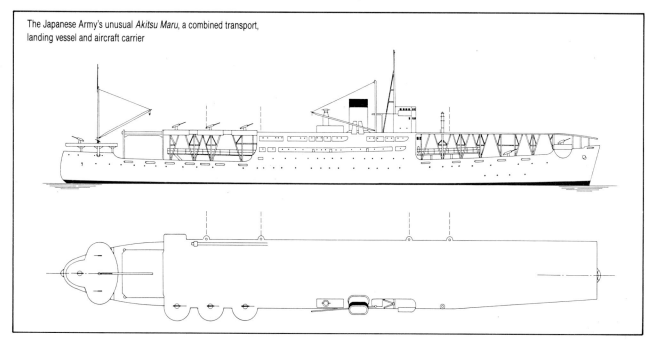

The Japanese Army's unusual *Akitsu Maru*, a combined transport, landing vessel and aircraft carrier

ing, but published sources vary on this point.

Akitsu Maru was launched on 17 September 1941 and completed on 30 December 1942; *Nigitsu Maru* was launched some time in 1942 and completed in March 1943. Little is known of the latter's career until she was sunk by the US submarine *Hake* on 12 January 1944, and it is unclear whether she ever embarked aircraft.

Akitsu Maru's first aircraft was the army's Kokusai Ki-76 liaison and artillery-spotter plane, a light, two-place 310hp high-wing monoplane with fixed landing gear, greatly resembling in form and function the German short take-off and landing (STOL) Fieseler Fi-156 Storch, whose early successes inspired its design. In late 1943 the vessel carried seven of these, modified to loft two 132lb depth charges for anti-submarine work. They were reportedly fitted with arresting hooks, but it is not known if they attempted landings. Their extensive system of flaps probably would have allowed touchdown, but the approach would almost certainly have been from the bow, since the aft derrick masked the after end of the flight deck.

By mid-1944, as the possibility of landing operations decreased and the toll taken by US submarines rose, the army decided to refit *Akitsu Maru* as an ASW escort carrier, equipping her with the Kayaba Ka-1 Autogiro, which thus became the first aircraft of its type to see operational wartime service afloat.

The aircraft was a 240hp two-place reconnaissance and artillery-spotter type patterned after the American Keller KD-1A Autogiro, a single example of which had been imported in 1939. The shipboard version was designated the Ka-1s; to permit it to carry two 132lb depth charges it had to be flown as a single-seater, with the rear cockpit faired over, an example of how, as noted in the previous chapter, the inability of the Autogiro to carry substantial weights aloft handicapped it for military service. Because their three rotors could be folded horizontally rearward, *Akitsu Maru* could carry as many as twenty of these aircraft, although it is not known if this many were ever actually embarked.

In her new guise, which superseded an earlier plan to convert her to a full flight-deck carrier, *Akitsu Maru* carried out only a few operational cruises before being sunk by the US submarine *Queenfish* in the Tsushima Straits on 15 November 1944.

The Japanese Army's third hybrid, *Kumano Maru*, was laid down on 15 August 1944 as a standard *M* type cargo-transport; while building,

it was proposed to alter her to the same design as *Akitsu Maru* and *Nigitsu Maru*, but she was ultimately given a different configuration with a short flush flight deck and a starboard midships horizontal funnel. Her particulars as completed on 30 March 1945 were

Displacement:	12,000t, 9502grt
Dimensions:	491ft oa × 64ft 3in × 23ft
Machinery:	2 sets geared turbines, 3 or 4 boilers, 2 shafts; 10,000shp = 19kts
Armament:	thirteen 3in AA, six 20mm or 25mm AA
Radius:	6000nm at 17kts
Bunkerage and complement unknown	

Capacity was twenty-five landing craft stowed below and eight aircraft on deck, or thirty-seven aircraft. There were stern and broadside launching doors for the landing boats as well as a stern derrick. Although the flight deck was unimpeded, with dimensions of 361ft by 70ft 6in, it was even less capable of landing-on operations than *Akitsu Maru* and *Nigitsu Maru*; even take-off would have been virtually out of the question except for the smallest and lightest aircraft.

It is highly doubtful that *Kumano Maru* saw any operational service or embarked aircraft before Japan's surrender only five months after her completion. She was employed in postwar repatriation service until sold for mercantile use in 1947 and is believed to have been scrapped in 1951.

By the early 1960s the amphibious assault helicopter carrier was an accepted type in the American and British navies, but these ships were usually converted aircraft carriers, in no sense hybrids. It was not until 1961 that someone had the idea of turning the four American *Iowa* class battleships into helicopter-carrier/gunfire support ships.

Ideas for converting the *Iowas* into something abounded in the 1950s, and it is not hard to see why; they were big, fast ships with a lot of useful life still left. After the Second World War they were too expensive to maintain in service, so one by one they went into reserve; only *Missouri* was kept in commission, reportedly in deference to President Harry S Truman's wishes. All four were placed back in service during the Korean War and proved valuable for shore bombardment, but after the war they slipped back into reserve; this time not even *Missouri* was spared. By March 1958, the US Navy had no battleships in commission.

There were soon proposals to convert the *Iowas*

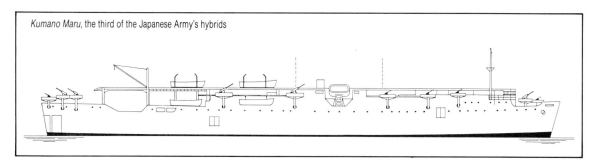

Kumano Maru, the third of the Japanese Army's hybrids

into ballistic or guided missile ships, or fast logistic support vessels or even fleet replenishment ships with all their turrets removed. All of these schemes were too expensive or too inefficient to progress.

While these schemes were being considered, amphibious tactics and 'vertical envelopment' by helicopter-borne troops were being developed. There was increasing concern, however, that one vital asset in amphibious operations was slowly dwindling: gunfire support. In the 1950s the US Navy still had a large number of gun-armed cruisers at its disposal for shore bombardment, but by the beginning of the 1960s many were reaching the end of their useful lives. Some of the younger hulls had been converted to missile ships, while others were more urgently needed as fleet flagships. There was a growing 'gun gap', and the Marine Corps was getting worried. By late 1962, there were only four all-gun 8in cruisers and two

The spacious quarterdeck of the USS *Iowa*, seen here in 1953 long after removal of the catapults, has made her and her sisters attractive candidates for several hybrid schemes (*National Archives*)

missile cruisers with six 8in guns left in service, a total of forty-eight 8in guns; it would take some time to bring them together from their scattered assignments if a need for an amphibious assault arose. The more numerous 6in cruisers were not considered powerful enough to deal with dug-in positions. As General Joseph Burger, Commanding General, Fleet Marine Force, Atlantic, observed, 'Aircraft and missiles cannot do the tactical support job the eights and 16-inch guns did in World War II and Korea'.

In response to this situation, Rear Admiral John S McCain, chairman of the Amphibious Warfare Evaluation Board, proposed in late 1961 the conversion of the *Iowas* into 'commando ships'. He envisaged the replacement of the after

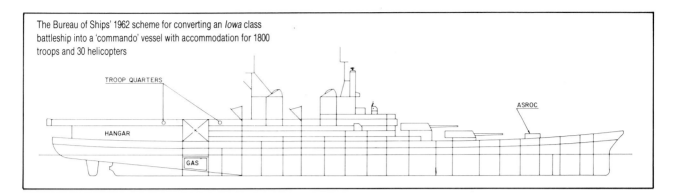

The Bureau of Ships' 1962 scheme for converting an *Iowa* class battleship into a 'commando' vessel with accommodation for 1800 troops and 30 helicopters

TROOP QUARTERS

HANGAR

GAS

ASROC

16in triple turret with a helicopter hangar and flight deck and the removal of most of the 5in dual-purpose guns to make way for landing craft. In an article in the *US Naval Institute Proceedings*, McCain outlined five tasks for the ships: 'command, gunfire support, over-the-beach assault, vertical envelopment, and logistic support'. He believed the ships could be especially valuable in small brushfire wars in the 'Afro-Asian' region, where the US Navy did not at the time have any standing forces.

The Marines liked the idea, as did others concerned with the navy's amphibious assault capability. The Bureau of Ships carried out a detailed study of the prospects for the conversion. Completed by mid-1962, it confirmed that the idea was feasible. The hangar aft would accommodate twenty helicopters and ten more could be stowed on deck. There would be room for 1800 troops, more than an *Iwo Jima* class helicopter assault carrier could embark. Fourteen LCM-6 landing craft would be carried on the side decks, providing a rough-weather landing capability. The conversion would also add sonar and an ASROC anti-submarine rocket launcher. The cost would amount to $65 million.

The commando assault conversion received some attention in the professional literature. An article in the 13 October 1962 issue of *Navy Times* outlined the conversion plan and was reprinted in the *US Naval Institute Proceedings* in February 1963, with an illustration based on a widely available commercial model kit of the *Iowa*. In spite of the attention, however, tight budgets eventually killed the idea.

It was not forgotten, however, especially by the Marines. The *New Jersey*, briefly recommissioned in 1968–69, proved that gunfire support was often more effective and accurate — and cheaper — than tactical air support, but political considerations put her back into mothballs before her planned second tour off Vietnam. In September 1972,

Colonel Robert D Heinl, USMC (ret) tried to make the recommissioning of the *Iowas* more attractive to the navy by pointing out that, with helicopter facilities in place of their after turrets, the *Iowas* would make good 'interim sea control ships'. The sea control ship (SCS) was an idea much discussed at the time; it was basically a small helicopter and V/STOL carrier for ASW and convoy protection roles, functions the CF of 1939/40 had been intended to fulfil. But, Heinl noted parenthetically, the converted *Iowa* would still be 'highly suitable' as commando ships, which was obviously what he was really after.

In 1979, an ex-air force pilot, Charles E Myers, Jr, began drumming up support for reactivating the battleships as 'interdiction assault ships' — gunfire support ships for amphibious operations. His proposal included the removal of the aft 16in turret to improve the helicopter facilities. Myers set about lobbying on behalf of his idea; at the same time, a very different mission was being considered for the ships by Admiral Thomas B Hayward, CNO. The expansion of the Soviet Navy had created a need, for the first time since the Second World War, for anti-ship warfare, rather than power projection over land; Hayward wanted a quick boost for the fleet's dwindling strength to meet this growing need. The number of carriers in commission had fallen to twelve front-line ships, and Hayward thought that the *Iowas*, armed with cruise missiles and perhaps carrying V/STOL aircraft, could substitute for carriers in low- to medium-threat environments, and supplement the carriers in high-threat conditions. Amphibious operations, and by extension the 'triphibious' gunfire support-vertical envelopment-landing craft assault hybrid conversion scheme, gradually slipped into the background; instead, the new studies focused on ways to improve the navy's surface warfare ability quickly. The *Iowas*, with their great size, high speed and tremendous 'survivability', were once

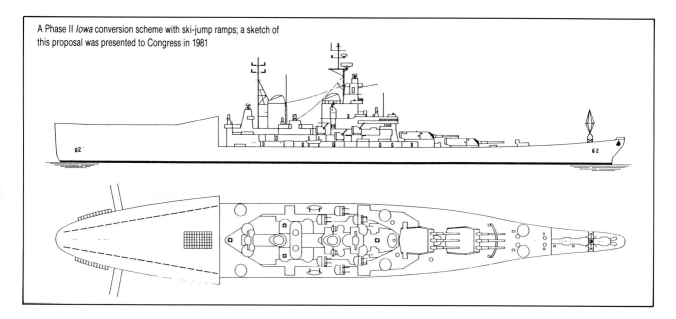

A Phase II *Iowa* conversion scheme with ski-jump ramps; a sketch of
this proposal was presented to Congress in 1981

again studied as platforms for such weaponry as
the Aegis integrated air defence system and
Harpoon anti-ship missiles. These studies
established 'Phase I' and 'Phase II' modification
programmes for the ships; Phase I would be the
initial configuration, limited to getting the ships
back in service with a minimum number of new
equipments, while the more extensive Phase II
modifications would be carried out during the
battleships' first major refits after recommissioning.

Even in Phase I, the main battery of the
reactivated *Iowas* would not be the 16in guns, but
eight newly fitted armoured box launchers for
Tomahawk cruise missiles. The Tomahawk comes
in several varieties, including an anti-ship model
and a strategic attack version for use against land
targets. Phase I also added Harpoon anti-ship
missile canisters to the battleships. The Sea
Sparrow short-range AA missile was apparently
too fragile to withstand the 16in gun blast, so the
reborn battleships' only modern anti-air weapons
are the four Vulcan-Phalanx 20mm gatling guns.

Although they could still act as shore-bombardment ships, and in fact have been used as such off
Lebanon, they were primarily seen as 'super-
cruisers', the centrepieces of Surface Action
Groups (SAGs). This outlook is apparent in the
various Phase II plans. These studies, completed
in late 1981, outlined six possible configurations;
in all, the ships' electronics and communications
equipment would be upgraded to allow them to
serve as flagships. Beyond that, there was a
considerable range in the types of modification
and their costs. The least expensive option was to

keep all three turrets; the most radical scheme
would have replaced all three with some 400
vertical missile launch tubes. The four mid-range
studies all involved the removal of the after turret
and its replacement by various combinations of
helicopter accommodation and missiles. Except
for the first scheme, all these would have reduced
the ability of the ships to provide gunfire support
for amphibious operations.

Only one of these Phase II alternatives
included a hangar and flight deck capable of
handling twelve AV-8B Harrier STOVL aircraft.
It is not clear how much design work was done for
such a reconstruction, but on 1 April 1981 the navy
did present to Congress a sketch showing the sort
of modifications involved. The forward portion of
the ship is basically unchanged, but aft is shown a
hangar structure and flight deck with ski-jump
ramps for Harriers. On the centreline at the
foreward end of the flight deck are vertical missile
launch tubes.

This sketch would seem to be the only official
illustration of what a flight-deck *Iowa* might have
looked like, but a similar scheme put forward by
the Martin Marietta Corporation was probably
the most widely illustrated of the Phase II proposals. In fact, a model showing this configuration was shown at the US Navy League
convention in April 1982 and eventually ended up
on display in the Pentagon.

The Martin Marietta scheme followed the basic
pattern of the Navy Phase II sketch. Forward, the
ship is little changed from its original reactivation
configuration. Aft, there is an 'A' shaped flight
deck 330ft by 150ft, similar to that in the navy

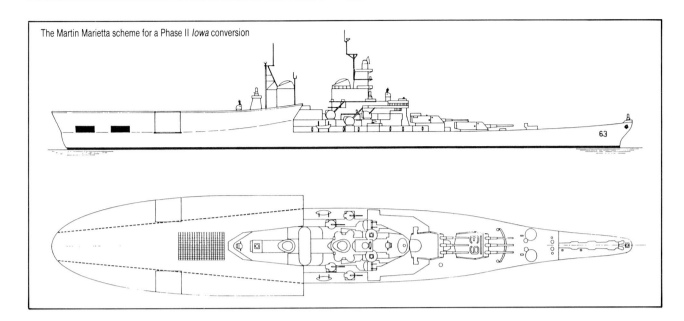

The Martin Marietta scheme for a Phase II *Iowa* conversion

sketch, but its two arms extend forward on each side of the after end of the original superstructure, giving a longer take-off run to the two ski-jump ramps. Lifts would connect the flight deck to the hangar deck. Aircraft capacity was estimated at twenty-five, a number of which would certainly have had to remain in a deck park. Interestingly, the only aviation ordnance allowed for in the proposal is 30mm ammunition and Sidewinder air-to-air missiles (AAMs); all the long-range offensive weaponry is concentrated in a 'missile farm' on the centreline of the flight deck just abaft the after superstructure. This contains 320 vertical launch tubes, apparently for Tomahawk and Harpoon SSMs, as the model has none of the guidance radars necessary for AA missiles.

There is a Vulcan-Phalanx gatling gun on each side of the superstructure and two on the centreline, one right forward in the eyes of the ship (which would have been a very wet place with any sort of a sea running) and one in place of the after main battery director. Two twin 5in/38 mounts are retained, while four vertically loading 155mm single gun mounts have been added. This unusual weapon, designed by the FMC Corporation, was designed to elevate to 90 degrees for loading; cartridges would be rammed straight up into the gun. This made for a simple mounting of reduced weight while still providing a fairly good rate of fire (10rpm).

Despite the shore-bombardment potential of the six 16in and four 155mm guns, the ship was clearly seen by its proponents as a surface combatant. The vast number of missiles — far more than any missile cruiser — and the aircraft would

be used together, the Harriers providing an over-the-horizon targeting capability for the long-range SSMs.

In addition to the Martin Marietta proposal, several unofficial conversion schemes had been inspired by the *Iowa* reactivation. In the July 1980 *Proceedings*, Howard Pulver put forward a flight-deck configuration similar to the Phase II Harrier-carrying study. Pulver replaced the after main battery turret with a 320ft by 100ft flight deck for helicopters and STOVL aircraft. This deck angled from starboard to port, presumably to allow short take-off runs by the AV-8A Harriers he saw as part of the ship's air group. Although he estimated that the hangar below the flight deck would have an area of 20,000sq ft, he did not propose a specific number of aircraft.

Other changes included new radars atop massive 'macks': combined masts and stacks. Pulver placed a Mk 26 twin-arm missile launcher forward of the remaining turrets, with two box-launchers for either Harpoon anti-ship or Standard AA missiles just below the after corners of the flight deck. Three Vulcan-Phalanx 20mm gatling guns were included, while the old 5in/38 battery was replaced by four 5in/54 lightweight gun mounts.

The one unlikely element in Pulver's scheme was the Mk 26 missile launcher on the fo'c's'le. Not only would it have been subject to heavy seas (the slender bows of the *Iowas* sometimes dig in deep and take a lot of water) and the tremendous blast overpressures from the 16in guns (a major consideration throughout the actual *Iowa* reactivation process), but the missile magazine would

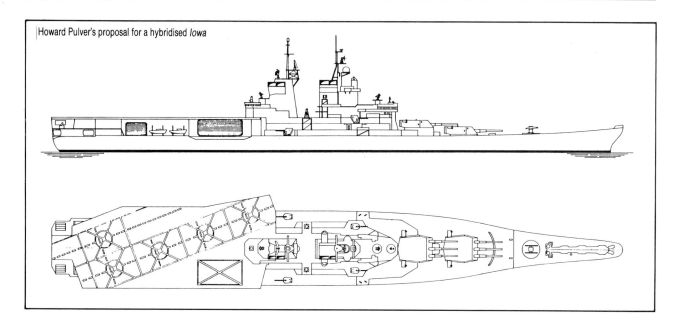

Howard Pulver's proposal for a hybridised *Iowa*

have been in a very narrow section of the hull, perhaps too narrow to accommodate a reasonable number of missiles. In placing a missile launcher so far forward, Pulver may have been guided by the 1950s missile-ship conversion studies; however in those sketches, horizontally loaded Talos missiles were projected; although the launchers were well forward, the magazines were farther aft, in a wider part of the hull. The Mk 26 launcher, on the other hand, loads vertically and consequently is directly above its magazine. In other respects, however, Pulver's proposal was fairly reasonable.

Another unofficial *Iowa* hybrid conversion was far more ambitious. It appeared in the *Proceedings* exactly one year after Pulver's scheme and was proposed by naval architect and former Second World War naval intelligence officer Gene Anderson. To a considerable degree, he followed the pattern of Pulver's ship; there was a Mk 26 launcher forward of the main battery turrets, and box launchers on each quarter, while the plan of the flight deck was very similar to the earlier proposal. Anderson, however, took things a step further, advocating the trunking of the boiler uptakes into one vast funnel, which would allow the flight deck to be extended 100ft farther forward. He also proposed installing a catapult and arresting gear, so that conventional high-performance jet fighters could operate from the ship; he believed that 'our Navy pilots are more than capable of flying on and off this converted ship in any kind of weather or visibility'. This seems doubtful, as the length of the landing deck is less than 400ft; however, Anderson did add a ski-jump launching path angled to starboard,

which would have improved STOVL operations considerably.

In addition to replacing the 5in/38s with four 5in/54s, as Pulver had, Anderson showed a light-weight 8in Mk 48 gun on each beam. This gun, which was developed specifically to improve the US Navy's shore bombardment firepower, was eventually cancelled due to its high costs. There were also to be landing craft 'hangars', like the boat hangars on *Yamato*, giving the ships another means of landing troops.

Anderson claimed *Ise* as his inspiration, having seen her just after the war, sunk in shallow water at Kure, but one must wonder if he had read Levert's *Fundamentals of Naval Warfare* at some point, for his flight deck, with its 'X' pattern, resembles that of Levert's battle-carrier. In fact, Anderson also called his *Iowa* conversion a 'battlecarrier'.

Whatever his inspiration, the cost of this sort of modernisation would have been prohibitive; the navy's waning enthusiasm for the far more modest Phase II proposals was a result of the tremendous expense entailed. In a hearing before a subcommittee of the House Armed Services Committee in December 1982, Rear Admiral Walter T Piotti, Director, Surface Warfare Division, stated that

... we have looked at all manner of schemes for increasing the aviation capability of [the *Iowas*] all the way up to and including the introduction of AV-8B's in significant numbers, the raising of the fantail to provide a below-decks hangaring capability, a ski jump takeoff ramp on board. That is very costly to the tune of about $1.3 billion, and very time consuming, estimates run up to 4 years to do it.

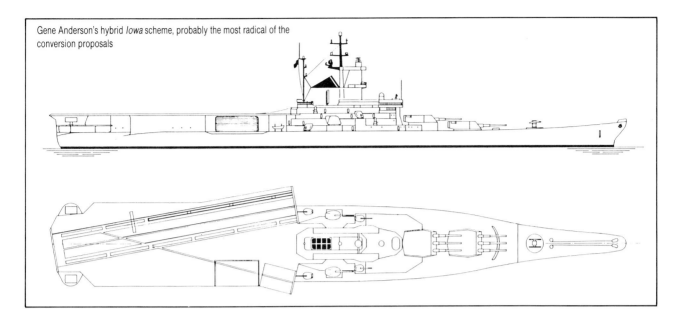

Gene Anderson's hybrid *Iowa* scheme, probably the most radical of the conversion proposals

Admiral Piotti concluded, 'I don't think we will go that route'. The issue was largely dead by 1984; Vice Admiral Robert L Walters told a Congressional committee that year that Phase II would be 'expensive and time-consuming and [would reduce] the conventional gunfire support capability unique to a battleship'.

This last factor may have played a larger role in the cancellation of Phase II than the cost of the project. Five of the six Phase II proposals had involved removing the after turret, and it is a safe assumption that the Marines opposed any reduction in the number of guns on the big ships. In spite of their 'super-cruiser' role within an SAG, the fact of the matter is that it is the big guns of the *Iowas* that are their most valuable attribute; it could be said with some justification that their use as surface combatants is just a way of keeping them busy between the relatively infrequent call for shore bombardment missions. Certainly, it is in the latter role that they have made the greater impression.

There are interesting parallels between the *Aikitsu Maru* and her army-built sisters and Admiral McCain's 'commando ship' *Iowa* conversion. Both were intended to be the central unit in amphibious operations, putting troops ashore via landing craft and supporting them with gunfire, although the 3in field guns on the Japanese ships would have been useful only during the opening stages of the assault due to their limited range. The aircraft complement had different roles in these vessels, however; in the *Aikitsu Maru*, light aircraft would have been useful only for liaison and spotting, while the commando ship's helicopters would have played an active role in putting troops ashore.

In an odd way, there is also a parallel between *Aikitsu Maru* and the various flight-deck *Iowa* schemes, for although the Japanese ship was intended to conduct amphibious landing operations she ended up as an escort carrier, while the *Iowas*, although initially seen as 'interdiction assault ships' supporting landings with their big guns, ended up being reactivated because of their ability to carry large numbers of missiles — the guns were just a bonus. *Aikitsu Maru*, designed for one job, ended up with another; the *Iowas*, ideal for one job, were reactivated for another.

Despite all the roles proposed for the *Iowas*, there seems little doubt that their big guns were the underlying rationale for their reactivation. And one suspects that, if the Marines have anything to say about it, they will keep those guns. Meanwhile, the prospect of hybrid *Iowas* diminished still further with the decision, announced in January 1990, that *Iowa* and *New Jersey* were to be decommissioned once again.

THROUGH-DECK CRUISERS

The limitations of the helicopter cruiser, noted in Chapter 14, were soon apparent to the navies operating this type of ship. Several of these navies therefore set about designing the next generation of the helicopter cruiser; these designs took advantage of the simultaneous development of STOVL aircraft. The result has been a series of hybrid or near-hybrid warships.

The first of these ships to be completed, the Soviet Navy's *Kiev*, is by any standard a hybrid. Although her design probably has its roots as far back as the early 1960s, the first knowledge the world at large had of her came on 8 January 1972, when the *Washington Post* reported that 'the latest US reconnaissance satellite photos' had revealed the construction at Nikolayev of 'either an oil super-tanker or a much more startling development: the first Soviet aircraft carrier'.

The construction of a carrier at Nikolayev was regarded as 'startling' because the Soviets had been pronouncing the aircraft carrier dead for so long. Yet this had not always been the case; carriers had been included in both prewar and postwar Soviet naval programmes. In his memoirs, Nikita Khrushchev, who emerged in the mid-1950s as Stalin's successor, admitted that carriers 'are the second most effective weapon in a modern navy (after submarines) . . . but we couldn't afford to build them. They were simply beyond our means'. But the American carriers, with their atomic bomb-carrying aircraft, still had to be countered, so Khrushchev sponsored the development of anti-ship missiles, which were capable of crippling the US carriers before they steamed within strike range of Soviet targets. These missiles could be launched from submarines, small surface ships and aircraft.

Since the Soviet Union could not build carriers, it had to be shown that such ships were not worth building. From the 1950s to the late 1960s, therefore, Soviet naval writers had only unkind things to say about the carrier; they were perhaps useful in limited, imperialist wars, the argument ran, but

were vulnerable to missile attack. One Soviet admiral described them as 'floating mortuaries'.

While the anti-carrier rhetoric was being mustered to justify the lack of Soviet carriers, a new strategic threat appeared: the ballistic missile-launching submarine. The Polaris SSBN required the development of ASW, which had long been neglected by the Soviet Navy. Because the first-generation Polaris missile had a range of only 1500nm, Soviet ASW surface ships might be able to locate and destroy the SSBNs before they could launch their missiles at inland targets. As we have seen, this line of thinking led eventually to the *Moskva* class helicopter-carrying cruisers; the increasing range of Polaris led the Soviet ASW ships farther afield in their search for the American submarines, so the helicopter cruisers were heavily armed with defensive missile systems to protect them when operating beyond the effective range of land-based Soviet aircraft.

This wider search for the ballistic missile submarines, coupled with new Soviet interests in distant parts of the world, expanded the operational horizons of the Soviet Navy. It became, for the first time, the 'oceanic' fleet Stalin had envisaged. The worldwide role of the navy was matched by a shift in the Soviet assessment of the aircraft carrier by the late 1960s; attacks were replaced with more favourable evaluations, especially of the carrier as a political tool. This revision of the official view was at least in part an ideological preparation for the coming of the first Soviet aircraft carrier.

Rumours of the construction of a new air-capable ship of some sort had circulated in the West since before *Kiev* had actually been laid down; for example, in its 1970–71 edition, *Jane's Fighting Ships* mentioned 'reports of an improved *Moskva*' under construction at Nikolayev. In an article published in the December 1970 *US Naval Institute Proceedings*, T G Martin mentioned these rumours and said, 'Perhaps more likely will be the building of a follow-on design, incorporating the lessons learned with the *Moskvas*'. He was exactly right; *Kiev* had been laid down only a few months before the article was published. However these reports were still rumours, unsubstantiated until US satellites revealed *Kiev* on the ways in late 1971.

The newspaper stories that followed on the Western discovery of the ship reveal how precise satellite intelligence has become; ten days after the *Washington Post*'s initial report on the possible Soviet carrier, the *New York Times* added

An American artist's interpretation of the Soviet *Kiev*, drawn in 1973 while the vessel was still under construction. Although details are incorrect, the general configuration was portrayed accurately

Displacement:	40,000t
Dimensions:	925ft oa (880ft wl) × 200ft (incl flight deck and sponsons)
Armament:	2 twin SA-N-3 'Goblet' missile launchers, 1 twin ASW launcher, 3 or 4 SA-N-4 launchers, twenty-eight 57mm guns, two 12-barrelled MBU ASW mortars
Aircraft:	25 VTOL, possibly 'Freehand' type; 25 'Hormone A' or 'Hind A' helicopters
Speed:	at least 30kts

that the ship under construction had 'what appear to be aircraft elevator wells and large tanks for aviation fuel'. Today, the building of a major warship cannot be kept secret, and even details of internal arrangements will be revealed to the orbiting spies as construction progresses.

Official confirmation of the Soviet carrier eventually came from Admiral Elmo Zumwalt, the CNO. In a Congressional hearing in March 1972, he stated that the ship at Nikolayev 'looks and feels like an air capable ship, aircraft carrier'. This testimony, however, was not released until August.

In early 1973, the Pentagon unveiled an artist's impression of the new Soviet ship, still more than two years from completion. The rendering showed a ship heavily armed with both missiles and guns, with a massive superstructure offset to starboard and an angled flight deck to port. A second unit was observed under construction soon after the sketch was released, and the ships were designated the 'Kuril' class by NATO. Their characteristics, as estimated at the time, are given above right.

The artist had clearly used *Moskva* as a guide for the details of superstructure and armament, and so showed both surface-to-air missile (SAM) launchers forward, whereas one is actually sited aft of the superstructure. On the whole, however, the artist had captured the general form of the ship, a convincing demonstration of the accuracy of satellite reconnaissance.

Soon Western naval publications were filled with conjecture on the role of the new ship, but despite the revelations of satellite observation, the purpose of a ship, and the process that led to its design and building, is not so easily uncovered. This uncomfortable fact must be kept in mind when discussing *Kiev* and her sisters; everything we know about Soviet expectations for these warships has been filtered through Western experience and expectations.

This point is highlighted by the one significant failure of the Western estimates to include SSMs; many Western observers assumed that *Kiev* would be an aircraft carrier on the American

The Soviet hybrid *Kiev* under way in the Mediterranean with helicopters and V/STOL aircraft on deck. The parallels between the ship and the preceding drawing are obvious (US Navy)

pattern, a power-projection ship with as many as sixty aircraft, and these aircraft would be the primary offensive weapons. But *Kiev*'s aircraft seem largely defensive; her main offensive weapons are the big carrier-killing missiles. This was a tactical doctrine alien to Western naval observers in the early 1970s, so the inclusion of powerful SSMs in *Kiev*'s armoury came as a surprise.

Such misplaced expectations persisted even after *Kiev* made her debut; her many weapons systems and comprehensive electronics suite were seen as an attempt to build a ship for independent operations, a 'self-escorting' carrier. The Soviet class designation of *Bolshoi Protivo Lodochny Kreyser* (large anti-submarine cruiser) was dismissed as an attempt to circumvent the Montreux Convention. This treaty, signed in 1936, governs the passage of warships through the Turkish Straits; although the convention does not explicitly bar the passage of aircraft carriers, it also does not specifically allow them to pass through the Dardanelles to the Mediterranean.

Other observers, however, noted that the *Kiev* class seemed a logical follow-on to the *Moskvas* not only in form but in function as well, and there is now every reason to believe that these ships really were intended to act as 'anti-submarine cruisers'.

Before examining their place in Soviet naval doctrine, however, it is necessary to describe the three ships of the *Kiev* class; much of the analysis of their role is based upon their known or estimated characteristics. All were built by the South Yard at Nikolayev; *Kiev* was laid down in September 1970, launched in December 1972 and commissioned in May 1975; *Minsk* was laid down in December 1972, launched in May 1975 and commissioned in February 1978; *Novorossiysk*, which differs from the earlier ships in some details of armament, was laid down in October 1975, launched in December 1978 and commissioned in August 1982. The particulars above right are those of *Kiev*.

A fourth ship built to the same basic design, *Baku*, also constructed at the South Yard, shows extensive changes and will be described in Chapter 18.

Virtually every writer remarks on *Kiev*'s impressive appearance. Her massive superstructure, offset to starboard but too large to be called an island, is dominated by a variety of electronic sensors and her fo'c's'le is jammed with weapons. From fore to aft, there are the two ASW mortars, the ASW missile launcher, a 76mm turret and a twin-rail SA-N-3 AA missile launcher. The big tubes for the SS-N-12 SSMs are mounted in pairs abreast the 76mm turret and SA-N-3 launcher; there are curved blast deflectors behind the after two twin-tube groups, and folding deflectors behind the forward group. A second SA-N-3 missile launcher and 76mm turret are mounted abaft the superstructure. One SA-N-4 launcher is sited on the port fo'c's'le abreast the second group of SS-N-12 tubes, while the other is mounted out-

Displacement:	32,000t standard; 37,100t full load
Dimensions:	895ft 8in oa (818ft 7in wl) × 107ft 4in wl (154ft 11in oa) × 32ft 10in
	(273m oa [249.5m wl] × 32.7m wl [47.2m oa] × 10m)
Flight deck:	620ft 1in × 67ft 11in (189m × 20.7m)
Machinery:	8 boilers, 4 sets geared turbines; 200,000shp = 32kts. 13,500nm at 18kts; 4,000nm at 31kts
Armament:	8 SS-N-12 'Sandbox' SSM launchers; 16 reloads; 2 twin SA-N-3 'Goblet' SAM launchers (72 missiles); 2 twin SA-N-4 SAM launchers (40 missiles); 1 twin SUW-N-1 ASW missile launcher; 2 RBU 6000 12-tube ASW mortars; four 76mm guns (2 × 2); eight 30mm six-barrelled gatling guns; ten 21in (533mm) TT (2 × 5)
Aircraft:	12 'Forger A' (Yak 36) V/STOL; 1 'Forger B' (two-seat trainer); 19 'Hormone A' helicopters; 2 'Hormone B' (SSM targeting) helicopters (these are being replaced by 'Helix-A' [Ka-27] helicopters)
Sensors:	Radars: 1 Top Sail air search; 1 Top Steer air/surface search; 1 Don Kay navigation; 1 Trap Door SS-N-12 fire control; 2 Head Light C SA-N-3 fire control; 2 Pop Group SA-N-4 fire control; 2 Owl Screech 76mm fire control; 4 Bass Tilt 30mm fire control
	Sonars: hull mounted and variable-depth towed sonars are installed
	Extensive ECM gear also fitted
Complement:	approx 1200

board of the after end of the superstructure. These launchers, usually covered by circular hatches, pop up to fire their short-range AA missiles. *Novorossiysk* has two SA-N-9 sextuple verticle missile launchers in place of the SA-N-4s. The 30mm gatling guns are mounted in pairs, one pair sponsored off on the port side just forward of the flight deck, another pair at the forward end of the island, and a pair on each quarter. The quintuple torpedo tubes are mounted in recesses in the hull sides just forward of amidships.

The flight deck is angled 4.5 degrees to port, and portions of it are covered with tiles to protect it against the blast of the jets during take-offs and landings. The extent of the hangar is uncertain, and one source states that there are two hangar decks, one for helicopters and one for STOVLs. Whether there are two hangar decks or one, the freeboard is relatively low, which rules out deck-edge lifts, given the rough northern waters that are the main operational areas of these ships; instead, there are two inboard lifts, one abreast the island and the second, half as wide, aft of it.

It was initially believed that the ship would carry the Yak 'Freehand' VTOL aircraft demonstrated at the Domodedovo air show in 1967, but the *Kiev* emerged with a more advanced aircraft, the Yak-38, given the NATO code name 'Forger'. This aircraft uses bent-elbow type nozzles to direct the thrust of the main engine; for landings and take-offs, the 17,985lb st main engine is supple-

mented by two 7875lb st lift engines just behind the cockpit. The small shoulder-mounted wings fold at mid-span and have four external pylons on the non-folding portion. The 'Forger' is just barely supersonic at 36,000ft, and has a range of about 200nm carrying AAMs or ASMs.

Overall, the 'Forger' is a less capable aircraft than the British Sea Harrier; for example, it could at first take off only vertically. The 'Forger''s three engines make short take-offs difficult, since the thrusts must be carefully balanced during the operation. Short take-off runs are now the usual procedure but require some form of automatic control system, whereas the Harrier's rolling take-off is very simple and manually controlled. The 'Forger' has a shorter range and can carry fewer weapons than the Harrier.

Since *Kiev* entered service in 1975 ballistic missile ranges have increased from 2500nm to more than 4000nm, and the new US Trident 2, intended for service throughout the 1990s, has a range of 6000nm. It seems unlikely that any ASW force could locate submarines that can hit their targets from almost anywhere in the world. But this has not invalidated the *Kiev*'s anti-submarine capabilities; there are strong reasons to believe that her role is now '*pro*-submarine' ASW. The ballistic submarine missile force is one of the cornerstones of the Soviet Union's strategic defences, and the *Kievs* can play a vital role in protecting these strategic assets against NATO air, surface and submarine ASW forces. Early Soviet SSBNs, with relatively short-range missiles, faced a difficult challenge in reaching their launch stations; to reach the open seas, they had to funnel through narrow channels, such as the Greenland-Iceland-United Kingdom (GIUK) gap. These narrow gaps therefore became the front line of the Western anti-ballistic submarine defences, with aircraft, attack submarines, surface ASW forces and ocean-bed surveillance devices guarding them. These were the 'choke points' where Soviet submarines could be trapped.

Admiral Sergei Gorshkov, head of the Soviet Navy from 1956 until his death in 1988, saw a clear parallel between the position of his submarine force and the German U-boats during the Second World War. He wrote disapprovingly of the lack of support the U-boats had received from the surface fleet and Luftwaffe; many of the potentially war-winning submarines were in consequence lost in travelling to their area of operations or while returning home. Guided by this insight, Gorshkov developed the pro-submarine doctrine; at first, this meant using surface ships and aircraft to help the submarines get past the Western ASW forces, but this has been modified by the increasing range of submarine-launched ballistic missiles. The Soviet SSBNs now can hit targets in the United States while in port; operating in waters close to the USSR — the so-called sanctuaries — they can be protected by other forces. The narrow passages, once a trap, have become a barrier through which Western attack submarines would have to pass to reach the Soviet SSBNs.

Kiev fits into this scheme of barrier defence in several ways. Her anti-submarine helicopters and weapons can help locate and destroy Western hunter-killer submarines attempting to infiltrate the sanctuary; her long-range SSMs and her STOVL aircraft can strike at surface ASW forces, and her area-defence AA missiles and aircraft can be used against ASW patrol aircraft. Her extensive command and control facilities make her a suitable flagship for the coordination of strikes by sea-based and land-based forces.

Gorshkov may well have gained political approval for the *Kiev* class as ballistic missile submarine sanctuary defenders; he was, however, well aware of the political value of a navy in peacetime, and the *Kievs*, with their impressive appearance, are well equipped to play a political role. And it is perhaps no coincidence that the Soviets developed an interest in amphibious warfare at about the same time as they undertook the construction of aviation ships; *Kiev* and her sisters could be used to cover landing operations, the sort of power-projection role US carriers have often assumed since the end of the Second World War. They could also be used for anti-ship and sea-control missions; although their Yak-38 aircraft would be of limited effectiveness in both power-projection and sea strike missions, the next generation of aircraft will almost certainly be more capable.

While the Soviet Navy was gradually developing its helicopter/VTOL anti-submarine cruiser, the Royal Navy was following a parallel path. HMS *Invincible*, the ship that emerged from this long evolution, is not as thoroughgoing a hybrid as *Kiev*, but she has had a tremendous influence on Western concepts of air-capable vessels.

Her origins can be traced to the late 1950s, when Staff Requirements were drawn up for an ASW escort helicopter carrier. It was seen as an ASW command and escort ship, carrying helicopters and directing their operations; it would also be able to act as a commando carrier for helicopter assault tasks. Such a ship would be large enough to warrant substantial defensive armament: Seaslug area-defence AA missiles.

One possible configuration for a helicopter cruiser was that of *Jeanne d'Arc*: a conventional centreline superstructure with a helicopter deck aft. A 1960 sketch was typical of a series of designs along this line; it called for a ship of 5940 tons deep displacement, 489ft long overall and capable of 26 knots. There would have been a Seaslug SAM launcher forward and two quadruple Seacat short-range SAM launchers. It would have carried eight helicopters, with a hangar below the flight deck.

Another possibility was a vessel akin to fixed-wing carriers: island superstructure and fore-to-aft flight deck. By 1961 the island-type seemed the better ship, able to operate more helicopters, and an 11,500 ton, 603ft long escort cruiser was sketched, with nine Sea King ASW helicopters operating from a flight deck that extended to the bow. A Seaslug launcher was located aft below flight-deck level, and a twin 4.5in gun turret was mounted forward of the island. A two-shaft steam plant would have driven it at 26 knots.

These projects were never more than sketches; the navy probably did not want to propose a small carrier-like ship while trying to gain political support for the CVA-01 programme, which dominated the plans and hopes of the Royal Navy in the first half the 1960s. This vessel was to be a 50,000 ton flight-deck carrier operating high-performance jets; escort cruisers would keep its flight deck clear of bothersome ASW helicopters. But CVA-01 was cancelled in early 1966 after an acrimonious debate with the RAF; it was expensive, and the political climate was one of retrenchment and cutbacks. The traditional 'East of Suez' role of the Royal Navy was to be reduced and eventually abandoned; in future, the Admiralty was to concentrate on operations in the eastern Atlantic in combination with other NATO navies. The existing carrier force was allowed to run down, the ships retired one by one, and no new carriers were to be built.

However, the ASW helicopter cruiser still had a place in Royal Navy planning even without the big carrier it was supposed to escort. It could escort American carriers in any NATO war, and it would be valuable in a limited war in which trade protection was necessary; with the RN's carriers

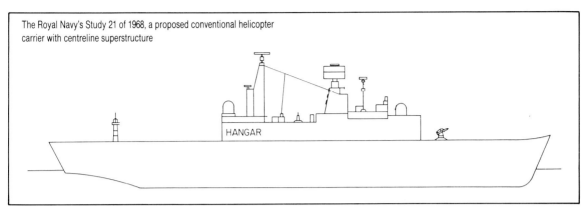

The Royal Navy's Study 21 of 1968, a proposed conventional helicopter carrier with centreline superstructure

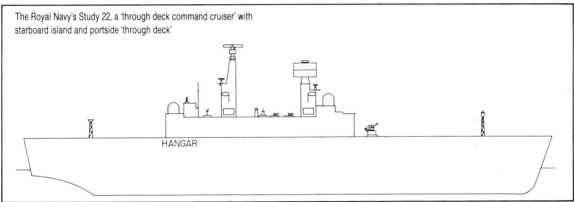

The Royal Navy's Study 22, a 'through deck command cruiser' with starboard island and portside 'through deck'

disappearing, large ships with adequate communications and staff facilities would be needed for fleet command. So the conversion of the *Tiger* class cruisers into helicopter cruisers, as described in Chapter 14, went ahead, while government approval was granted for design studies of a purpose-built helicopter cruiser in 1967. Again, the two helicopter-cruiser configurations were considered. The more conventional cruiser looked less like a carrier and so might not arouse those opposed to any carrier schemes, but the ship with a 'through deck', a euphemism for the forbidden flight deck, could operate Harriers more effectively, allowing the aircraft a short take-off run, increasing their payload. Sir Michael Le Fanu, who became First Sea Lord in 1968, pushed for the through-deck design because of this greater potential.

However, a conventional cruiser was sketched; designated Study 21, it was a 12,500 ton ship with a centreline superstructure and a Sea Dart AA missile launcher forward. The flight deck was aft, and there was a hangar for six Sea King helicopters in the after part of the superstructure. Study 22 was a 17,500 ton 'Through Deck Command Cruiser' with an island superstructure to starboard and the 'through deck' to port. This design also featured a Sea Dart launcher forward

of the island. The hangar would have been in the hull below the flight deck and nine Sea Kings would have been carried.

Study 22 became Study 23, an 18,750 ton through-deck ship. The configuration was justified on the basis of increased helicopter complement, and the design was completed toward the end of 1970. Displacement had grown to 19,500 tons. In spite of opposition from the RAF, the first ship of a three-ship class was ordered in April 1973; she was christened *Invincible*, a name last used for a battlecruiser — even here, the navy seemed to be avoiding any hint that the new ship might in any way be a carrier. Her characteristics as built are given below.

Displacement:	16,000t standard; 19,500t full load
Dimensions:	632ft wl; 677ft oa × 90ft wl; 104ft 6in flight deck × 26ft deep
Flight deck:	550ft × 44ft 4in
Machinery:	4 Rolls-Royce Olympus gas turbines, 2 shafts, 112,000shp max, 94,000shp sustained = 28kts. 5000nm at 18kts
Armament:	1 twin Sea Dart SAM launcher
Aircraft:	5 Sea Harrier STOVL, 9 Sea King helicopters
Sensors:	Radars: Type 1022 air search; Type 992R surface search; 2 Type 909 fire control; 2 Type 1006 navigation
	Sonar: Type 2016
Complement:	557 + 318 air group

HMS *Invincible* at Portsmouth in February 1989, soon after the modernisation described in the text (*Courtesy of Rob Cabo*)

Invincible (originally CAH 01, now R 05) was laid down by Vickers at Barrow-in-Furness on 20 July 1973, launched 3 May 1977, and commissioned on 11 July 1980. Her construction had been continually delayed by labour disputes and changes in the design, including a 1976 decision to make possible the embarkation of a Royal Marine Commando of 960 men. *Illustrious* (R 06, ex-CAH 02) was laid down by Swan Hunter, Wallsend, on 7 October 1976, launched on 1 December 1978 and completed on 20 June 1982; *Ark Royal* (R 07, ex-CAH 03) was laid down on 14 December 1978, launched on 2 June 1981 and completed on 1 November 1985; she was also built by Swan Hunter.

Invincible is the first two-funnelled British carrier since *Eagle* of 1923; this is just one result of the choice of machinery. *Invincible* has four Olympus TM3b gas turbines; two are coupled to each shaft. While the gas turbines halve the engineering staff compared with a steam-driven ship of comparable power, they require large air intakes and uptakes, reducing the space available for the hangar, which has wide sections fore and aft but a narrow section abreast the uptakes.

'Upkeep by Exchange' (U × E) also affected the design. This system cuts down on shipboard maintenance by providing for the replacement rather than repair of equipment; for example, *Invincible* normally carries two spare Olympus turbines. This system requires large storage space for such equipment and clear routes for its removal.

As a result of gas turbines, U × E and modern standards of accommodation, *Invincible* is a voluminous ship for her relatively small displacement, which makes for a shallow draught and a high-sided hull; add to this the large island and it is easy to see why *Invincible*'s first captain described her as 'a handful' in confined waters on a windy day. He was otherwise well satisfied with her handling, however; she can turn 180 degrees in 800 yards at 28 knots thanks to her twin rudders, and two sets of fin stabilisers make her a steady ship. She is also a dry ship due to her considerable freeboard.

Invincible and her sisters are equipped to act as fleet flagships, with extensive communications gear, medical facilities, etc. There is also an admiral's bridge, below the navigation bridge and behind the forward Type 909 radome, a position from which the admiral 'cannot actually see enough to interfere with the running of the ship', according to one source.

As built, the ship's only weapon was the GWS 30 Mod. 2 Sea Dart AA missile launcher. Different reference books credit the ship with a capacity of either thirty-six or twenty-two missiles. The original design also featured four Exocet SSM launchers to starboard of the Sea Dart. These were never fitted, being deleted from the design while *Invincible* was under construction.

The Sea Dart launcher has been described as 'awkwardly located', and fitting it in certainly must have presented the designers with some difficulties. In the original Study 22 design, the launcher had been located directly forward of the island, presumably offset to starboard like the island itself. In the final design it was moved forward to the fo'c's'le. It is possible that the missile magazine was squeezed out of its original location by other equipment, or that it cut into the already scarce hangar space. Another consideration was certainly the blast of the rocket booster; early published sketches showed no blast shield behind the launcher, but the completed ship has an elaborate blast shield to protect aircraft on deck.

The flight deck is 550ft long and the take-off runway is 40ft wide; it is angled about 0.5 degree to port. There are two lifts, each 32ft by 55ft, large enough for the next generation of ASW helicopters and STOVL aircraft. The ski-jump ramp was devised while *Invincible* was under construction, and she was fitted with a 7 degree ramp; a greater angle would have given better Harrier performance but it also would have blocked the Sea Dart launcher's field of fire to port at low angles.

The question of whether the *Invincibles* would actually operate Harriers was settled by the time the ski-jump was added. In 1975 orders were placed for twenty-four FRS (Fighter/ Reconnaissance/Strike) Mk 1 Sea Harriers. Development of this navalised Harrier had begun in 1973; changes from the RAF Harriers included a new nose to house a Blue Fox radar and a raised cockpit with bubble canopy that gave the pilot a much better view aft and down. The space under the cockpit was used for some of the electronic gear demanded by naval operations. The result was a handsome aircraft, 47ft 7in long, with a wingspan of 25ft 3in. The outrigger landing gear arrangement means that folding wings cannot be fitted, but the nose folds to port for storage, reducing the aircraft's length by about 5ft. Maximum speed is in excess of 640 knots; radius of action varies with mission and load, from 450nm on reconnaissance missions to 280nm in the strike role.

On 2 April 1982 2000 Argentine troops landed at Port Stanley in the Falkland Islands, quickly overwhelming the eighty-four-man Royal Marine garrison. Three days later *Invincible* left Portsmouth with the light carrier *Hermes* and twenty-eight other warships. *Hermes* had recently been fitted with a 12 degree ski-jump for Sea Harrier operations; intended to carry five Sea Harriers, she sailed from Britain with twelve aboard, while *Invincible* had eight. Eight more Sea Harriers and ten RAF Harriers would join the

task force later, for a total of thirty-eight; of these, six Sea Harriers and three RAF Harriers would be lost during the campaign. None was lost in aerial combat, while Sea Harriers destroyed twenty-three enemy aircraft in the air and five on the ground. The Harriers proved extremely manoeuvrable in combat thanks to VIFFing — Vectoring In Forward Flight — using the rotating nozzles to reduce turn radius or decelerate suddenly. They also had an outstanding record for availability, *Invincible*'s Sea Harriers flying 99.97 per cent of their assigned sorties.

Although *Hermes* was the task force flagship, *Invincible*, with her up-to-date communications and control equipment, directed fighter cover and air defence throughout the campaign. Despite her small size, she was able to operate her aircraft almost continuously in the South Atlantic's severe weather conditions. She operated as many as ten Sea Harriers, twice her designed complement.

Invincible was not relieved until after the Argentine surrender. Her newly completed sister, HMS *Illustrious*, arrived in the South Atlantic on 27 August, and *Invincible* was finally able to shape a course for home. She was one of the last ships of the original task force to return to Britain.

Illustrious had been rushed to completion a year ahead of schedule, but arrived too late to see action in the war. She had two American Vulcan/ Phalanx close-in weapon systems (CIWS) for last-ditch defence against anti-ship missiles by the time she arrived in the South Atlantic, one on the starboard quarter of the flight deck and the other forward near the Sea Dart launcher.

Ark Royal completed with more radical changes. Her 12 degree ski-jump ramp blocks the Sea Dart launcher on some bearings, confirming that the Sea Harriers are the carrier's main AA weapon. She was fitted with three CIWS, one in the extreme bow, one in a sponson on the port quarter and another on the starboard side of the island. She carries eight Sea Harriers, nine ASW Sea Kings, and three Sea Kings equipped with Airborne Early Warning (AEW) radar, the need for which was demonstrated during the Falklands campaign. The other ships are being brought up to the same standard during their long refit and reserve periods; only two of them are operational at any one time. *Invincible* paid off for modernisation in April 1986 and emerged in January 1989 with the 12 degree ski-jump, new sonar, a new search radar and her Sea Harrier capacity

Two views of HMS *Ark Royal*, which was completed with changes from the first two vessels of the class (*Courtesy of Rob Cabo*)

increased to nine. She received the Dutch Goalkeeper anti-missile 30mm gatling gun in place of the Vulcan/Phalanx. These changes added about 250 tons to her displacement. Long-range plans also call for the addition of lightweight Seawolf missiles, which proved invaluable during the Falklands campaign.

★   ★   ★

It was perhaps inevitable that someone would try to interpret the term 'through-deck cruiser' in a literal sense. In the January 1970 issue of the British *Marine News*, journal of the World Ship

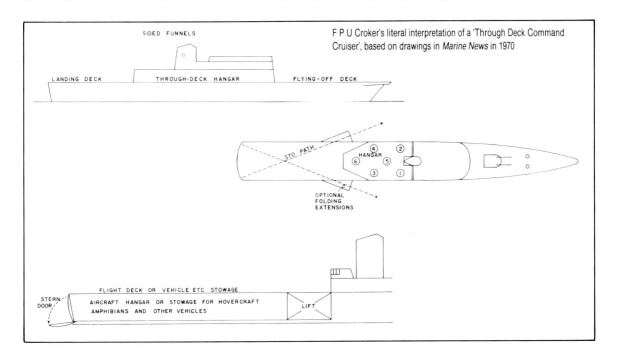

SIDED FUNNELS

F P U Croker's literal interpretation of a 'Through Deck Command Cruiser', based on drawings in *Marine News* in 1970

LANDING DECK — THROUGH-DECK HANGAR — FLYING-OFF DECK

STO PATH

HANGAR

OPTIONAL FOLDING EXTENSIONS

FLIGHT DECK OR VEHICLE ETC STOWAGE

STERN DOOR

AIRCRAFT HANGAR OR STOWAGE FOR HOVERCRAFT AMPHIBIANS AND OTHER VEHICLES

LIFT

Society, F P U Croker made just such an attempt; the results form an interesting footnote to *Invincible*'s design as well as forming an object lesson in the dangers of taking a political euphemism seriously.

'Details of the through-deck have not been published', Croker said, 'but the name implies some kind of hangar with doors fore and aft, leading to a flying-off deck on the focsle and a landing pad on the quarter deck'. Croker illustrated this intriguing interpretation of the term with a ship that has a superstructure amidships with a hangar running its length. Sided funnels are shown, so that the uptakes would not interfere with the free passage of aircraft from the landing deck aft to the flying-off deck forward.

This hangar arrangement would present an interesting operational problem: aircraft stowed in the hangar for maintenance or repair would certainly interfere with the fore-to-aft passage of other aircraft, unless the ship's beam was so great that a clear passage could be kept free at all times.

Croker followed this interpretation — fascinating but not necessarily a hybrid — with a definite hybrid: a centreline superstructure, flight-deck aft, guns-forward arrangement similar to *Blake* and other helicopter cruisers. He proposed an unusual style of flight operations, however: in order to garner the advantages of the Harrier's short take-off performance, he suggested an X-patterned take-off run. Aircraft would start at the fantail and taxi diagonally across the deck, launching off folding extensions that gave them a slightly longer run. He chose an armament of two 6in guns because 'long range missiles of the "Sea Dart" variety would be superfluous' because of the aircraft; he did not specify what purpose the guns would serve.

A third possible configuration was proposed, a ship with a hangar beneath an aft flight deck, as in *Jeanne d'Arc* and *Vittorio Veneto*. However, Croker added a stern door, as on the amphibious assault ships *Fearless* and *Intrepid*. This would allow the ships to carry 'hovercraft amphibians or other vehicles' as well as or in place of aircraft — similar to the Japanese Army's *Kumano Maru* (see Chapter 15).

Croker's analysis of the possibilities of naval V/STOL aircraft was perceptive, and each line of development he suggested has appeared in subsequent hybrid designs, even his 'through-deck' (or 'through-hangar') ship, a literal interpretation of a deliberately misleading designation.

★ ★ ★

The term 'through-deck cruiser' has proved politically useful for at least one other navy besides that of Britain. The Italian Navy's *Giuseppe Garibaldi* was often so described during the long debates over her construction; legislation dating from Mussolini's day forbade the operation of fixed-wing aircraft by the navy, and the Italian Air Force saw in the navy's plans for a helicopter carrier with a continuous flight deck the thin end of the fixed-wing wedge. Air force suspicions may have been heightened by the fact that the new design called for a ski-jump bow (allegedly for improved sea-keeping). The ship was therefore often described by its proponents as a through-deck cruiser, able to operate more helicopters more efficiently than the *Dorias* or *Vittorio Veneto*. It was argued that the ability to operate STOVL aircraft such as the Harrier was just a bonus. In the end, the navy's carefully composed arguments and neutral terminology seem to have paid off, first in getting the ship authorised, and finally in obtaining the political green light for acquiring Harriers, which was finally granted in late 1988.

The design of *Giuseppe Garibaldi* was finalised in 1980; she was laid down in March 1981 and commissioned on 9 August 1987. Her characteristics as completed are given below.

Displacement:	10,000t standard, 13,850t full load
Dimensions:	590ft 7in oa × 109ft 7in × 22ft
	(180m oa × 33.4m × 6.7m)
Flight deck:	570ft 11in × 99ft 9in (174m × 30.4m)
Machinery:	4 gas turbines, 2 shafts; 80,000shp = 30kts. 7000nm at 20kts
Armament:	4 OTO Melara/Matra Teseo Otomat SSM launchers; 2 Albatros octuple SAM launchers; six 40mm/70 (3 × 2); six 12.75in (324mm) ASW TT
Aircraft:	16 Sea King helicopters
Sensors:	Radars: 1 SPS 52C long-range air search; 1 SPS 768 air search; 1 SPS 774 air/surface search; 1 SPS 702 surface search/target indication; 1 SPN 728 air control; 1 SPN 703 navigation; 2 RTN 30X Albatros fire control; 3 RTN 20X 40mm fire control
	Sonar: 1 DE 1164 bow-mounted
Complement:	550 + 230 aviation personnel

Garibaldi carries a fairly substantial battery, and the four Otomat missiles have a range of 100nm. She therefore falls into a grey area, not quite a hybrid but more heavily armed than a conventional carrier. She could in many ways be considered a very capable escort carrier, a logical extension of the design rationale of her helicopter-cruiser predecessors.

There can be no question that *Kiev* and her sisters are hybrids, and they have been referred to as such by at least one writer. They are capable of performing a variety of roles, including some for which they may not have originally been intended. One that comes to mind is that originally suggested by some Western analysts: independent operations in low- to medium-threat situations, the sort of role suggested for the cancelled Harrier-carrying *Iowa* Phase II conversion. The *Kievs'* aircraft, missiles and guns give them a layered defence against air attacks, while their SS-N-12 SSMs have a 1000kg (2200lb) warhead capable of seriously damaging

any ship in existence. Another role suggests itself: providing ASW escort for the next generation of Soviet carriers, just as *Invincible* was originally intended to do. Given aircraft with higher performance, they could also be used to intercept US bombers carrying cruise missiles before they get close enough to the USSR to launch.

The nomenclature of the entire class has evolved in an instructive fashion; *Kiev* started out as a 'large anti-submarine cruiser' but in 1978 she became a *takticheskoye avionosnyy kreyser* — Tactical Aircraft-Carrying Cruiser — and some Soviet senior officers have simply called the *Kievs* 'aircraft carriers'.

The *Invincibles* are more difficult to categorise. Had they been completed with Exocet launchers, a good case could be made for classifying them as hybrids. In addition to their ASW and AA roles, they would have carried an anti-ship missile, a missile whose use would have required the ship to close to within 20nm of the enemy. The dichotomy of carrying both long-range strike aircraft and a short-range surface weapon goes back to the very first hybrid designs; although the Exocets' bolt-on canisters have nothing like the influence of heavy artillery on the ship's design, they resemble guns in that their use involves hazarding the ship to enemy fire. No responsible commander would take such a risk while he still had Sea Harriers at his disposal. Moreover, the likelihood of enemy surface forces surprising the ship at short range — once one of the prime justifications for heavy low-angle batteries on carriers — is, given modern sensors, very remote. The removal of the Exocets therefore implies no real reduction in the ship's striking power. On the other hand, both the Sea Dart and the Exocet positions deprived the ships of some aviation capacity. Although the Exocets were air-brushed out of the official sketches around 1975, the recess in the parking area for them is still there.

As completed, the ships are essentially carriers with heavy defensive batteries. The deletion of the Exocets — definitely a cruiser item — was just one of several steps that have moved the *Invincibles* more and more toward the carrier end of the spectrum. The decision to increase the ski-jump ramp angle in the ships, in spite of the reduction in Sea Dart effectiveness this entails, is another step in this process; it would not be surprising if the Sea Dart launchers were one day removed from the ships entirely.

The designation of these ships, like that of the *Kiev* class, has evolved away from the 'cruiser' end of the scale. Authorised as 'Through Deck Command Cruisers' (TDCCs), they became known next as CAHs, generally construed as 'Cruisers Assault Helicopter' (even though the commando assault role was very definitely a secondary one), but sometimes taken to stand for 'Cruisers, Heavy, Helicopter carrying'. The 'C' seems to have become associated in people's minds with 'carrier', however, and since 1980 they have been classed as 'ASW Aircraft Carriers'.

Giuseppe Garibaldi, last of the 'through-deck cruisers' to go to sea, is the least hybrid-like of the group. She is to all appearances a conventional aircraft carrier, with a flight deck extending from bow to stern. Her missile battery, although substantial, is inconspicuously located below the flight deck aft, almost an afterthought to the design. It exercises nothing like the influence of *Kiev*'s massive missile tubes or *Invincible*'s Sea Dart launcher on the ship's design, clearly demonstrating the potential of 'bolt-on' missile canisters.

The importance of these ships, especially *Invincible* and *Kiev*, for the prospects of modern hybrid ships lies in the influence they have had on designers around the world. The term 'through-deck cruiser', originally a politically inspired circumlocution, enjoyed something of a vogue in naval circles in the mid-1970s, and the basic pattern of *Kiev* and *Invincible* has been repeated in a number of other designs that will be examined in our final chapter.

CHAPTER 17

SUB AQUAE AD ASTRA

In 1925 the naval writer and analyst Hector C Bywater described an imaginary US-Japanese conflict in his book *The Great Pacific War*. In it he introduced a craft that would become a standard bugaboo in later American war-scare fiction: the monster Japanese submarine. Bywater envisaged giants of 7000 tons, heavily armoured for surface action, with a range of 24,000 miles and carrying two 8in guns (which, oddly enough, was the armament fitted to the French submarine *Surcouf*, completed in 1933).

Japan did not fulfil Bywater's prophecy for two decades, and when it did the result was not a monster submarine-cruiser, but a new type of hybrid, the submarine aircraft carrier.

The idea of mating craft that operated under and over the sea dated from the First World War, when both Germany and Britain tested the combination, albeit unsuccessfully. Later, aircraft-carrying submarines were experimented with, designed or planned by the navies of Britain, the

Italy's *Giuseppe Garibaldi* at La Spezia in August 1987, soon after her commissioning (*Courtesy of Rob Cabo*)

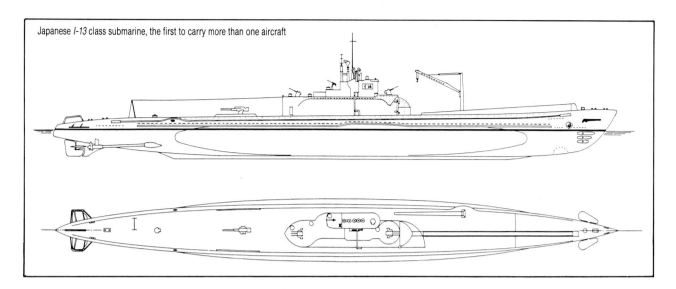

Japanese *I-13* class submarine, the first to carry more than one aircraft

United States, France, Germany, Italy, Poland and the Soviet Union. Almost all eventually gave the concept up. Not so Japan; from 1927 until the very end of the real Pacific war, the IJN clung to the idea tenaciously, operating thirty-eight aircraft-carrying submarines altogether (although some were later stripped of aircraft equipment, usually to accommodate *kaiten* suicide torpedoes).

The great majority of these craft, however, cannot be considered hybrids; their aircraft, like those of cruisers, were intended simply to extend scouting range. Submarine aircraft were employed extensively during the Pacific war, making scouting flights over Pearl Harbor, the US west coast, many Pacific islands, major cities of Australia and New Zealand, Diego Suarez and the African coast. These seaplane scouts were almost always undetected and often gleaned useful information, although their success was frequently marred, in Western eyes at least, by being abandoned by their parent submarine after their report had been received. This was often due to the difficulty of arranging a successful rendezvous after the aircraft had completed its mission. In August 1942, in the only heavier-than-air attack ever mounted against the North American mainland, a seaplane from submarine *I-25* twice dropped incendiary bombs on Oregon, hoping to kindle forest fires.

The first three Japanese submarines constructed with aircraft facilities carried a dismantled float biplane in two parallel, cylindrical hangars aft of the conning tower. The second two were also given aft-launching catapults. This arrangement had several disadvantages: the cylinders, although streamlined, made the boats handle more clumsily underwater, and the assembly of the aircraft on deck took considerable time, requiring dangerously long stays on the surface. The submarines with catapults had to sail backwards to generate wind-over-deck for launch.

These defects were corrected in the large submarines authorised under the Third and Fourth Replenishment Programmes of 1937 and 1939. The craft were divided into three categories: Type A, more or less flotilla leaders, with accommodation and communications equipment for the command of groups of submarines; Type B, patrol; and Type C, attack. The first two types carried a single aircraft housed in a long, low hangar forward of the conning tower and faired into it, opening to a catapult nearly flush with the forward deck casing and stretching almost to the bow. The catapult placement necessitated mounting the deck gun aft of the conning tower (an arrangement also adopted in US submarines for an entirely different reason). In these vessels the earlier biplanes were replaced by a new aircraft, the Yokosuka E14Y1 (Allied code name Glen), a light (340hp) two-place twin-float low-wing monoplane, ingeniously designed for rapid folding and unfolding.

The first submarine that can be considered a hybrid was the *I-13*, laid down in February 1943 as the second unit of the A2 type of the A category. During construction she was redesigned at the behest of Yamamoto to carry two aircraft instead of one. Six sisters were subsequently ordered.

The redesign added about 600 tons to the displacement and altered the superstructure considerably. The forward catapult was retained, but the hangar was placed roughly amidships, offset

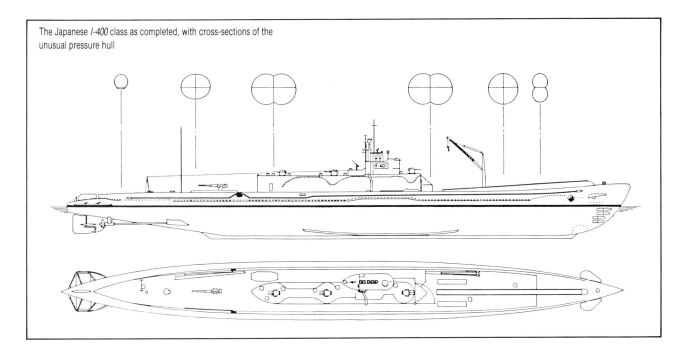

The Japanese *I-400* class as completed, with cross-sections of the unusual pressure hull

to starboard; it was faired into the conning tower, which was offset to port. Because the hangar was partly under the conning tower, it did not have to be extended forward, which would have required lengthening the hull; in fact, overall length was unchanged from that of the A2 type, although beam and draught were somewhat increased. Because of the danger of interception by enemy aircraft while on the surface launching or recovering the seaplanes, a substantial light AA armament was installed.

Particulars of the AM type, as it was designated after the redesign, were as follows.

Displacement: 3603t surface, 4762t submerged
Dimensions: 372ft 9in oa × 38ft 6in × 19ft 4in
Machinery: 2 diesels, 4400bhp; electric motors, 600hp; 2 shafts =
               16.75kts surface, 5.5kts submerged. 21,000nm at 16kts
               surface; 90nm at 3kts submerged; endurance of 90 days
Armament: six 21in TT (bow), 12 torpedoes; one 5.5in, seven 25mm
               AA (2 × 3, 1 × 1)
Complement: 108

Maximum diving depth was nominally 330ft.

Only two of the class were completed, *I-13* on 16 December 1944 and *I-14* on 14 March 1945. Construction of *I-1* and *I-15* ceased at an advanced stage in March 1945 and the remaining three units were cancelled before being laid down.

The AM vessels were intended to operate in the scouting line, their aircraft supplementing or supplanting those of the cruisers. By the time of their completion this role had been completely invalidated. Consequently, the two units completed were given a more offensive part to play,

acting in concert with other submersible hybrids, the giant *I-400* class, the largest and longest-ranged submarines ever built until the nuclear-powered American and Soviet monsters of recent years.

This class, designated STo, an abbreviation of *sen-toku* (special submarine), was designed to combine the functions of the A, B and C types in one vessel. Like the AMs, they were ordered into being by Yamamoto, against the advice of some staff officers who had reached the conclusion that the big submarines, by now a Japanese speciality, were too awkward in underwater handling and too easy to detect. But the admiral's order could not be gainsaid, and eighteen of the type were authorised under the Modified Fifth War Replenishment Programme of 1942. All but five, however, were cancelled before laying down and only three were completed.

The original STo design called for a craft displacing 4550 tons on the surface and carrying two aircraft. This was altered to provide for three aircraft, resulting in an increase in displacement of about 700 tons, enlargement of the hangar, and, for greater surface stability, a wider beam in relation to length.

The ingenuity of the design began with the hull. The forward section was given a vertical figure-8 configuration, housing torpedo rooms on two levels. As they ran aft, the two cylinders merged into a single cylinder; the pressure hull then became a horizontal figure 8, likened by several writers to the form of a pair of eyeglasses, with a

Submarines *I-400* (centre) and *I-14* (foreground) in Japanese waters soon after the end of the Second World War. They are alongside US submarine tender *Proteus*, to which *I-14* surrendered at sea (*Naval Imaging Command*)

longitudinal bulkhead between the two partial cylinders.

Topside, the superstructure followed the AM pattern, with a 115ft long hangar offset to starboard of and faired into an extremely large conning tower. Still farther to starboard ran what might be called a sub-hangar, a tubular space housing the seaplanes' floats. A strong AA battery of ten 25mm guns was arrayed atop the 130ft long conning tower structure in one single and three triple mounts, and there was a 5.5in gun on the aft deck casing.

Forward, a compressed air catapult, offset to starboard to align with the hangar door, stretched 85ft 4in toward the bow on a raised, streamlined casing. For handling the seaplanes there was an electrically powered derrick to port, with a lift capacity of 5 tons. It retracted horizontally into the deck casing when the vessel submerged, as did the 43ft high wireless mast, which was raised and lowered by an electric motor. In addition to the three seaplanes, components to assemble a fourth were carried.

One surface-search and two air-search radar sets were installed, the former also intended to track the submarines' own aircraft. External surfaces were coated with a supposedly sound-absorbent material to avoid asdic/sonar detection; its efficacy remains moot.

Another feature of doubtful value was an automatic trim control system designed to allow the submarine to 'hover' in a stationary position 130 to 165ft below the surface, thus keeping it in a fixed position for rendezvous with returning aircraft.

I-400, name ship of the class, was laid down on 18 January 1943, followed by *I-401* to *I-405*. *I-400* was completed on 30 December 1944, *I-401* on 8 January 1945 and *I-402* on 24 July 1945. *I-402* was converted to a submersible tanker while under construction, which accounts for her delay in completion; she therefore vanishes from our story. Work on *I-404* and *I-405* ceased in March 1945 and all the other projected units were cancelled in 1945.

Particulars of *I-400* and *I-401* as completed were

Displacement:	5223t surface, 6560t submerged
Dimensions:	400ft 3in × 39ft 4in × 23ft
Machinery:	4 diesel engines, 7700bhp; electric motors, 2400hp; 2 shafts = 18.75kts surface, 6.5kts submerged. 37,500nm at 14kts surface, 60nm at 3kts submerged; endurance of 90 days
Armament:	eight 21in TT (bow), 20 torpedoes; one 5.5in, ten 25mm (3 × 3, 1 × 1)
Complement:	144 (also given as 187 and 213)

The vessels proved as unwieldy when submerged as had been feared, but they achieved a remarkably fast diving time for craft of their size, able to submerge to periscope depth in fifty-six seconds. Maximum diving depth was about 330 to 360ft.

As with *Oyodo*, development and production of aircraft for the ships was to proceed in parallel with their construction. Thus on 15 May 1942 the Aichi Aircraft Company was given specifications for a 'special attack bomber', a speedy seaplane for catapult launching able to carry a torpedo or a heavy bomb load. The result was the Aichi M6A1 *Seiran* (Mountain Haze; there was no Allied code name because the existence of the type was not known until after the war), 'bearing the distinction of being the only submarine-borne aircraft to have been built anywhere in the world with offensive missions as its primary role'.

It was a two-place low-wing monoplane with two large jettisonable floats, a maximum speed of 295mph and a range of 642nm. It could carry a single torpedo or 1760lb bomb, or two 550lb bombs. The engine was a 1400hp in-line liquid-cooled type, chosen in preference to a radial because the latter took up too much space to allow arming the aircraft while they were still in the submarine's hangar.

There were ingenious features to permit shipboard carriage: the wings, which had a span of 40ft, pivoted to fold flat against the fuselage, while the tailplanes folded downward and the tip of the fin rudder folded to starboard. In spite of this it was a tight fit; the propeller had a 6in clearance within the 11ft 6in diameter of the cylindrical hangar. The floats, as mentioned above, were housed separately and had to be attached before launching. To aid such assembly at night, main attachment points were coated with luminous paint.

It was calculated that under ideal conditions a specially trained four-man crew could prepare a *Seiran* for launching in just under seven minutes. In practice, it took more than twice that number of men nearly half that time merely to attach the floats. Pumping preheated lubricants into the seaplanes' engines while they were in the hangar reduced warm-up time on the catapult, but even so it took thirty to forty-five minutes to get the full complement into the air.

The prototype *Seiran* first flew in November 1943; altogether, twenty-eight were produced, including two trainer versions with retractable wheel undercarriages replacing the floats. A special unit, the 901st Air Group, was formed to operate them from the submarines and began training in late 1944.

Initially, the *I-400s* were reportedly to be used to launch aerial attacks on US cities; New York and Washington were considered as targets. In early 1945 it was decided instead to employ their aircraft, together with those of the two AM boats, to attack the Gatun lock gates of the Panama Canal, thus severing this major US supply line to the Pacific. For this purpose, a special unit was formed, consisting of *I-400, I-401, I-13* and *I-14* and designated the First Submarine Flotilla. It was commanded by Captain Tatsunoke Ariizume, a veteran submariner. Practice in launching and recovering the seaplanes, and rehearsal of the attack on a full-size floating model of the locks, was to be carried out in the Inland Sea. However, it was delayed when *I-401* was damaged by an air-laid mine while on a voyage to Manchuria to obtain the diesel fuel that was in such short supply in Japan. It was perhaps in response to this that the *I-400s* were equipped with degaussing gear, probably the only submarines of the era so fitted. *I-400* was dispatched in place of her damaged sister, and Ariizume used the delay forced on him by *I-401*'s repairs to have snorkels fitted on all four vessels.

The four submarines and their aircraft finally assembled in early May at Nanao Bay for a six-week training period during which two of the *Seirans* were lost, one crashing into the sea, the other hitting a mountain.

Ariizume had been a strong advocate of the canal attack from the start, but to his chagrin the high command changed targets just when all was in readiness for it. The new target was Ulithi atoll, a major American fleet anchorage and believed to be a concentration point for troops destined for the invasion of the Home Islands.

For Operation *Haikari*, as the Ulithi strike was code-named, the flotilla assembled at Maizuru in northern Honshu. In early July, *I-13* and *I-14* sailed from there to Truk, where they were to disembark aircraft for a night reconnaissance over Ulithi to confirm the presence of worthwhile targets. *I-401*, the flagship, and *I-400* followed two days later, taking independent routes to a rendezvous point from where the pre-dawn attack would be launched. It was to be a suicide mission, the *Seirans* flying without floats. *Kaiten* from other submarines were to take part if possible.

I-14 arrived at Truk as scheduled but *I-13* never showed up. Her loss is officially credited to attacks first by aircraft from the escort carrier *Anzio* and then by destroyer *Lawrence C Taylor*, although one reliable Japanese source doubts this on the basis that the site of her supposed destruction was too far from the route she was scheduled to take to Truk.

I-400 and *I-401* were at sea on 16 August preparing for the attack the next day when a wireless signal arrived informing them that Japan had capitulated. The submarine carriers, like all other Japanese warships, were to proceed to the nearest Japanese port, flying a black flag denoting surrender and ridding themselves of all offensive armament. *I-400* and *I-401* shot off their torpedoes, then destroyed their aircraft, the former by dumping them overboard, the latter by launching them off the catapult to crash into the sea. *I-14* apparently left hers at Truk.

All three were intercepted and captured at sea, *I-400* surrendering to destroyer *Blue*, *I-401* to submarine *Segundo*, and *I-14* to submarine tender *Proteus*. They continued on to Japan with small prize crews aboard. The Americans were astonished at the size and appearance of their prizes, for US intelligence had received not a shred of information that these craft existed.

After some refurbishing, the three submarines, manned by American crews, sailed in company for Pearl Harbor on 11 December 1945, arriving on 6 January 1946. The voyage gave the Americans a chance to evaluate the vessels. 'The *I-400*'s broad beam, deep draft, and ample bow buoyancy tank gave her a dry bridge and an easy roll and pitch', her American executive officer wrote much later. 'For peacetime surface cruising, this submarine could not be beat, but ... when submerged in combat such a huge, low-speed, low-endurance target with a shallow test depth could not last long against a modern ASW team'.

This officer and others were eager to try diving the big boats to see how they behaved underwater, but it was not to be. After thorough examination they were taken to sea and sunk as gunnery and torpedo targets.

The AM type submarines and the *I-400s* had considerable potential for surprise pinpoint attacks on vulnerable targets like the Panama Canal, but they came too late, were too few, and were squandered under a vacillating and ill-conceived strategy. As submarines they were failures; the *I-400s*, especially, illustrate how the compromises necessary to create a hybrid can fatally flaw a design. To achieve their air capability and its concomitant long range and surface stability, they sacrificed underwater manoeuvrability, evasiveness and endurance. Their fighting ability also suffered; the torpedo armament, although among the heaviest of any Japanese submarine, was two tubes fewer than that mounted on American boats less than a third the size. Their displacement could have permitted them to carry more numerous and/or heavier guns (although by the time of their completion surface gunnery action by submarines was largely a thing of the past).

Had all eighteen *I-400* class boats been secretly completed in 1941 or early 1942, they might have achieved worthwhile results in attacks on what were then the virtually undefended coasts of the continental United States. But the idea of using a handful of them to attack US cities in 1944 or 1945 was absurd. It could have accomplished nothing of material consequence, and it certainly would have further enflamed the already rabid American racial hatred of Japan.

The proposed attack on the Panama Canal was a far sounder proposition. Success, however, seemed unlikely. Because the war had progressed so far across the Pacific, the Japanese believed the Canal Zone would be lightly defended. But 'lightly' is relative; there remained stationed in the Zone fighter planes that not only greatly outnumbered the few *Seirans* the submarines could launch, but also flew faster and carried an armament far heavier than the single rear-cockpit machine guns of the seaplanes. It is difficult to believe that the Japanese aircraft could have avoided the radar detection that would have unleashed the fighters against them.

In any case, the blocking of the canal would have been an inconvenience rather than a decisive blow. At most, it would have caused a delay of a few months in American preparations for the assault on the Home Islands. The same held true for the Ulithi operation. Even if the raid were successful, Japan's fate had already been sealed; it had been isolated by submarine and mine from its overseas resources, its greatest cities had been razed by fire-bombing, its industry was at a virtual standstill; worst of all, the atomic bombs had fallen. Six seaplanes could not save the Japanese empire.

Writing soon after the war, a former Japanese officer said of the *I-400s*: '[They] will be principally remembered for what they were and not for their

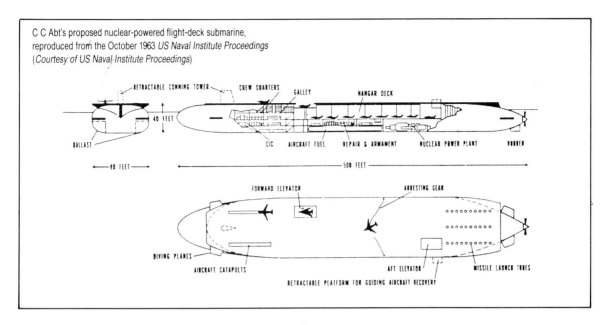

C C Abt's proposed nuclear-powered flight-deck submarine, reproduced from the October 1963 *US Naval Institute Proceedings* (*Courtesy of US Naval Institute Proceedings*)

accomplishments . . . and the shadow cast by their immensity may well project itself on future submarine designs'. Yet during the nearly four decades since that assessment was written, the shadow cast by the *I-400*s has been a pale and sickly one. The concept of the aircraft-carrying submarine fell into disrepute as unworkable and outmoded. What was largely forgotten, however, was the strategic implication of the *I-400*s. Unlike all previous aircraft-equipped submarines, they were not intended to launch a seaplane or two for fleet reconnaissance or to spot prey for a mercantile raider; they were designed for what today would be called power projection — the extension of seapower over land via the air.

The only serious postwar project was an idea strikingly similar to the Japanese submarine carriers: the Douglas Attack Aircraft Model 640, which was designed in 1952 to fit the dimensions of the hangars for Regulus missiles mounted on a few US submarines. This project never got beyond the draughting board, hobbled perhaps by the same problems of aircraft assembly and recovery as its Japanese predecessors. Little else was heard of the submarine carrier.

Since then there have been revolutionary advances in submarine technology that in theory could fit the craft far more capably for the power-projection role. Size has increased to the point at which quite a number of aircraft and all their accoutrements could be carried, while nuclear propulsion grants virtually unlimited range and high submerged speeds. This combination of high underwater speed and great endurance makes possible operations in any of the world's seas for as long as necessary with greatly increased chances of avoiding detection. A submarine carrier seemingly would have all the advantages of a nuclear-powered surface carrier plus the asset of invisibility.

Other developments make, again in theory, cooperation of submarine and aircraft more feasible and more efficient. Inertial navigation systems, for instance, could solve what was the greatest problem of the past — reuniting the submarine and its aircraft after the completion of a mission. It was because of this difficulty that many Japanese submarines abandoned their seaplanes.

One problem remains unsolved: how to minimise the vessel's vulnerability while launching and recovering aircraft, operations that must be carried out on the surface. The shortest possible exposure is necessary, and in the past very short launch times were achieved when only a single aircraft was involved. But the more aircraft to be launched, the more surface time required. The jet-powered aircraft offers a slight, but only very slight, advantage in this respect, for it requires no warming up.

There would seem to be no easy way out of this difficulty unless something as *outré* as underwater launching is devised. At first this idea seems suitable only for bad science fiction — the mid-1960s television series *Voyage to the Bottom of the Sea* featured a nuclear submarine named *Seaview* that housed a 'flying sub' in its nose — yet in 1965 a study was undertaken for the US Navy by the General Dynamics Corporation of an aircraft that could function under water. A tentative design resulted. In the same year Donald and Bruce Reid, a father and son team of Wanamassa, New Jersey, claimed to have constructed such a craft. The General Dynamics scheme came to nothing, and no more seems to have been heard from the Reids, but perhaps the concept should not be dismissed as total fantasy.

Submarine recovery of aircraft was even more of a problem and more time-consuming than launching. Jockeying a seaplane to its recovery device is at best a tricky and often lengthy process, the difficulties of which multiply exponentially if the wind and sea are anything other than calm. A radical solution to this problem would be recovery directly aboard the surfaced vessel, as aboard a flight-deck carrier. Just such a solution was proposed in 1963 by C C Abt, who, writing in the *US Naval Institute Proceedings*, envisaged a submersible flight-deck vessel.

Abt argued that such a craft would be valuable in carrying out operations for which the surface carrier is too vulnerable but which still require manned aircraft for accurate delivery of firepower. Under these conditions, he asserted, 'a submarine-aircraft team would appear to present a nearly ideal military symbiosis. The submarine would supply the heavy fire power (both conventional and nuclear), while the aircraft would detect and identify tactical targets for the submarine, do artillery spotting, and bombardment and group support missions requiring such rapid reaction time and target discrimination as to be beyond the capability of the submarine's relatively long-range tactical rockets'.

Abt's proposed ship displaced 10,000 to 12,000 tons (whether this represents surface or submerged tonnage is unclear), its dimensions would be 500ft by 80ft by 40ft deep. To achieve the surface stability demanded by flight operations, its hull takes the form of a squashed cigar, with the flight deck covering most of its top and overhanging a tumblehome. Below, a hangar deck houses twenty to thirty aircraft; there is a forward lift offset to starboard and an aft lift offset to port. Two parallel flush-deck catapults are mounted forward with a retractable conning tower, or sail, between them. The flight deck has a single arresting line, and a portside retractable aircraft landing-guidance platform is placed aft. The submarine's armament consists of twenty-seven vertical launch tubes for intermediate-range ballistic missiles aft, arranged in three rows of nine. A nuclear powerplant of unspecified horsepower gives a speed of 30 knots on the surface and 35 knots

submerged. In an odd echo of Japan's submarine operations, Abt suggests that his vessel could also be used for clandestine supply missions in wartime.

The design is flawed in many respects. Realising that maintenance of watertight integrity of the lifts would be a major concern, Abt restricts their size to 12ft by 25ft. Yet he wants them to accommodate 'tactical strike aircraft of the 30,000-pound STOL type'. No such aircraft small enough to fit the lifts' dimensions existed in 1963 and none exists today. Another liability is the overhanging flight deck; such projections would probably make enough noise at high underwater speed to make detection by passive sonar relatively easy. The retractable sail, like the lifts, would require a substantial aperture in the pressure hull, and also a complex mechanism. All in all, it would be a bad submarine, seriously hampered in its underwater performance, especially its diving depth, by the aviation facilities.

Like so many hybrid designers before him, Abt substantially overestimates the number of aircraft his ship could carry. The authors asked D K Brown, former deputy chief naval architect of the Royal Navy, and Anthony Mammola, a designer for the Electric Boat Division of General Dynamics, to evaluate the proposal. Brown pointed out that design studies some years ago concluded that a submarine would have to displace approximately 1800 to 2000 tons per aircraft carried. Using this ratio, the twenty to thirty aircraft Abt specifies would require a displacement of between 36,000 and 60,000 tons. Such a size is not beyond the bounds of contemporary submarine technology but would be fabulously expensive, for exceeding Abt's estimated construction cost of $200 million per unit (a figure based on the 1963 value of the dollar and which would be far higher after a quarter-century of inflation).

Brown and Mammola both criticise Abt's hull form as less efficient and necessarily heavier than a cylindrical shape, and both express doubt about the craft's ability to achieve adequate submerged depth.

If the Abt design makes for a poor submarine, its promise as a carrier is equally dismal. Maintaining constant coverage over a beachhead or other similar operations proposed by the author would require aircraft to be continually rearmed and refuelled for their sorties. This would entail frequent and extended periods on the surface, exposing the submarine carrier to just the sort of detection and counterattack from which its sub-

A submarine equipped with SkyHooks for Harrier type aircraft as proposed by Terry Treadwell

mersibility is supposed to protect it.

Sustaining high-intensity air operations seems to undermine the virtues of a submarine carrier; as a breed, they seem far better suited to the role of quick, surprise strikes on vulnerable targets — as the *I-400*s were intended to perform. Such a vessel, less ambitious and theoretically more feasible than Abt's submarine carrier, has recently been suggested by Terry C Treadwell. This scheme would feature a submersible mounting for a pair of SkyHooks for VTOL aircraft. These devices would permit quite rapid launching and recovery times, estimated by Treadwell as three minutes and two minutes, respectively.

This is not a fully developed scheme such as Abt's, and the submarine in question is therefore described only briefly, apparently based on a British Aerospace sketch: 'cigar shaped . . . strong and streamlined with a prominent tower amidships and a hump smoothly angled downwards behind it acting as a launching ramp for . . . aircraft'. 'Launching ramp' is something of a misnomer, for the VTOL aircraft would not be launched from it; it is instead the area from which the aircraft would be picked up by the SkyHook cranes. These last would be retractable for underwater cruising, folding into long, low projections extending aft from the conning tower. The mecha-

nism for this would complicate the vessel's design and present an interesting engineering challenge, to say the least.

Treadwell indicates Sea Harriers as the submarine's aircraft, perhaps with their undercarriages eliminated since they would not be required for either launch or recovery, an idea suggested for shipboard aeroplanes as early as 1918. With its outrigger landing gear done away with, a Harrier could have folding wings, making its accommodation less difficult in a cramped submarine, and reducing the size of the hangar hatch needed, an important consideration in achieving a reasonable diving depth.

Intriguing as the concept of the submarine-aircraft carrier is, it would appear to be simply one more cul-de-sac down which hybrid design has strayed. Although it is now more technologically possible than ever before, there seems no strategic or tactical role it could play that could not be performed equally well and less expensively by other weapons systems. As an over-the-beach support vessel, it sacrifices the submarine's undetectability; this leaves only the quick, one-time

strike by a few aircraft on a vulnerable target —
the Panama Canal attack model, if you like — and
no navy seems willing to spend so much on a ship
of such limited utility. The cost of carrying even a
couple of aircraft aboard a submarine is too high.
As D K Brown concluded in his evaluation of the
Abt design, 'Submarine carriers are not impossible, but they would be limited and very expensive'.

THE 'NEW CAPITAL SHIP'?

Before turning to hybrid schemes that may
yet come to be, it is necessary to examine
their technological basis. The interplay of technical feasibility versus tactical/strategic desirability has always played a strong role in the
history of hybrid warships; of these two considerations, however, technical feasibility must surely
come first. No matter how useful a ship with a
given set of chracteristics may be, it is only a pipe-
dream if it is impossible to build.

We have seen over and over again how hybrids
armed with guns faced many difficult technical
problems. The guns had a tremendous impact on
flight operations: they required firing arcs that cut
into aviation facilities, stirred up turbulence that
made flight operations dangerous, and their blast
could damage aircraft on deck. Modern missiles
eliminate or greatly reduce these conflicts; they
often require no arcs of fire because their guidance
becomes operational after they leave the ship, so
their blast can be effectively directed away from
the aviation areas. Some missile launching
devices, such as the Vertical Launch System
(VLS), are virtually flush with the deck, and do not
cause any turbulence at all, while other launchers
are far smaller than gun turrets. Still others, such
as canister launchers, have less impact on the
ship's structure because they do not require extensive below-deck spaces. Perhaps most significant
of all is the fact that the range of an SSM, unlike
that of a gun, is often comparable to that of
aircraft. This is one technological development
with enormous tactical consequences.

STOVL aircraft also contribute to the technical
feasibility of the hybrid. They have far less
influence on ship systems than conventional aircraft, as they can operate from flight decks far too
small for other types. They therefore do not
squeeze out other weapons systems. Yet STOVLs
have a performance comparable to conventional
aircraft, unlike helicopters, thereby significantly
extending both the defensive and offensive reach
of a warship. STOVL aircraft also seem likely to

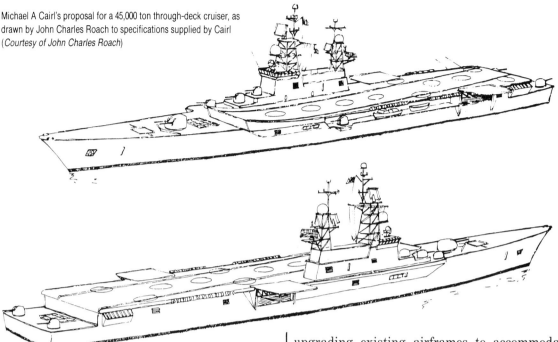

Michael A Cairl's proposal for a 45,000 ton through-deck cruiser, as drawn by John Charles Roach to specifications supplied by Cairl (*Courtesy of John Charles Roach*)

help in extending a hybrid's useful life, for although they will certainly grow heavier as their capabilities and performance improve, the deck area they require will need little if any linear enlargement. Still another important advantage of modern aircraft is the fact that aviation fuels such as the US Navy's JP-5 are much less volatile than aviation petrol; thus a modern hybrid need be no more 'timid' than any other warship when going into a surface action.

A final, subtle factor that may operate in favour of the hybrid is the longevity of modern aircraft. Interwar designers of hybrid warships almost universally failed to realise that the rapid turn-over in aircraft types could outmode their vessels in a very short time. To cite only one example, the American flying-deck cruiser of 1931 was inadequate for the aircraft of 1934, the year the first such ship might have been completed had it been authorised. By the end of the decade, the outlook for hybrid warships was even worse: the CF-2 design of 1940 was barely capable of operating the aircraft of that very year, and that marginal capability was based on the operation of relatively low-performance aeroplanes. The operation of front-line fighting aircraft was beyond the CF-2's abilities the day it was designed.

Today, military aircraft have grown so complex that they require many years to design, test and manufacture; they are so expensive to purchase, maintain and replace, that every effort is made to keep them serviceable by modifying and upgrading existing airframes to accommodate new weapons, sensors and powerplants. Today's individual military aeroplane is a costly, valuable asset to be husbanded for as long as possible. What this means for the hybrid is that it is unlikely to become quickly outmoded by new types of aircraft it cannot operate. The service life of a warship will undoubtedly remain longer than that of its aircraft, but the difference may not be all that great.

For all these reasons, the hybrid warship seems more feasible today than ever before. Whether or not it is a viable idea in terms of military utility is another question entirely.

The military viability of one type of hybrid warship was an issue examined by Michael A Cairl in an article in the December 1978 *US Naval Institute Proceedings*. Entitled 'Through-Deck Cruiser: The New Capital Ship', the article was clearly inspired by the recent appearance of *Kiev* and *Invincible*. Cairl argued that similar ships should eventually replace the big US carriers, which he regarded as expensive and inflexible. Their lack of defensive armament necessitates a large number of escorting vessels, which in turn are costly and virtually useless outside the carrier task force; Cairl therefore preferred a ship with a variety of weapons, which would be able to survive without escorts in low- to medium-threat situations. Such ships would be useful in 'showing the flag' and in maintaining a political presence in crisis situations without being quite as overt a

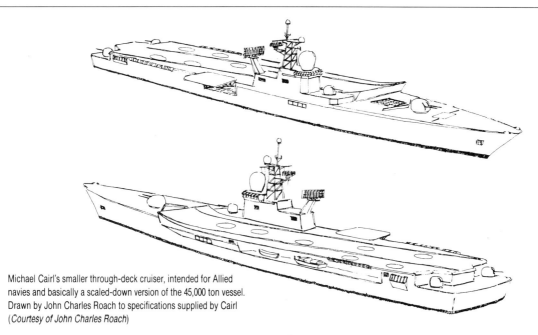

Michael Cairl's smaller through-deck cruiser, intended for Allied
navies and basically a scaled-down version of the 45,000 ton vessel.
Drawn by John Charles Roach to specifications supplied by Cairl
(*Courtesy of John Charles Roach*)

political lever as an entire carrier task force. To
fulfil these duties, Cairl suggested a vessel of the
following characteristics.

Displacement:	c45,000t
Dimensions:	886ft oa × 102ft
Machinery:	gas turbines, electric drive; 27-28kts
Armament:	two 8in (1 × 2); six 76mm (6 × 1); two VLS installations for AA and ASW missiles; two Harpoon canisters; CIWS
Aircraft:	25-30 V/STOL aircraft and helicopters
Sensors:	air search: SPS-48; unspecified fire control, surface search radars and sonar

Cairl shunned nuclear propulsion because of its
great cost; in its place, he proposed gas turbines
with an electric drive train, using super-conducting components, rather than mechanical reduction gearing. This would allow better subdivision
and remove the machinery from the midships area
— the exhaust vents are located on each side of the
after end of the flight deck. Additionally, he
specified a moderate speed of 27 or 28 knots; this
would reduce the weight and volume of the machinery plant, allowing more room for other systems.
The dimensions of the ship were set by the requirement that it should be able to transit the Panama
Canal for fast response in crisis situations. Cairl
also proposed a smaller version of this type of ship
for other Western navies, but he provided few
characteristics. The illustration of his smaller
through-deck cruiser showed a ship armed with a
twin turret forward, probably for 8in guns as in
the larger ship, three 76mm guns, and a single
vertical launch missile system.

The twin 8in turret was to be a development of
the lightweight 8in gun then under development,

while the 76m guns would be standard OTO
Melara mounts. The vertical tubes for AA missiles
and ASROC ASW rockets were located just forward and abaft the flight deck, while a single
Harpoon canister is shown fixed on each side of
the superstructure. Although acknowledging that
his ship would require advanced electronics, Cairl
ruled out complex systems such as Aegis, the US
Navy's integrated air defence system; Cairl
regarded Aegis as 'untried' and probably out of
date by the time his ships would come into service.
Aviation facilities followed the through-deck
arrangement of his models, *Kiev* and *Invincible*,
with a slightly angled flight deck complete with
ski-jump ramp; folding deck-edge lifts served a
344ft hangar.

Cairl's ship is open to criticism on a variety of
counts, some of which were brought out in a rather
harsh letter to the *Proceedings* by Norman
Friedman. Friedman pointed out that it is the
expensive electronics that make up the major
portion of escort ship costs, and that systems such
as Aegis are necessary to deal with massive
saturation attacks; he doubted whether Cairl's
ship could squeeze the same electronic capability
into its combined cruiser/carrier hull. He also
objected to Cairl's 'tightly-packed' ship, which
would allow little room for modernisation and refit
as the vessel aged.

The most damning fact of all was the dramatic
reduction in fleet air capability inherent in Cairl's
scheme. If the thirteen US carriers active in 1978
were replaced by eighteen 'through-deck cruisers',
as Cairl proposed, the total number of embarked
aircraft in the US fleet would have been halved.

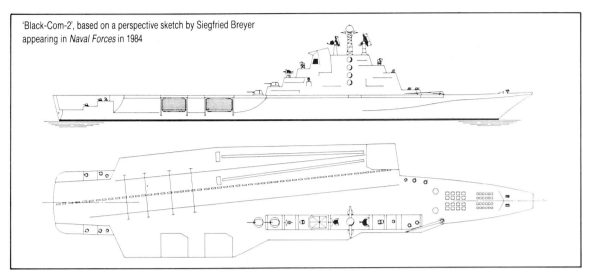

'Black-Com-2', based on a perspective sketch by Siegfried Breyer appearing in *Naval Forces* in 1984

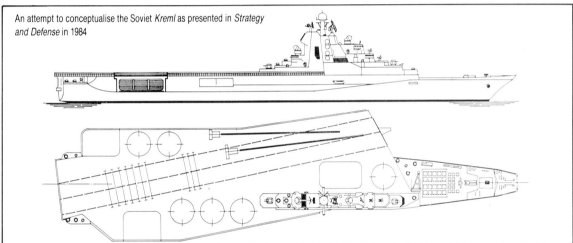

An attempt to conceptualise the Soviet *Kreml* as presented in *Strategy and Defense* in 1984

This reduction could not be made good by any combination of guns and missiles.

Other criticisms can be directed at the details of the design. The deck-edge lifts on a ship of this size might be unusable in heavy seas, making rough-weather air operations difficult. More serious, the intention to hazard a major aviation vessel in the sort of close-inshore operations implied by the presence of 8in guns is very questionable indeed. The environment of a hostile coast is perhaps the most dangerous of all for a warship, with anti-ship missiles and aircraft popping up from the ground clutter with little or no warning, exposure to artillery fire and mines, and the thousand other perils demonstrated in such operations during the past fifty years. Moreover, sea room for aircraft operations would be limited, and in the final analysis air operations are still the ship's major function. It seems almost axiomatic that major aviation vessels should not operate too near a hostile coast; the range of their aircraft make such

operations unnecessary, and the dangers are very great.

Cairl's intention to replace the US Navy's carrier task forces with a greater number of 'one-ship' task forces seems unrealistic at every point. His proposal clearly demonstrates how a hybrid ship may be technologically feasible and yet militarily impractical. However this does not vitiate the concept of the hybrid, only the idea of the hybrid as replacement for the big carrier.

In early 1984, rumours about a 60,000 to 70,000 ton follow-on to the *Kiev* class began to circulate in Western naval publications. These rumours were confirmed when satellite photographs revealed the construction of such a vessel at Nikolayev's South Shipyard in August of that year. These photos showed that the central portion of the ship, presumably the hangar, was completed almost to

A bow view of the Soviet *Baku* shows the massive missile battery on the fo'c's'le. Three Ka-27 helicopters are parked on the flight deck (*Department of Defense/US Navy*)

Displacement:	75,000t
Dimensions:	1099ft 2in oa × 131ft 3in (hull), 295ft 3in (max) (335m × 40m [90m max])
Machinery:	2 nuclear reactors, 4 turbines, 250,000shp = 30–32kts
Armament:	20 tubes for SS-N-19 anti-ship missiles; 2 tubes for SS-N-14 (plus reloads) ASW; 1 RBU-6000 ASW mortar; 12 tubes for SA-N-6 AA missiles; four 76mm guns (2 × 2); nine 30mm gatling guns
Aircraft:	70 'navalised' Su-27 'Flankers', plus helicopters
Sensors:	air search: Top Sail, Top Steer; surface search: Palm Frond; fire control: Eye Bowl (SS-N-14); Top Dome (SA-N-6); Bass Tilt (30mm)
Complement:	5000 plus a marine infantry contingent of 1500

the flight deck, but the bow was far less complete, a tantalysingly blank canvas for the imaginations of Soviet Navy watchers. Almost inevitably, the heavy armament of the *Kievs* led to speculation that these big carriers would also have heavy missile and gun batteries forward. Norman Polmar speculated that the new ships would be 'heavily laden with weapons and electronics', and one contributor to the *Proceedings* went so far as to describe the ship as an 'air-capable battleship', or 'BBVN' (Battleship-Aircraft Carrier, Nuclear-powered). Another writer drew a parallel between the potential Soviet ship and the US Navy's 'self-protecting CVAN' of 1955 (see Chapter 13).

All this speculation resulted in some interesting sketches in various naval journals. One illustration appeared in *Naval Forces* in an article by Siegfried Breyer. Citing an unnamed 'Japanese study', the sketch showed a typical super-carrier flight deck mated to a *Kiev*-style superstructure and weapons systems from the large cruiser *Kirov*. There was a heavy suite of anti-ship (SS-N-19) and anti-aircraft (SA-N-6) missiles and 100mm guns.

There was a similar sketch in the October 1984 issue of the magazine *Strategy and Defense*. This was a somewhat more detailed bit of prediction than *Naval Forces* had attempted. The vessel had the following characteristics.

The vessel again is a cross between a *Kirov* class battlecruiser and a flight-deck carrier. The ship has the battlecruiser's bow, complete with an extensive suite of weapons, while aft the steeply angled flight deck has two catapults, one centre-line and two deck-edge lifts. The writer dubbed this vessel *Kreml* ('Kremlin'), one of several names rumoured for the new ship.

Like Cairl's through-deck cruiser, this combination battlecruiser/carrier is a flawed idea, and for many of the same reasons. The truncation of the flight-deck and hangar to make room for missiles reduces the ship's true striking power — its aircraft — to an unacceptable degree; anti-ship missile batteries cannot compensate for this reduction. Even granting that it could carry seventy 'Flankers', a similar-sized American carrier accommodates about eighty-five aircraft of various types, representing a greater potential for both offence and defence.

In one sense, however, *Kreml* may not be so wide of the mark. In the late 1960s, the Soviets apparently considered just such a hybrid ship. As described by Michael MccGwire in the August 1989 *Proceedings*, it would have been

a nuclear powered ship twice as large as the *Kiev*. This 'universal' ship would combine the characteristics of the *Kirov* and *Kiev* in a single hull, and would be ready for delivery in 1982.

However, Admiral Gorshkov regarded such ships as a mistake, calling them 'unsuccessful'. The 'universal' ship therefore progressed no further.

The direction of aircraft carrier development selected by the Soviets began to emerge when *Baku*, *Kiev*'s half-sister, made her debut in 1988. *Baku* is clearly a development of *Kiev*, but the basic design has been greatly modified. There are several changes in detail; for example, she has 100mm twin mounts in place of her predecessors' 76mm guns, and the forward portside sponson for

the 30mm gatling guns has been eliminated, the guns being moved to the superstructure. More significant, however, is *Baku*'s enlarged super-structure, which is even more massive than *Kiev*'s. This is due at least in part to the four phased-array radar panels similar to those used in the US Navy's Aegis system. The Soviet system is believed to be less advanced than Aegis, lacking the ability to control area-defence AA missiles. *Baku* has no SA-N-3 long-range AA missile launchers; the only AA missiles are SA-N-9 point-defence weapons, which implies that the aircraft have taken over the role of long-range air defence. Similarly, the SUW-N-1 long-range anti-submarine launcher is also gone, which may indicate that *Baku* relies more heavily on her helicopters for ASW than her half-sister.

Taken as a whole, *Baku* is a bit more of a carrier than the earlier ships, relying more on her aircraft for her offensive and defensive capabilities. Her massive anti-ship missile battery is the only thing that keeps her in the hybrid class; the twelve tubes for SS-N-12 anti-ship missiles (eight tubes in the forward group, with four more tubes just abaft them) may still be considered necessary because her aircraft cannot as yet carry weapons heavy enough to knock out an American carrier.

Tbilisi, the Soviet Union's first full flight-deck carrier, finally appeared in late 1989. The trends evident in *Baku* are taken one stage further in *Tbilisi*; she has the same phased-array radar installation on her massive superstructure, and she lacks a long-range AA missile battery. Although reports that *Tbilisi* would carry a pow-erful shipboard surface-to-surface armament persisted even after the ship began her trials, it is clear now that *Tbilisi* mounts only self-defence missiles and guns. She is a pure carrier, and her sixty aircraft are her principal defence and sole

A portside view of *Baku* under way in the Mediterranean. (*Department of Defense/US Navy*)

means of offence; they are launched by a steep ski-jump ramp forward, rather than by catapults. Her air group will probably include MiG-29 'Fulcrum' and Su-27 'Flanker' fighters and Su-25 'Frogfoot' attack aircraft, a more formidable force both in number and capabilities than the twelve 'Forgers' carried by the *Kievs*.

The ideological problem of *Tbilisi*'s classifica-tion has yet to be solved; although Admiral of the Fleet V N Chernavin, C-in-C of the Soviet Navy, referred to her as an 'aircraft carrier', *Pravda* felt compelled to correct him, calling her a 'heavy aircraft-carrying cruiser'. Chernavin described her main role as the provision of 'long-range [fighter] cover for our vessels when shore-based fighters are unable to help', and her aviation complement certainly seems skewed toward fighter aircraft. But the Soviets are aware of the inherent flexibility of carrier aircraft, including their suitability for American-style 'imperialist' power projection. In this regard it should be noted that the 'Frogfoot' is a *ground* attack aircraft similar to the US A-10 Thunderbolt, more suited to supporting troops ashore than to anti-ship strikes.

Photographs of the launch of *Tbilisi*'s sister ship, *Riga*, indicate that she follows the pattern of the first carrier, but reports on the third carrier, *Ulyanovsk*, vary. She may be 10,000 tons larger than *Tbilisi*, and may be equipped with catapults. Whatever modifications this third ship may embody, it seems clear that with *Tbilisi* and her sisters the Soviets have built their first true aircraft carriers.

If recent Soviet trends and long-standing American practice are any indication, the flight-deck carrier is likely to continue as the strike

The US *Spruance* class destroyer *Leftwich*. Features of this class have
made it an attractive candidate for various hybridisation schemes
(*Courtesy of Rob Cabo*)

vessel *par excellence* of the superpower navies.
Hybridising such ships seems as fundamental a
mistake as mounting heavy artillery on carriers
was in the 1930s, for such a process inevitably
reduces the carrier's true military potential — its
air squadrons. This does not eliminate the hybrid
from the ranks of effective warships, however;
there are other roles for which the modern hybrid
may be suited, such as those of the escort vessel
and the cruiser.

The utility of the hybrid as an air defence escort,
either in fleet work or convoy protection, is apparent; stationed on the periphery of the screen, a
hybrid could contribute to the defensive CAP,
either by refuelling and replenishing aircraft
based on aircraft carriers or by adding its own
aircraft to the fighter ring guarding the task force
or convoy. In this role the hybrid would operate
relatively high-performance STOVL aircraft such
as the Sea Harrier.

The hybrid has another potential escort role,
however: ASW. Although this form of defence has
been dominated by the helicopter for three
decades, there is good reason to believe that it may
eventually be displaced by VTOL aircraft.

This rather surprising state of affairs is the
result of modern sonar developments. When operating in deep water, low-frequency sonars are
capable of detecting submarines at 'convergence
zones' great distances from the ship. This occurs
because the sound waves directed down into the
water undergo refraction due to the increasing
water pressure; they eventually return to the
surface in a zone about 5nm wide about 30nm from
the ship. Because the detection zone is so far from

the ship, and is so narrow, a quick response by
ASW forces is required if this phenomenon is to be
used to advantage. A helicopter, with its limited
speed, might take a quarter of an hour or more to
get to the zone; by that time the submarine could
be 8 or 9nm from the point of detection. A VTOL
aircraft such as Boeing's tilt-rotor Osprey, which
flew for the first time in March 1989, could cover
that same distance in about five minutes, by
which time a fast submarine could travel only
about 3nm — a 28sq mile area to search, instead of
more than 250sq miles. The advantages of an
ASW VTOL aircraft at such detection ranges are
obvious.

The air defence and ASW potential of VTOL
aircraft has led to the consideration of a new type
of vessel, the 'air-capable' warship. There are links
between the modern air-capable ship and the
flying-deck cruiser of the 1930s, both in form and
intended functions; another interesting reflection
of the 1930s is the fact that the air-capable ship
has come at one point to the attention of the US
Congress.

In the Fiscal Year 1978 shipbuilding programme, Congress approved the construction of a
single air-capable *Spruance* (DD963) class destroyer. This would have involved simply increasing the size of the hangar and flight deck, allowing
the ship to operate up to four helicopters, or,
ultimately, some form of VTOL aircraft. The US
Navy did not really want this ship, and in the end
managed to get the funds redirected to a standard
unit of the class. However, the basic idea has
inspired several other projects.

One of the earliest of these designs to appear
was the work of Dean A Rains and Donald B
Adams, both of Ingalls Shipbuilding Division, for
a 'flight deck DD 963'. This proposal resembled
Croker's 'through-deck cruiser', and called for a
complete revision of the *Spruance* design. The
beam would be increased from 55ft to 68ft, the

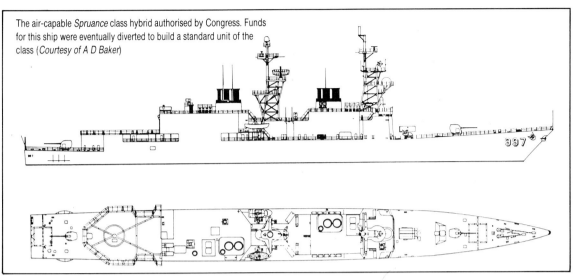

The air-capable *Spruance* class hybrid authorised by Congress. Funds for this ship were eventually diverted to build a standard unit of the class (*Courtesy of A D Baker*)

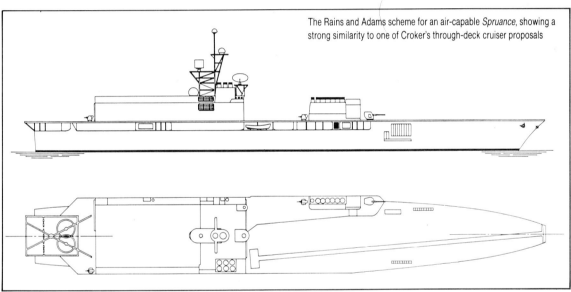

The Rains and Adams scheme for an air-capable *Spruance*, showing a strong similarity to one of Croker's through-deck cruiser proposals

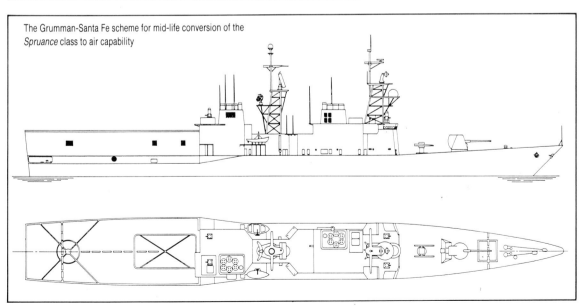

The Grumman-Santa Fe scheme for mid-life conversion of the *Spruance* class to air capability

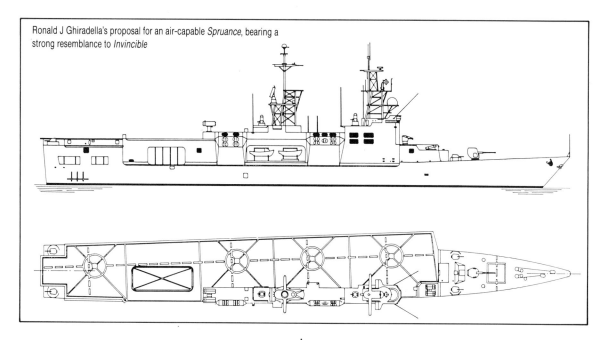

Ronald J Ghiradella's proposal for an air-capable *Spruance*, bearing a strong resemblance to *Invincible*

superstructure would be rearranged and a hangar built on the main deck; there would be a flight deck forward of the hangar, including a ski-jump in some versions of the design, and a landing deck abaft it. In no meaningful sense a hybrid, this was really an attempt at a small carrier.

Another *Spruance* conversion design was worked out by the Grumman/Santa Fe Corporation and bears a strong resemblance to traditional hybrids. This scheme is one of several proposed 'mid-life' modernisations of the *Spruance* class ships. It shows the basic destroyer design from the bow to the after superstructure, but aft a large hangar has been built onto the hull, with a flight deck above. The resulting 9000 ton ship could embark as many as eight helicopters or four ASW VTOL aircraft; the sketches show an early version of the never-built Grumman turbofan Model 698 aircraft. This gull-winged aircraft featured swivelling engine nacelles attached to the fuselage and was intended to travel at up to 500 knots.

Still another *Spruance*-based VTOL design bore a strong resemblance to HMS *Invincible* and was intended to provide the advantages of STOL operations. Proposed by Commander Ronald J Ghiradella, US Naval Reserve, it featured a basic *Spruance* hull lengthened to 606ft overall; the gas turbine uptakes are trunked to starboard where an island superstructure is located, making room for a 470ft flight deck angling to port. Forward, there are conventional weapons: a 5in gun and Harpoon anti-ship missile canisters, with 30mm guns sited on each quarter to provide close-in AA defence, and a Basic Point Defense Missile System is

located aft of the island. There is a long, narrow lift (62ft by 26ft) aft of the island. Ghiradella foresees two hangar decks, the main one on the original main deck, with a lower hangar deck extending from the lift aft to the stern. In spite of the fact that the lift is too narrow to handle Harriers, Ghiradella gives the aircraft complement as twelve 'medium-sized' helicopters and four 'Harrier-type' aircraft.

Despite the large size of the *Spruance* hull, it is clearly at the lower limit of effective STOVL aircraft operations; critics of such designs have argued that ship motion would be too lively for STOL operations. Yet an even smaller 'air-capable' ship has been proposed. This vessel would be based on the 'deep vee' hull form, a broad-beamed and semi-planing hull, allowing greater topweight and speed equal to that of longer, narrower ships of similar displacement. Hydro Research Systems has based an 'air capable frigate' on such a hull, the NHP 3000. This intriguing little ship, only 367ft long by 46ft 7in at the waterline and displacing 3400 tons, would carry four large ASW helicopters in a hangar with a 285ft long flight deck above. It is not difficult to picture such a ship, with suitable modifications, operating Harriers. Although the shipboard weapons are not specified, the sketch seems to show a lightweight 5in gun forward with a Sea Sparrow launcher superimposed abaft it, a pair of close-range air defence weapons such as the US Vulcan/Phalanx, and canisters for eight Harpoon SSMs.

In many ways the most interesting hybrid escort design is a Vosper Thornycroft proposal

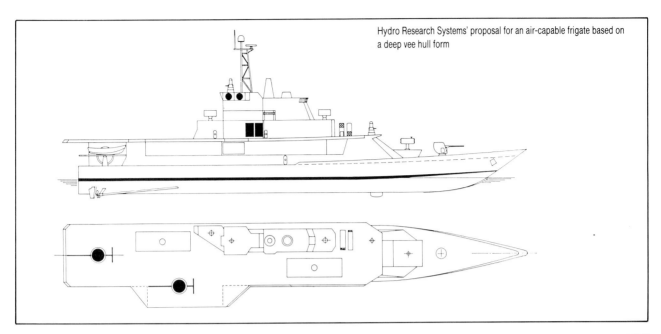

Hydro Research Systems' proposal for an air-capable frigate based on a deep vee hull form

that takes full advantage of British Aerospace's SkyHook, the crane-like Harrier launching and recovery device. This design shows a ship of moderate size with a conventional forward section, complete with gun and centreline superstructure. Aft, however, the ship is given over to Harrier operations. There is a hangar in the after end of the superstructure, topped by a SkyHook on each beam. Harriers would be launched through doors in the hangar's sides, sliding out on cradles to be picked up by a SkyHook. Recovery would reverse the procedure. There is a small flight-deck right aft, which has a helicopter on it in the illustrations.

The characteristics of the design are

Displacement:	5200t
Dimensions:	416ft 8in oa, 393ft 9in wl × 65ft 7in
Machinery:	45,000hp = 26kts+. 490 tons fuel; 4500nm at 16kts
Armament:	one 100mm (1 × 1), 2 Goal Keeper CIWS
Aircraft:	5 Harriers, 1 helicopter
Sensors:	surveillance and aircraft direction radar, navigation radar, hull-mounted sonar
Complement:	338

Although no other weapons are mentioned in the company's brochure, the superstructure also seems to contain a VLS for some type of missile, perhaps Seawolf; a vertical-launching version of this light AA missile will soon enter service aboard the Royal Navy's 'Duke' class frigates.

One of the most interesting features of this design is the inclusion of a 250ft 'skeletal ski-jump' along the centreline of the superstructure, to be used for launching Harriers. The twin funnels and the masts are on each side of the ship, giving

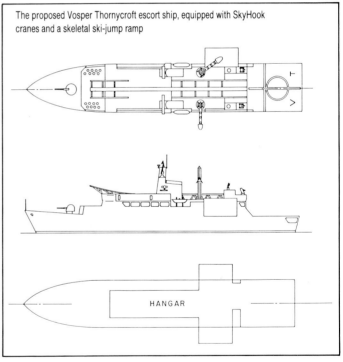

The proposed Vosper Thornycroft escort ship, equipped with SkyHook cranes and a skeletal ski-jump ramp

HANGAR

sufficient clearance for the Harrier's 25ft wingspan, and the rails slope up to form a ski-jump over the bridge. Aircraft would be placed on the rails by one of the SkyHooks, and then take off along the rails (presumably on some sort of cradle), permitting the increased payloads associated with the ski-jump launch.

This is one of the few schemes to depart completely from the conventional aviation ship configuration, taking advantage of the Harrier's remarkable flexibility and the possibilities of the

An artist's conception of the Vosper Thornycroft escort ship at sea, handling Harriers and a helicopter. The configuration in this drawing differs somewhat from the previous illustration (*Courtesy of British Aerospace*)

SkyHook. It is certainly one of the most imaginative aviation ships ever devised.

The various designs for 'Harrier carriers' are almost always for small ships, because the perceived purchasers of such vessels are the second-rank naval powers. The 'flight-deck DD 963' and the Vosper Thornycroft design were both intended to provide shipboard aviation to smaller navies and so resemble Sir George Thurston's hybrid battleships of the 1920s: multi-purpose ships intended to capture the attention of countries whose naval aspirations are constrained by limited budgets. As such, they are not independent ships; they must have escorts if they are to operate. The same limitation applies to a hybrid cruiser scheme that appeared in the September 1977 issue of the *Proceedings*. The article, written by John Fozard, one of the men involved in the Harrier's design, was for the most part concerned with the potential of the Harrier and did not describe the small sketch accompanying the text, so the roles intended for the cruiser-sized ship illustrated can only be surmised. The ship bore a superficial resemblance to *Blake*, and has something of that ship's patchwork quality about it. There was a gun forward, presumably a 4.5in, with a twin-arm missile launcher abaft it, and a centreline forward superstructure block. The after superstructure, which had a second missile launcher on its top, was offset to starboard to allow room for the flight deck, which had a ski-jump ramp. The hangar was below the flight deck.

Overall, it is an uninspiring design, clearly intended simply to illustrate the fact that almost any type of ship can operate Harriers. In recent years, a more convincing rationale for the hybrid cruiser has emerged. Its proponents advance a radical notion regarding cruiser operations: a return to the traditionally independent role of the big cruiser. In this self-sufficient arena, the advantages of carrying a few aircraft of greater performance than helicopters are obvious.

The cruiser's loss of most of its independent

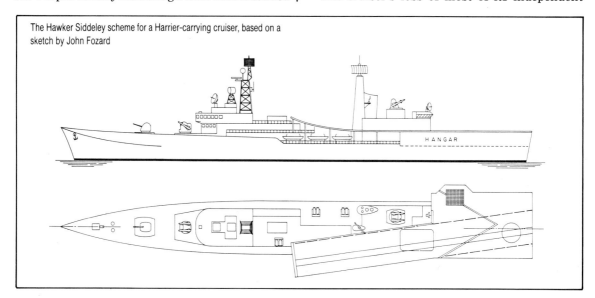

The Hawker Siddeley scheme for a Harrier-carrying cruiser, based on a sketch by John Fozard

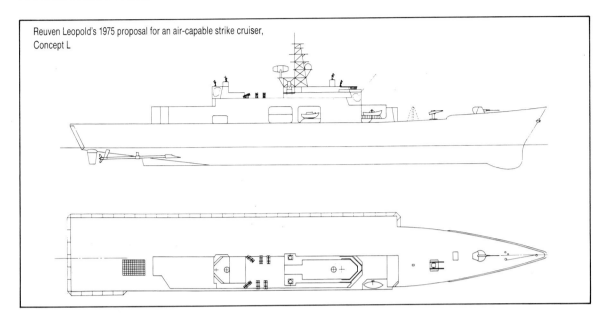

Reuven Leopold's 1975 proposal for an air-capable strike cruiser, Concept L

functions in the course of the Second World War has already been noted; it emerged from that conflict as a carrier escort vessel, a role for which its size and speed suited it. Its size was especially useful when the first generation of AA missiles emerged in the late 1950s. These early weapons were unreliable because of their delicate vacuum-tube electronics; during the past three decades the introduction of transistors and solid-state electronics has made possible vast improvements in missile reliability and accuracy. A parallel development has led to combined sensing/control systems of great capacity, such as the US Navy's Aegis, which is specifically intended to deal with saturation attacks. While certainly highly valuable in the carrier escort role, Aegis also offers some hope of restoring the cruiser's former independence by giving a single ship so equipped a chance to deal with massive attacks.

This was the rationale behind the US Navy's 'Strike Cruiser' (CSGN) programme, initiated in the early 1970s. Its intention was to produce a powerful and independent surface combatant; to some degree, this development programme paralleled that of the first US 'treaty' cruisers of the *Salt Lake City* class, a response to new technologies that led to the design of a big, new type of cruiser for wide-ranging duties. The strike cruiser stood in almost exactly the same relation to earlier guided-missile cruisers as the *Salt Lake City* had in relation to the previous fleet-screening ships of the *Omaha* class. It was perhaps inevitable that the suggestion would be made to increase their capabilities by including aircraft, just as James L Bates had suggested during the preliminary design of the *Salt Lake City* class in 1925.

In this case, the idea was put forward by Reuven Leopold, who was the technical director of the Naval Ship Engineering Center, and as such was involved in the design of the strike cruiser. Most CSGN schemes had featured more or less conventional helicopter facilities, while some made provision for operating a couple of STOVL aircraft, but in 1975 Leopold completely recast the ship in order to give it a more effective aircraft complement. His series of alternative flight-deck CSGN designs was based on the fact that the actual structure of a ship is no longer the major element in its cost; instead, the electronics, weapons and, in nuclear ships, the machinery constitute the major expenses. Therefore, a flight-deck for STOVL aircraft, while increasing the size of the CSGN by about 4000 tons, would not increase its cost greatly. The addition of good aviation facilities would make for a far more formidable ship, better able to take care of itself during independent operations. Leopold worked out three versions of the basic design: concept K, based on the existing CSGN hull design; concept L, which featured a redesigned hull better suited to the new ship; and concept M, a larger vessel which added a second 8in lightweight gun. Concept L had the following characteristics.

Displacement:	18,896t light, 21,146t full load
Dimensions:	666ft (oa) × 79ft 10in × 25ft 6in
Machinery:	2 nuclear reactors; c30kts
Armament:	one 8in gun (1 × 1); two 20mm Vulcan/Phalanx CIWS; 1 twin-arm Mk 26 Standard missile launcher; 1 VLS missile installation; canisters for Harpoon SSMs
Aircraft:	6 STOVL
Electronics:	Aegis system

The aircraft are hangared in the superstructure, eliminating the need for a lift. (This arrangement comes full circle from the Beardmore design of 1912, mentioned in Chapter 1, in which the hangar layout was virtually identical to Leopold's.) Both a twin-arm launcher and a VLS were included because the VLS could store only the SM-2 medium-range AA missile; the lancher forward would handle the long-range versions of this missile. Presumably, Tomahawk cruise missiles, perhaps in box launchers, would eventually have been installed. The CSGN design also featured fairly extensive use of armour, with box protection for magazines and other vital compartments. It was to be equipped to act as a flagship.

The CSGN was eventually cancelled because of its great cost, but Leopold did not give up on his flight-deck cruiser. In a 1978 article describing possible future trends in warship design, he suggested a hybrid cruiser based on his CSGN proposal. He described the advantages of an 'organic air capability' in these terms.

> Through the use of aircraft, a ship's sphere of influence will be greatly expanded by the over-the-horizon target detection, classification and engagement capability. . . . With the availability of V/STOL aircraft within the next decade, it is expected that . . . more space and weight will be devoted to air capability on our future surface warships.

The over-the-horizon targeting capability is especially important. Many anti-ship missiles have ranges of several hundred nautical miles, but this great range is useless unless the ship knows what it is shooting at, and roughly where the target is. Satellite guidance is one possibility, but in time of war satellites may be blinded or destroyed by enemy action. An alternative is the 'forward pass', whereby an aircraft provides targeting data to a missile launched from a ship. Here the advantage of 'organic air' is clear; in fact, it may be that only a ship with some form of aircraft guidance for its weapons will be able to use them effectively. There is in this a certain parallel to the gunfire spotting provided by observation aircraft for battleships in the 1920s and '30s.

The 'forward pass' could, of course, be provided by any suitable aircraft, but for a ship on independent operations, such as the strike cruiser, this duty would necessarily fall to its own aircraft. Helicopters are capable of doing this job, but they are slow and vulnerable, while a STOVL aircraft could not only provide guidance for the ship-launched weapons but attack with its own anti-

ship missiles, thereby greatly complicating the defenders' task.

Leopold therefore envisages a warship of nearly 10,000 tons for the early twenty-first century that is very similar to his larger flight-deck CSGN. There is a gun forward, vertical-launching missile installations forward and aft, CIWS on each quarter, and a superstructure to starboard that includes hangars for several STOVL aircraft. There is a through deck and an Aegis-style electronics suite. Propulsion would be by gas turbines with super-conducting electrical drive; this may be where Cairl got the idea for such a powerplant for his through-deck cruiser, which appeared some months later.

Leopold continued to advocate such a ship even after he left the navy's employ. In 1984 he was one of the members of a conference on the navy's future sponsored by the Hudson Institute, a defence-related research centre. In discussing the future of the surface force, he pointed out that 'there is a big gap in the size of our combatants, which are below 10,000-ton displacement, and the carriers, which are more than 90,000 tons'. If the concept of the SAG is to be maintained after the reactivated *Iowas* are retired, something will be needed to take their place. Furthermore,

> Assuming the SAG concept has merit, the two major deficiencies it suffers are: (1) the lack of an effective, integral antiair warfare capability; and (2) the lack of an over-the-horizon targeting capability for the Tomahawk.

To make good these deficiencies, Leopold proposed a

> 20,000-ton, nuclear-powered, through-deck cruiser that carries Aegis with SM-2 antiair missiles. It has the Tomahawk, but it also has the aircraft needed for over-the-horizon surveillance and targeting.

Leopold makes a good case for his flight-deck CSGN, which is in many ways akin to the flying-deck cruiser of the 1930s. Certainly, the arguments for this type of vessel are far sounder than any scheme to replace the flight-deck carrier with hybrids. If there are to be hybrid warships in the future, they will surely follow the pattern set by Leopold's designs.

The story of the hybrid warship has been a long one, and proposals for its construction numerous, yet few vessels have been built to this pattern. The reasons for this dearth have been many and

Reuven Leopold's design for an 'under 10,000-ton warship of early 21st century', featuring electric propulsion as shown in the cutaway portion of the sketch (*Courtesy of US Naval Institute Proceedings*)

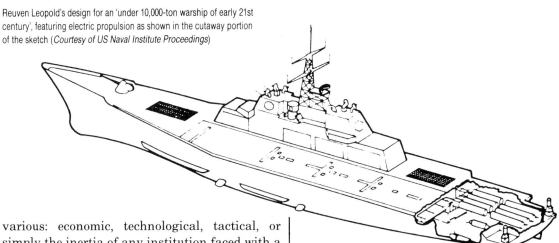

various: economic, technological, tactical, or simply the inertia of any institution faced with a new idea. The differing types of hybrid ships have been equally diverse, from battleship-carriers to carriers armed with heavy artillery, to flying-deck cruisers and submersible carriers. They have covered a spectrum of feasibility, from the possible to the wildly improbable. Through it all, the central theme of increasing the capability of warships by the addition of aircraft has kept its place. The question is no longer one of technical feasibility; the modern missile-armed, STOVL-equipped hybrid is a proven quantity. Instead, it is the military validity of the idea that will determine whether the hybrid has a future.

Some hybrid ideas, such as the heavily armed carrier, do not measure up to this test. By reducing the aircraft complement of the carrier for the sake of missiles, they cause a real reduction in the ship's combat effectiveness. Missiles have yet to reach the point where they can effectively replace manned aircraft; for the foreseeable future, aircraft will be necessary for the location, selection and designation of targets. One aircraft is worth more than one missile by any measure, and so the substitution of missiles for aircraft is a bad bargain. A carrier heavily armed with missiles is worse than a cul-de-sac; it is a positive step backwards. To arm a carrier with guns for shore bombardment, as suggested by Cairl, represents a signal failure to grasp the fact that the major virtue of aircraft is their ability to act *at a distance* from the carrier, thereby securing for the ship a certain measure of safety.

However the hybrid cruiser, as exemplified by Leopold's flight-deck CSGN, seems a militarily valid idea, if systems like Aegis truly provide the capability for the survival of independent warships. Everything hinges on this last point. If Aegis or its equivalents can indeed cope with massive attacks from several directions at once,

then the combination of missiles and aircraft makes sense for a cruiser. The aircraft can see over the horizon to target the ship's long-range weapons and carry out their own attacks; they can provide an outer defensive zone against air attacks, and prosecute ASW contacts. The ship's missiles can deliver large warheads to distant targets, as long as the necessary guidance is available from some source, and greatly complicate the problems facing a defender. Cruise missiles such as Tomahawk turn every ship that carries them into a strategic threat, and the more platforms there are for these weapons, the greater the threat. In addition, a nuclear-powered ship is largely independent of supporting bases or supply vessels. Nuclear power also allows greater loads of ammunition and fuel to be carried. The flight-deck CSGN can carry almost half the aviation ordnance as the *Enterprise* of the Second World War and almost twice as much fuel for its aircraft. And although six STOVL aircraft may not sound like much of an aviation complement, it should be noted that *five* Sea Harriers can lug aloft a greater weight of ordnance than *twenty-four* Vought Vindicators of 1940. What this weight of ordnance corresponds to in relative hitting power is impossible to calculate, but the guided anti-ship missiles of today are surely many times more effective than the 1000lb bombs of the Vindicator. By this measure, the flight-deck CSGN is indeed a ship to be reckoned with.

There hangs over this type of modern hybrid only one question: can it operate independently? If Aegis is as effective as advertised, then the hybrid cruiser may well be the ship to fill the gap between carrier escort and carrier. But if such electronic systems prove unable to cope with the level of attack which a ship on independent operations can reasonably expect to encounter — which would probably be less than the all-out saturation attack a carrier battle group would face — then the 'cruising ship' is as much a thing of the past as it was in 1945.

In this last case, some form of hybrid warship might still be found useful in the task force screen, relieving the carrier's squadrons of duties such as ASW or forming part of the outer AA defences. Or the chimera of a two-for-the-price-of-one ship may yet appeal to an ambitious second- or third-ranked naval power; but such ancillary types of warship lack the fascination that was first summoned up by Sir George Thurston's image of a 'solitary and powerful unit'. This image lay behind not only Sir George's schemes, but many of those which followed: the flying-deck cruiser in the distant scouting line; William Gibbs' giant battleship-carrier 'let loose' on the oceans; the absurd German schemes for preying on Allied commerce; Levert's 'battle-carrier', faster and longer-ranged than any escort; the Bureau of Ships' 'self-protecting' CVAN — all seen by their proponents as the ideal independent warship. Leopold's flight-deck CSGN is only the latest, and perhaps the most feasible, in that long progression.

APPENDIX A

WHAT'S WRONG WITH THIS PICTURE?

Having reviewed the history of hybrid warships from their beginnings to the present, it may be useful to take a look at a design that has no history behind it and see if a judgement regarding its feasibility can be made.

The design appeared in a naval war-gaming magazine, the *Alnavco Log*, in 1974. Don Carey, the author of the article, offered an alternative version of history in which the Japanese, instead of building the conventional *Yamato* class battleships, build battleship/carriers. The author dubbed these putative hybrids the *Tosa* class; the hypothetical characteristics of these ships are given below.

Displacement:	78,000t (standard?), 93,200t full load
Dimensions:	875ft (wl), 915ft (oa) × 110ft (wl), 160ft (oa) × 40ft (full load)
Flight deck:	575ft × 125ft
Machinery:	12 boilers, 12 turbines, 6 shafts; 450,000shp = 40kts
Armament:	six 18.1 in (460mm) (2 × 3), eighteen 3.9 in (100mm) (9 × 2), ninety-six 25mm (28 × 3, 12 × 1), eight 24in (600mm) torpedo tubes
Aircraft:	80 (types unspecified)
Armour:	main belt 12in; hull (other than main belt) 4in; flight deck 6in; bomb deck (hangar deck floor level) 4in; hangar deck sides and bulkheads 6in; transverse bulkheads 3in; turrets 20–25.5in; tower 12in; magazine 4in
Complement:	2500

The author notes that there are to be six shafts, the outer pair to protect the inner shafts and rudders from torpedo damage. There are to be four rudders placed in the race of the four inner propellers. There would be twelve engine rooms and twelve boiler rooms.

The first things to clear up are the factual errors in the design. The greatest of these is the horsepower; citing machinery three times as powerful as the experimental destroyer *Shimakaze*'s powerplant, the author rates his hybrid at 450,000shp. The *Shimakaze*'s machinery, however, was rated at 75,000shp, although she did achieve 79,240shp. Clearly, the author somehow *doubled* the output of the machinery of the destroyer, thereby doubling his hybrid's horsepower. A machinery installation such as that proposed would actually be

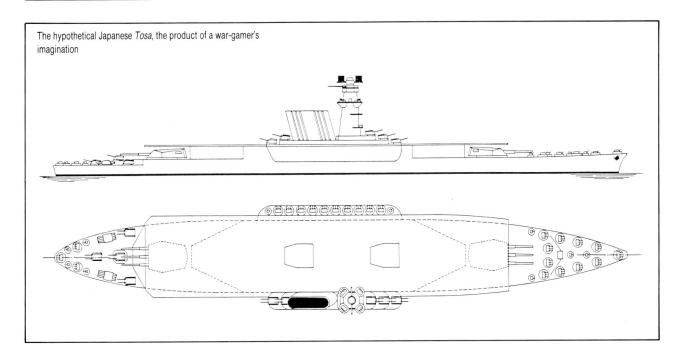

The hypothetical Japanese *Tosa*, the product of a war-gamer's imagination

rated at 225,000shp, and might achieve as much as 240,000shp. Under no circumstances would this be sufficient to drive the ship at 40 knots; a comparison with other ships indicates a speed nearer 32 to 33 knots. Another problem is the efficiency of six shafts; with a beam of only 110ft, the propellers would be so close to each other that they would interfere with one another, adversely affecting the ship's speed. However, now that we have reduced the shaft horsepower to 240,000, a four-shaft machinery plant is possible without overloading the individual propellers.

The aircraft capacity presents another problem. A generous estimate of the hangar space available yields about 380,000sq ft; the Japanese carrier *Taiho* had *two* hangar decks, each as large as the *Tosa*'s, yet she carried seventy-three aircraft, and twenty-one of these were disassembled spares. We may therefore estimate that the *Tosa* might have been able to carry about forty operational aircraft, rather than the eighty supposed by its creator. This overestimation of aircraft capacity is typical of many unofficial hybrid designs.

The size of the flight deck also has to be revised downward. The model illustrated in the article featured a flight deck that extended over the main battery turrets — some 60 to 70ft — without any indication of cantilever support or stanchions. As stanchions would interfere with the arcs of fire of the main battery turrets, it would probably be necessary to trim the extensions back considerably to ensure their structural support. This sort of mistake originates in the scale of the model: at 1/1200, a thin flight deck extension looks quite solid; a drawing at a larger scale makes it clear that it is an impossible structure.

There are other problems with the design; the proposed ship is enormous, larger than any of the preliminary designs for the *Yamato* — designs that were rejected because they were too large for Japanese harbours. Even the 'Super-Yamato' design involved a ship of about 70,000 tons standard displacement. Obviously the *Tosa* would have been too big for the existing dockyards and harbours. Had the Japanese decided to build hybrid battleship/carriers, they would probably have been similar in size to the *Yamato*.

We are therefore left with a 65,000 to 70,000 ton ship, capable of 30 to 33 knots, with a main battery of six 18.1in guns and about forty aircraft. This is a fairly close match to the characteristics of the Gibbs and Cox Design B for the Soviet Union, described in Chapter 10. The same characteristics could be embodied in a 45,000 ton battleship and a 20,000 ton carrier; in fact, the 20,000 ton carrier could accommodate more aircraft. In addition, a carrier and a battleship could manoeuvre independently, while *Tosa* cannot separate her gunnery and aviation features; in a surface engagement with a carrier and a battleship, *Tosa* would have to steer a course to fight the enemy battleship, which would probably make aviation operations impossible because of the wind (not to mention the blast from her own guns). The battleship and carrier, however, could manoeuvre independently, so the battleship could engage her guns fully while the carrier could launch her aeroplanes without interference. A few hits from guns could render the *Tosa*'s flight deck inoperable, in spite of its heavy armour (which probably could not be as heavy as the author states, because of the topweight it represents; Gibbs did not try to armour the flight deck or hangar of Design B). And the aircraft and their fuel represent a considerable hazard to a ship in a gunnery engagement. Clearly, this hybrid idea will not fly.

In addition to the *Tosa* class, the author proposed an *Aso* class, 29,850 tons and armed with six 12.2in guns and fifty aircraft, and an *Ayase* class, 15,050 tons and armed with six 6.1in guns and fifty aircraft. The same problem of overestimating the aircraft complement is apparent with these smaller designs; the *Zuiho*, a pure aircraft carrier of 11,000 tons, carried only thirty aircraft. We may estimate that the *Aso* might carry thirty aircraft at most, and the *Ayase* fewer than twenty. With a reduced aviation complement, the *Ayase* seems too weakly armed for independent operations, but the *Aso* is certainly a reasonable proposition for commerce raiding; its 12.2in guns could deal with any cruiser, and the aircraft could be usefully employed in finding targets for the ship and harassing larger pursuers.

In commerce raiding or commerce protection, the gun-armed hybrid might have found roles it could perform better than 'pure' cruisers or carriers. Certainly, the American flight-deck cruiser of the early 1930s and the various German hybrid designs considered during the Second World War were intended to fill such roles. Unfortunately for the mythical *Aso* class, the Japanese showed little interest in commerce raiding — or, for that matter, commerce protection. So, although the ship might have made a successful commerce raider, there was no impetus to build such a vessel. Like so many hybrid designs, it is trapped somewhere between technological feasibility and military utility.

APPENDIX B

MERCHANT HYBRIDS

All the hybrids we have considered, whether visionary, planned, projected, converted or constructed, have been warships. Over the decades, however, there has also been a number of real or imaginary hybrid merchant vessels.

The most notable to date have been the British merchant aircraft carriers (commonly known as MAC ships) of the Second World War, which will be discussed presently. Created as a stopgap measure to help protect Atlantic convoys from German submarines, they were identical in purpose to vessels proposed a quarter of a century earlier by another of the colourful and unusual characters who people hybrid history, John Lawrence Bogert.

Bogert was a man of many parts. An American naval architect and marine engineer, he was a member of the Columbia College (later Columbia University) class of 1878, and was the institution's oldest graduate when he died in 1956 at the age of ninety-seven. He held forty US patents, served for many years as associate editor of the New York-published *Marine Journal*, remained an active and avid swimmer until late in life, and sang regularly with the New York Oratorio Society for more than half a century. The most unusual aspect of his career, however, was a long battle with the US Navy in which he sought to be declared 'Father of the Flat-Top Plane-Carrier', a title he used in later years on his office letterhead.

The claim stemmed from his submission to the Navy Department in May or June 1917 (the exact date is in doubt) of a proposal for a 'mothership for airplanes and submarine destroyer' that he dubbed *Democracy*. This 'combination of the bomb-dropping armed airplane with armed freight ship', as he later described it, was in fact a small flight-deck carrier. Bogert's plans called for a 540ft by 80ft vessel of about 15,000 tons, capable of at least 16 knots, and armed with four 5in/51 guns in fore and aft sponsons on each beam. The ship was apparently to be propelled by three diesel engines of unspecified output.

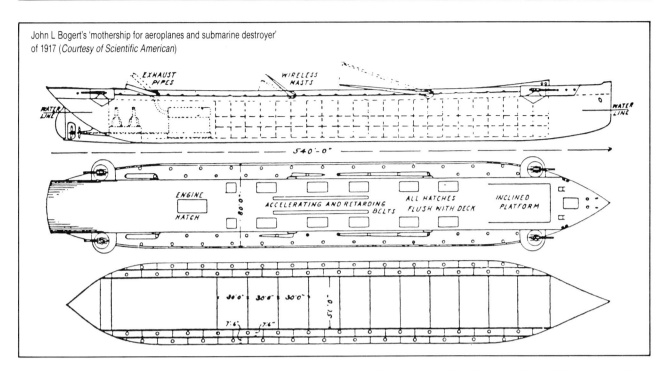

John L Bogert's 'mothership for aeroplanes and submarine destroyer' of 1917 (*Courtesy of Scientific American*)

An elaborate and unusual scheme of under-water protection was devised, which was described by *Scientific American* in 1917 as consisting of

> . . . on each side a double wall of anti-torpedo compartments. They are 7 feet 6 inches wide by 10 feet deep and 30 feet in length. Each is provided with manholes which, when the ship is ready for sea, are closed by watertight covers. It is the intention to use these compartments for storage of special kinds of cargo, which would be resistant to the torpedo and would act with a water-excluding effect in case of injury.

The vessel's conventional mercantile hull is topped by a 50ft wide, clear, flat deck that near the bow curves upward over a pilot house and was intended to assist aircraft in taking off. Hinged exhaust funnels are located on each beam aft; farther forward on each beam are a pair of retractable wireless masts. Both sides of the flight deck are lined by flush-deck cargo hatches, six on each beam.

Approximately amidships, flush with the deck, are two parallel 'accelerating and retarding belts' for use by aircraft. Bogert was especially fond of this device for launching aeroplanes, and was still promoting it in 1945: 'The endless belt construction involves constructing the hubs of the plane's landing wheels . . . so that the wheels are free to turn forward, never backward. The result is . . . that when the plane is pushed . . . onto the accelerator endless belt it immediately partakes of the forward speed of the belt less tire slippage'.

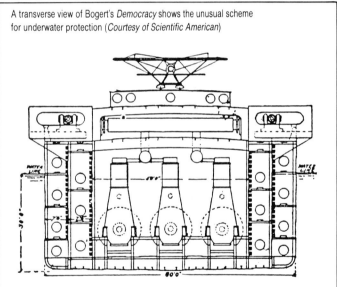

A transverse view of Bogert's *Democracy* shows the unusual scheme for underwater protection (*Courtesy of Scientific American*)

In its 'retarding' mode the belts would presumably be travelling in the opposite direction, but Bogert is vague on this point, and this function for the belts disappears in later versions of *Democracy*'s design.

Bogert envisaged the ship as carrying 'three large-size, bombing hydro-aeroplanes . . . provided with pontoons for landing on the sea . . . housed within the pontoons, are the usual landing wheels . . . the bottom of the wheels projecting sufficient to keep the surface of the pontoons clear of the deck'. These putative amphibious float-planes would therefore be similar to the Caudron

The Hamburg-Amerika Linie liner *Pennsylvania* fitted with an aircraft platform for an experimental take-off that failed to occur (*Courtesy of L L von Münching*)

biplanes that made take-offs from the British *Hermes* and French *Foudre* before the First World War; the same configuration was later employed by a number of amphibians.

Bogert planned for one such ship to accompany each convoy. Its aircraft, carrying depth charges, would scout ahead and around the procession, while the vessel's gunners would be ready to cope with any surfaced U-boat. Bogert specified the 5in calibre in the correct belief that later German submarines would carry 5.9in guns.

Bogert's prediction that aircraft would provide invaluable protection to convoys was fully borne out in the Second World War. Moreover, his carrier design was far more feasible than many other early proposals for aviation vessels. Its worst flaws were lack of aircraft-arresting gear (if the 'retarding belt' is discounted) and the upward-inclining portion of the deck. The latter, so similar to the ski-jump ramps of today's STOVL carriers, would have hindered rather than assisted take-off by the aeroplanes of 1917. A downward inclination would have been far better, and was used on many launching platforms or decks of the era. A final drawback is the low position of the pilot house, which would have made ship-handling difficult.

Hard on the heels of *Democracy*, Bogert graced the Navy Department with another carrier scheme, this one for a conversion of the interned and confiscated German liner *Kaiser Wilhelm II* into an aircraft 'mothership'. This, however,

seems a straightforward aviation vessel rather than a cargo-carrying hybrid, and so falls outside our consideration. It may be noted in passing that the design was nowhere near as original a concept as *Democracy*, the central superstructure and funnels being retained, while a *Campania*-like launching platform was added forward; aft, there was to be a landing deck that no doubt would have presented hazards similar to those of *Furious* and *Vindictive*.

Bogert waged a tireless campaign on behalf of his *Democracy*, both in public print and private letters, but the navy rejected the proposal three times during 1917–18. The stated reason was that mercantile tonnage was in too great demand to spare any for a purely experimental vessel. Unstated, but perhaps an additional reason, was the fact that the navy possessed no aircraft capable of oceanic shipboard work.

Bogert based his later claim to be 'Father of the Flat-Top' on several rather shaky premises. One was that the escort carriers of the Second World War were converted from or built on merchant hulls and were therefore identical to his 1917 proposal. 'Once a cargo vessel, always a cargo vessel', he maintained, refusing to concede that the CVEs lost their mercantile character in the process of conversion.

Nor would he accept the primacy of HMS *Argus* as the first flight-deck vessel, claiming that his 1917 patent application for such a craft predated the British ship. He also laboured under the strange delusion that aircraft could not, and never did, land aboard *Argus*. While admitting that *Argus* could launch aircraft, as late as 1946 he declared that the fact that she was *'fitted with ducts for discharging smoke and funnel gases at the stern* is clear proof, if one were needed, *that aviators did not fly in over the stern'*. This was written in the same year *Argus* was broken up after a career that had seen thousands of landings on her deck by more than forty different types of aircraft.

Oddly, the navy apparently never disabused Bogert of this bizarre belief. Instead, in one of the refutations of his claim, it muddied the waters further by confusing *Argus* with the Beardmore aviation vessel proposed in 1912 (mentioned in Chapter 1), probably because *Argus* was constructed by Beardmore.

The navy never did accord Bogert the recognition he sought, but in 1951 he received a private civilian award, the William A Moffett Maritime Aviation Trophy, donated by Lily W Reed, the founder of the National Maritime & Aeronautical Association. The concept of a flat-deck vessel for aircraft take-off and landing had occurred many times to many persons in many places long before Bogert put pen to paper, and his reasoning that the CVEs remained merchant ships was totally specious. Nevertheless, the inventor went to his grave convinced, as he wrote to Navy Secretary James Forrestal in 1946, 'John L. Bogert's ideas licked the German U-boats and won the "Battle of the Atlantic" '.

Bogert's *Democracy* and most other merchant hybrids were inspired by wartime needs, but there were a few merchant hybrids whose purposes were totally peaceful. Several of these schemes were based on the economic incentives offered by governments for rapid mail delivery. For many years, the major transoceanic mail-carrying craft were the great passenger liners, because their speed was so much higher than that of cargo ships. The value of rapid mail delivery was such that a few shipping firms were attracted to the idea of speeding delivery by flying aircraft from the passenger vessels while they were still a day or two from their destination. As early as November 1910 the Hamburg-Amerika Linie installed a flying-off platform on the stern of its liner *Kaiserin Augusta Victoria* for an experimental take-off after the vessel sailed from New York, but bad weather prevented it. The attempt was rescheduled a few days later, from the firm's liner *Pennsylvania*, but this time pre-sailing damage to the aeroplane aborted the scheme.

Aircraft aboard the stern catapult on French liner *Ile de France* in 1928 (R D Layman collection)

The idea was revived in 1928 with the installation of a catapult on the stern of the French liner *Ile de France*, from which a seaplane was launched for a 400 mile flight to New York City.

The most successful use of shipboard mail-carrying aircraft began in July 1929. The Norddeutscher Lloyd liners *Bremen* and *Europa* both had catapults specially designed and constructed by Ernst Heinkel Flugzeugwerke GmbH mounted between their funnels. These devices launched aircraft on nearly 200 flights, to New York on westbound Atlantic crossings and to Bremerhaven on eastbound legs. Successively improved types of Junkers and Heinkel aircraft were employed, all single-engined twin-float monoplanes, and they eventually extended range to 1250 miles and reduced New York-Berlin mail delivery to four and a half days, a span comparing favourably with today's. The use of the liners' aircraft ended in 1936 with the stationing of special catapult ships in the Atlantic to serve German air routes to North and South America.

It may have been the example of the German liners that inspired the famous designer Norman Bel Geddes to include provision for aircraft in a 1932 proposal for a highly streamlined ocean liner, an extremely visionary 1088ft vessel displacing 70,000 tons. His illustrations show a catapult and two twin-engined seaplanes abaft the second funnel in a streamlined hangar with retractable covering.

None of these vessels, real or imaginary, could be considered hybrids, but they are indicative of a trend toward the mercantile hybrid that might

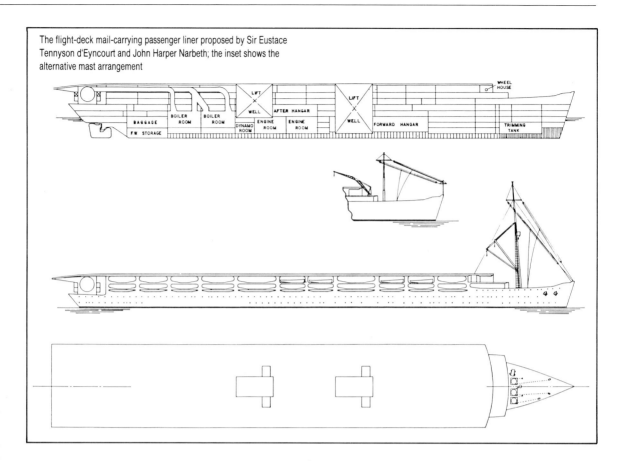

The flight-deck mail-carrying passenger liner proposed by Sir Eustace Tennyson d'Eyncourt and John Harper Narbeth; the inset shows the alternative mast arrangement

have developed had not the passenger/mail-carrying aeroplane advanced so greatly in size, capacity, speed and range.

An extreme extension of this trend was worked out even before the catapult liners entered service; a proposed flight-deck mail-carrying passenger vessel was discussed in detail at the 64th session of Britain's Institution of Naval Architects on 21 March 1923. It was the brainchild of two prominent Admiralty warship designers, Sir Eustace Tennyson d'Eyncourt and John Harper Narbeth. In 1923 D'Eyncourt was serving his final year as Director of Naval Construction, a post he had held since 1912; Narbeth was responsible for the design of most of the first generation of Royal Navy aviation vessels. In their liner design they were assisted by the equally distinguished C J W Hopkins. All three had been involved in aviation vessel design from the *Ark Royal* of 1914 to the flight-deck vessels *Argus, Eagle* and *Hermes*, and their collective experience in that field was without question the greatest in the world at the time.

Their plan provided for a moderately sized vessel fitted in all respects as a luxury liner, but in place of the normal superstructure they installed a flight deck. The rationale was to provide exchange of mail, passengers and light cargo via air to and

from ports at which the steamer itself would not stop.

The design had the following characteristics.

Displacement:	24,000t full load
Dimensions:	670ft oa × 80ft wl (92ft over bulges), 100ft at the flight deck
Machinery:	water-tube boilers, geared turbines; 40,000–45,000shp = 24kts (average sea speed 21–22kts at 60% power). Oil 2500t
Cargo capacity:	1500t
Accommodation:	1250 passengers in 4 classes; crew of 460 incl approx 20 aviation personnel

Auxiliary power was to be provided by four electric generators, two driven by steam, two by diesel engines.

The 565ft by 100ft flight deck terminated 100ft abaft the bow; immediately under its forward end was the bridge, with wings on each beam for vision aft. Forward, on a short fo'c's'le deck, was a tall semi-retractable mast carrying running lights and fitted with derricks to handle aircraft and cargo. An alternative arrangement provided a shorter, totally retractable mast to carry the lights, with cranes just forward of the flight deck replacing the derricks.

The level just below the flight deck was open for much of its length, thus helping to maintain uniform air flow on the flight deck and allowing stowage of enough boats to accommodate 1800 persons. There were two aircraft hangars, each two decks high, the forward hangar completely below the waterline, the after hangar right at waterline level. Each hangar was served by a 46ft by 26ft lift.

The two turbine compartments were aft of the forward hangar and directly below the after hangar. Abaft the engine rooms were the two boiler rooms, whose trunked uptakes led to a wide common duct just below the flight deck; exhaust gases would be vented through large circular vents on each beam aft, an arrangement generally similar to the 'tunnel funnels' of *Argus*, but the aft placement of the liner's boilers would have minimised the problem of hangar overheating encountered on the carrier.

The hull featured integral bulges to protect it against icebergs and collisions in peacetime. It was calculated that they would also contribute to the ship's stability, an important point in passenger liners where excess rolling could lead to unhappy travellers. In time of war, of course, the bulges would furnish protection against torpedoes and mines. The Washington Treaty had only recently been signed, and d'Eyncourt and Narbeth may have seen their ship as a way of increasing the Royal Navy's potential wartime carrier tonnage (a factor in several other merchant hybrid designs). They brushed aside this possibility, however, stating that 'This proposal is put forward as a commercial proposition and not as a subsidiary naval vessel. . . . It is fully recognized that the nearer this vessel can approach to ordinary commercial purposes the better'. Certainly the placement of the hangars, dictated by the need for as much above-water cabin space as possible, would have been a tremendous liability in wartime, since both would have provided vast and easily flooded compartments in the event of underwater damage.

The paper opined that this type of vessel could 'not only expedite the present mail and passenger services, but . . . offer facilities for rapid communication with ports or inland localities which have hitherto been very badly served by offshoots from the regular passenger and mail services'. Among examples cited as to how this might benefit empire trade routes was the case of a vessel bound from Britain to Australia via the Suez Canal. With only one stop at Port Saïd, the ship could aerially serve Lisbon, Gibraltar, Algiers, Malta, Naples, Port Sudan, Aden, British Somaliland, Colombo and Bombay.

In addition to this mail and passenger service, it was suggested that ' "joy rides" from the ship would be very profitable, and small two-seater machines could be provided for such a purpose. By this means on many routes passengers could view towns and country of great interest from the air, without going ashore, or stopping the vessel'.

It was even envisaged that with mooring and towing equipment fitted, the carrier-liners could be integrated into the empire airship routes then being planned, a venture that collapsed after the crash of the airship R.101 in 1930. Also, 'Arrangements could . . . be made . . . to carry and to use kite balloons for sport or trade purposes'.

There was some doubt about the number and type of aircraft to be embarked; the number might run from eight to twenty-two, but would depend on 'the type and construction of the aircraft, as well as their extreme dimensions. It would be necessary to modify existing commercial types by fitting the wings to fold back, or the tails to hinge, in order to be able to adopt lifts of a reasonable size and to stow a good number of machines of sufficient carrying capacity'. This would certainly have been necessary in the case of two types suggested, the de Havilland DH.9c, a two-passenger modification of the wartime DH.9a reconnaissance-bomber, and the de Havilland DH.34, a larger six-passenger model, both single-engined biplanes.

The rationale of the d'Eyncourt-Narbeth proposal received generally favourable comment during the discussion that followed the presentation of their paper. Among those favouring it were two well known figures in aviation circles, Admiral Mark Kerr and RAF Wing Commander T R Cave-Browne-Cave. What technical criticism was voiced centred on the length of the flight deck, with suggestions that it be lengthened or supplemented by a catapult, and the obstacle presented by the mast. The latter does indeed seem the design's major flaw. D'Eyncourt and Narbeth had foreseen that the mast might be 'open to objection as being in the way of aircraft', but believed 'this view is not sound, for machines rise in a very few yards, and after a very short time are well in the air and can be maneuvered to either side of the mast and shrouds . . . and in case of failure to alight the machine would get away clear of the vessel long before reaching the mast'. This optimism was not shared by some veteran aviators in the audience; oddly enough, no one commented on the lack of arresting gear in the design.

★   ★   ★

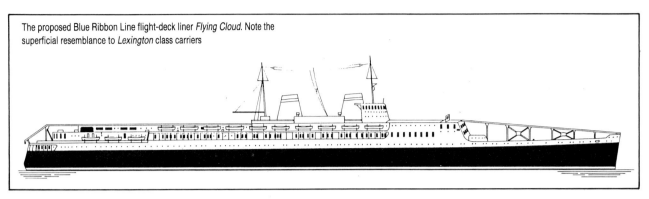

The proposed Blue Ribbon Line flight-deck liner *Flying Cloud*. Note the superficial resemblance to *Lexington* class carriers

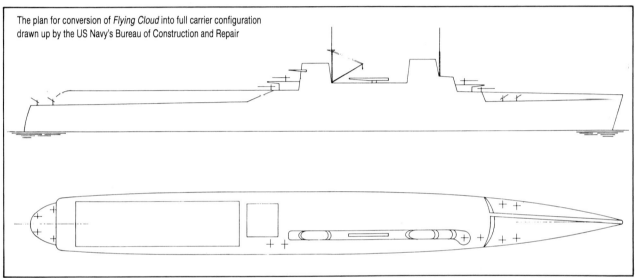

The plan for conversion of *Flying Cloud* into full carrier configuration drawn up by the US Navy's Bureau of Construction and Repair

Nothing came of the d'Eyncourt-Narbeth proposal, but an even more ambitious scheme along the same lines was put forward a year later. A venture by the Swiss firm Brown Boveri and Company and the New York Shipbuilding Corporation (then a division of Brown Boveri's US subsidiary), it envisaged a fleet of high-speed flight-deck liners for ultra-fast transatlantic service. The vessels' aircraft were to be used for the same sort of mail and passenger service as proposed by d'Eyncourt and Narbeth.

Lawrence R Wilder, chairman of New York Shipbuilding, was the driving force in the project and by 1927 he had obtained considerable financial investment and prestigious endorsements. Two firms, the Transoceanic Corporation of the United States and the Blue Ribbon Line, had been formed to manage and operate the service, and the design of the liners had been completed.

There were to be six Blue Ribbon Line vessels, the first to be christened *Flying Cloud* after one of the most famous of Donald Mackay's clipper ships. Of 35,000 tons, these liners were to measure

900ft by 90ft and be driven by turbines producing 130,000 to 160,000shp for a maximum speed of 35 knots and a normal sea speed of 31 knots.

Topside, two large funnels, two masts and a rather skimpy bridge structure were offset to starboard on a flight deck extending the entire length of the vessel. Forward, this deck sloped toward the bow, supported by stanchions over an open fo'c's'le; the stern featured a sharply downward-angled extension quite similar to those installed on the aircraft decks of the liner *Pennysylvania* and the cruiser *Pennsylvania* in 1911. A single large lift slightly aft of midships connected to a hangar deck immediately below; there was space for twenty-four aircraft.

Flying Cloud bore a superficial resemblance to the carriers *Lexington* and *Saratoga*; indeed, the liner and the carriers were roughly comparable in tonnage, dimensions, horsepower and speed. One doubts the resemblance was coincidental, for *Saratoga* had been under construction at New York Shipbuilding's Camden, New Jersey, yard all the while the Blue Ribbon project was taking shape. In fact, the liner was designed for rapid conver-

Merchant aircraft carrier *Empire MacAlpine*, first of a class of specially built grain carriers, with Fairey Swordfish ranged on deck (*Fleet Air Arm Museum*)

sion to a full-scale carrier in the event of a national emergency, with aircraft capacity enlarged to an estimated 100. For this reason, the US Navy may have been quite happy to see some of its carrier design features incorporated in *Flying Cloud* or even willing to pass some design tips along.

The navy's Bureau of Construction and Repair did in fact later draw up plans for converting *Flying Cloud* and its sisters into warships. A catapult and aircraft crane between the funnels were added, and the flight deck shortened aft to allow the installation of four single 5in/25 AA guns on the quarterdeck. Four more such guns, two on each beam, were placed forward, while a low-angle battery of four single 6in guns would be mounted in superimposed pairs fore and aft of the superstructure.

It has been suggested that the liner was designed in carrier form with an eye to obtaining government financial support of the venture. Such support was indeed sought; although Wilder had pledges of $50 million in private capital, far more money was required to meet construction costs, estimated at $21 million per vessel. In late 1927, therefore, the Blue Ribbon Line requested a loan from the US Shipping Board Construction Fund for 75 per cent of the cost of the six ships, or approximately $92.5 million. Shipping Board hearings on the application were held in January 1928, but Wilder's arguments for the project fell on deaf ears. The request was rejected by the board on 27 April 1928 on the grounds that the project was 'technically open to criticism, economically unsound and financially nebulous'.

This was not quite the end of the Blue Ribbon Line; Wilder continued to press the project until his death in 1937, but that complicated story is beyond the scope of this book.

Hindsight suggests that the Shipping Board's rejection of the Blue Ribbon project, while undoubtedly based on what seemed sound judgement at the time, robbed the American govern-

ment of an economic bargain and the US Navy of an invaluable reserve. For an investment of only $10.5 million more than the price of the two *Lexingtons* (whose construction costs had risen to about $40 million apiece, an increase of more than 90 per cent over the original estimate), *six* ships of roughly comparable size, speed and aircraft capacity could have been obtained. As merchantmen, these vessels were not limited by the Washington Treaty restrictions on individual or total carrier tonnage, and they were deliberately designed to permit conversion to full carrier form in a matter of months. It seems likely that their aircraft complement was overestimated; certainly they could not have been as efficient as purpose-built warships, and they would no doubt have been more vulnerable to bomb, shell, and torpedo. Nevertheless, it requires little imagination to conceive what effect their existence might have had on Pacific strategy, Japanese as well as American.

There is a certain irony in the Shipping Board's rejection of the *Flying Cloud* project, for in 1939, the US Maritime Commission, successor to the Shipping Board, produced the P-4-P design for a liner with offset funnels, intended for rapid conversion to a flight-deck carrier in wartime. Although it would not have carried aircraft commercially, one cannot help thinking that very much the same thing could have been achieved a full decade earlier if only Walker had been heeded. But, like *Flying Cloud*, the P-4-P came to nothing.

Two more American schemes for liner-carrier combinations were subsequently advanced: the 'Yankee Clippers' of 1937 and the 'Liberty Liners' of 1949 and 1961. Nothing came of them, and the ships cannot be considered hybrids for they were intended not to operate aircraft commercially but

to serve as naval carriers in wartime. To this end the design of both types featured telescopic masts and — shades of Giuseppe Rota — retractable funnels.

When hybrid merchant ship-aircraft carriers finally did come into existence, in the form of the aforementioned British MACs, they bore a considerable superficial resemblance to the vessel envisaged by Bogert a quarter of a century earlier and were intended for precisely the same purpose: protection of convoys against submarines in oceanic areas beyond the range of land-based aircraft.

The MACs were a logical extension of the catapult aircraft merchant ships (CAMs) of 1941, which carried fighter planes to ward off German aircraft. Credit for conceiving the MAC idea has been assigned to various persons: Captain M S Slattery, the Royal Navy's Director of Air Material, is one; Sir Douglas Thomson, the Ministry of War Transport's parliamentary private secretary, is another; while John Lamb, marine superintendent of the Anglo-Saxon Petroleum Com-

pany, is said to be responsible for bringing oil tankers into the scheme.

Whatever the case, the concept was thrashed out in sessions of the Board of Admiralty and technical experts during May and June of 1942, and formal authorisation of the plan was given on 2 June. It was strictly an expedient. 'It was . . . never intended', one chronicler of the MACs has written, 'that [the ships] should be more than an interim measure in the anti-submarine campaign. Primarily for defensive and reconnaissance duties with the convoys, they satisfied the requirements of a short-term policy, and filled the gap until naval auxiliary carriers became available'.

Original naval staff requirements relating to ship speed, flight-deck length and hangar capacity (all factors determining the type of aircraft that could be carried) had to be scaled back to adjust to the capacity and skills of the merchant shipbuilding yards that were to construct or convert the vessels. It was laid down from the start that all the MACs were to be diesel-powered, thus eliminating the complicated construction required to vent the greater volume of gases produced by steam engines.

Another precondition was that the vessels would be strictly merchantmen, with civilian crews, flying the red ensign, and subject to mercantile procedures and regulations. The aircrews would be aboard as supernumeraries, in the same manner as naval gun crews. This situation was fraught with possibilities for friction, but in fact a high degree of comradeship developed between the merchant mariners and the Fleet Air Arm personnel.

Altogether, nineteen MAC ships entered service between April 1943 and May 1944. They were of three general types: six specially constructed grain carriers (*Empire MacAlpine* class), nine converted oilers of the Anglo-Saxon Petroleum Company (*Rapana* class) and four oilers reconfigured while building (*Empire MacKay* class). The class names were unofficial, taken from the name of the first vessel of each category to enter service.

Because the vessels were produced by eleven different yards, there were many minor variations among them. The *Rapana* class was fairly uniform, with deadweight tonnage of 11,009 and 461ft 8in flight decks. The grain carriers varied between 7930 and 8360 deadweight tons with flight decks ranging from approximately 413ft to approximately 424ft. Deadweight tonnage of the *Empire MacKays* varied from 11,000 to 11,508; their flight decks averaged about 461ft. Speeds in all classes were 11 to 13 knots.

The normal superstructure in all MACs was eliminated, replaced by a small starboard island, farther forward on the grain carriers than on the oilers. The steel flight decks were external, not strength, decks, largely prefabricated and installed with expansion joints. Engine room gases were exhausted through side openings vented to permit discharge on each beam.

The six grain carriers had belowdecks hangars, uniformly 142ft × 38ft, able to accommodate four aircraft with wings folded, and served by single 42ft by 20ft electrically powered lifts with a capacity of 5 tons.

The internal arrangements required by the oilers made installation of hangars impossible, so their aircraft were stowed in a 100ft aft deck park, protected by a system of screens and palisades that was often inadequate to prevent weather damage.

Armament of all the MACs included one 4in LA gun aft. The grain vessels mounted two 40mm and four 20mm AA guns; the others had seven to nine 20mm guns.

Nominal aircraft capacity on all the merchant carriers was four machines, but because of their lack of hangars the oilers usually embarked only three. Originally, equipping the MACs with the American Vought-Sikorsky OS2U Kingfisher was contemplated, but in the end the Fairey Swordfish, with its slower landing speed and shorter take-off run, was found more suitable. This modest, seemingly anachronistic biplane proved to be the Royal Navy's ubiquitous aerial work-horse of the Second World War, as valuable flying from the decks of the MACs as it was everywhere from the first day of the conflict to the last. MAC Swordfish fought numerous skirmishes with U-boats, employing bombs, depth charges and rockets, and toward the end were equipped with radar and the jet-assisted take-off (JATO) system. It is doubtful that the MAC aircraft ever sank a submarine by independent action, but they assisted in some kills and inflicted a not-insignificant amount of damage. More importantly, they forced many a U-boat to keep its head down in the presence of a convoy, in the long run a contribution probably more important to the preservation of merchant ships than the actual destruction of the enemy submarines.

The MAC aircraft were organised as No 836 Squadron, the largest in the Fleet Air Arm, with nineteen flights designated by the letters A to S; one flight was assigned to each ship.

The converted oiler *Macoma* was the last MAC to commission, in May 1944. By this time enough CVEs were available, and plans to create thirteen more MACs were cancelled. No 836 Squadron was disbanded on 21 May 1945 and the entire system officially terminated on 28 June. By then the merchant carriers had spent 3057 days at sea with Atlantic convoys and their Swordfish had logged 9106 hours in the air in 4177 individual flights.

With the end of hostilities all the MACs were rapidly converted or reconverted to normal mercantile configuration, and all underwent various changes of ownership, name and/or nationality. All were scrapped as the years passed; the first to go was *Adula* in 1953.

The idea of merchant conversions, auxiliaries or commercial aircraft-carrying ships seems to have lapsed in the decades following 1945. However, the US Navy has fairly recently revived the MAC concept in what it calls the ARAPAHO system, based on the combination of containerships and the rotary-wing aircraft. It is predicated upon the fact that the size, stability and deck strength of a containership permits installation of landing pads larger and stronger than those of small surface combatants, thus allowing operation of heavier aircraft, and a greater number of them, while the ship's standard cargo containers can house much if not all of their equipment, personnel and fuel. It is proposed to create a number of units that could, without use of specialised labour, rapidly convert a containership into a helicopter

British Aerospace's proposed SCADS ship (*Courtesy of British Aerospace*)

carrier whose aircraft would perform anti-submarine and early-warning duties for convoys, supplement the aircraft of conventional carriers, or substitute for such aircraft in areas or situations where carriers would be unavailable.

The ARAPAHO system was tested aboard the 18,000 ton containership *Export Leader*, operating from Norfolk, Virginia, in October 1982. During 40 hours at sea, the vessel logged 223 deck landings, forty-five of them at night, involving seven helicopters of four different types.

The feasibility of the system seems clearly demonstrated, and creation of a force of ARAPAHO vessels could undoubtedly, as its advocates claim, be a powerful 'force multiplier' for any navy. The hybrid nature of such vessels is also clear, for it is estimated that even after installation of the ARAPAHO system they would retain 85 to 90 per cent of their cargo-carrying capacity.

★   ★   ★

An even more ambitious use of the containership as an aviation vessel was demonstrated during the British campaign to retake the Falkland Islands from Argentine forces in 1982. Among the multitude of merchantmen taken over to supplement Royal Navy warships were four container

vessels converted into aircraft ferries: sisters *Atlantic Conveyor* and *Atlantic Causeway* (14,867 tons, 22 knots), *Contender Bezant* (11,445 tons, 19 knots) and *Astronomer* (27,867 tons, 22 knots). All were modified in an astonishingly short time considering the complexity of the work required, none taking more than ten days.

All were intended primarily for helicopter basing, maintenance, repair and refuelling, but the potential for V/STOL operation by a containership was shown by *Atlantic Conveyor*, the first to enter service. Sailing from Devonport on 25 April with a complement of helicopters, she took aboard eight Fleet Air Arm Sea Harriers and six RAF GR.3 ground-attack Harriers at Ascension Island on 5 May. On 19 May these were flown off to carriers *Hermes* and *Invincible*, providing badly needed reinforcements.

Six days after this demonstration of the V/STOL potential of the containership, *Atlantic Conveyor* was struck by two air-launched Exocet missiles that started disastrous fires; she sank on 19 May while under tow. No Harriers were aboard when the missile hit, but several helicopters were lost with the ship.

Meanwhile, *Contender Bezant* had embarked four Harriers at Ascension and carried out deck landing trials with them before sailing for the zone of hostilities, where *Atlantic Causeway* had arrived on 27 May. *Astronomer*, largest and best equipped of the aircraft ferries, did not reach the islands until after the conflict ended, but along with *Contender Bezant* and *Atlantic Causeway* performed valuable helicopter support work in the aftermath of the campaign. In 1983 *Atlantic Causeway* was chartered by the Royal Navy for experimental work with Harriers and anti-submarine helicopters, temporarily renamed *Reliant* before reverting to mercantile service and her original name.

These four converted vessels can be considered hybrids in a sense, for in addition to their aviation role they served as store ships, able to embark thousands of tons of earth-breaking and earth-moving equipment for airfield construction, tents, clothing, rations and ammunition for troops ashore, AA missiles and their launchers, and a myriad of other combat-related items.

The success of these masterfully improvised craft led to a more advanced concept for a merchant aviation vessel, British Aerospace's proposed Shipborne Containerised Air Defence System (SCADS) ship. Several types of SCADS ships have been put forward, all designed to take advantage of the flexibility of containerised weapons systems; one scheme envisages a pre-prepared package of components, including pre-fabricated ski-ramp flight decks and helicopter pads, that could transform a containership of about 30,000 deadweight tons into a floating base for six Sea Harriers and two helicopters within 48 hours. As with the Falklands aircraft ferries and the ARAPAHO system, standard containers would provide shelter for the aircraft and help house their support systems and personnel. Self-defence weaponry would include SeaWolf missiles and decoy launchers.

Classification of such ships as hybrids would depend on whether they were used for cargo-carrying as well as aviation purposes. The SCADS Harrier-carrier conversion would require 233 containers, while containerships of suitable size have a capacity of 2000 containers; clearly, a considerable cargo load could be carried in addition to the SCADS equipment.

The recent emergence of the containership into the aviation role would seem a continuation of the ancient maritime practice under which any vessel able to mount a weapon, from a galley in the Egypt of the Pharoahs to a twentieth-century ocean liner, might be pressed into service as a warship. Again, *plus ça change, plus c'est la même chose.*

BIBLIOGRAPHICAL NOTES

The following abbreviations have been used for frequently cited publications
Combat Fleets: Combat Fleets of the World
Conway's: Conway's All the World's Fighting Ships
Jane's: Jane's Fighting Ships
NYT: New York Times
USNIP: United States Naval Institute Proceedings
WI: Warship International

Introduction
On the inclination to disperse aircraft rather than concentrating them in carriers, see the joint essay 'Capital Ships' in Charles W Domville-Fife, ed, *Evolution of Sea Power* (London: Rich & Cowan, 1939). Other topics mentioned will be covered in more detail in the relevant chapters.

Chapter 1: Trying on Wings
The Beardmore design is described and illustrated by the present authors in *Before the Aircraft Carrier: Development of Aviation Vessels 1849-1923* (London: Conway Maritime Press, 1989), pp33-34, based on material in Sir Arthur W Johns' 'Aircraft Carriers', *Transactions of the Institution of Naval Architects*, vol LXXVI (London, 1934), pp1-19. Structural and other details of *Furious* as she was originally designed can be found in Oscar Parkes' *British Battleships*, revised edition (London: Seeley Service, 1966), pp621-24, and in R A Burt, *British Battleships of World War One* (Annapolis: Naval Institute Press, 1986), pp303-15. Her initial redesign and early operations are discussed in C A Jenkins, *HMS Furious/ Aircraft Carrier 1917-1948, Part 1, Profile Warship 23* (Windsor, Berks: 1972); R D Layman, '*Furious* and the Tondern Raid', *WI*, vol 10, no 4, 1973, pp374-85, and W G Moore's autobiography *Early Bird* (London: Putnam, 1963), pp94-128. This last describes the great strain on the ship from the firing of the 18in gun. An overall history of *Furious* is given in Douglas Stuart Jordan, 'Fisher's Folly - the Fabulous *Furious*', *USNIP*, vol 81, no 6 (June 1955), pp667-77. Much of the information on *Vindictive* came from a detailed chronological history compiled by R H Nailer, former chairman of the World Ship Society's Naval Subcommittee, publisher of the Society's *Warships Supplements;* the authors are grateful to Mr Nailer for supplying a copy before its publication.

The genesis of the *Hawkins* class is thoroughly described in John Roberts and Alan Raven, *British Cruisers of World War Two* (Annapolis: Naval Institute Press, 1980), pp51-61. Wind tunnel tests of the *Vindictive* models are described in D K Brown's 'Early Aircraft Carrier Projects', *Warship no 36*, pp218-22. *Vindictive's* Baltic operations are described by Geoffrey Bennet's *Cowan's War: The Story of British Naval Operations in the Baltic, 1918-1920* (London: Collins, 1964). Her use as a CMB depot ship is noted in Augustus Agar's *Baltic Episode: A Classic of Secret Service in Russian Waters* (London: Hodder

and Stoughton, 1963). Particulars and appearance of *Vindictive* after her 1923-25 reconstruction are especially well given and illustrated in the 1928 edition of *Jane's*.

Finally, those interested in the German seaplane carrier projects (which were not hybrid ships, but which provide an interesting comparison to contemporary British thinking) can find information and illustrations of *Roon* and *Stuttgart* in Erich Gröner's *Die deutschen Kriegsschiffe 1815-1945*, Band 1: *Panzerschiffe, Linienschiffe, Schlachtschiffe, Flugzeugträger, Kreuzer, Kanonenboote*, revised and updated by Dieter Jung and Martin Maass (Munich: Bernard & Graefe Verlag, 1982), pp78-79, 131-33.

Chapter 2: Flights of Fancy
One of the best works on the growth of the 'air power' doctrine is Michael S Sherry's *Rise of American Air Power: The Creation of Armageddon* (New Haven: Yale University Press, 1987). For an analysis of Mitchell's conflict with the US Navy, see Charles M Melhorn, *Two-Block Fox: The Rise of the Aircraft Carrier, 1911-1929* (Annapolis: Naval Institute Press, 1974). For the British side of postwar naval aviation, see Stephen Roskill's *Naval Policy Between the Wars, vol 1: The Period of Anglo-American Antagonism, 1919-1929* (London: Collins, 1968). The *Hood* type hybrid appeared in *USNIP*, vol 49, no 241 (March 1923), p482. A search of standard sources has revealed no information about Strother. Biographical information on Sir George Thurston comes mainly from an obituary in *Engineering*, vol 169, no 4384 (3 February 1950), p131 and another obituary in the London *Times* for 25 January 1950, p7. His 1914 battleship designs can be found in the *Transactions of the Institute of Naval Architects*, vol LVI (1914), pp1-32. His 'Capital Ship of the Future' article appeared in the 1920-21 edition of *Brassey's Naval and Shipping Annual* (London: William Clowes), pp70-81. His article on 'The Influence of the Washington Conference on Naval Design', which included his first hybrid scheme, the 'experimental battleship', appeared in the 1923 edition of the same annual (pp85-99). Extracts of this article appeared in the May 1923 issue of *Scientific American* (vol 128, no 5, p304), the July 1923 *USNIP* (vol 49, no 245, pp1221-1223) and in the 20 October 1923 issue of the *Literary Digest* (vol 79, no 3, pp23-25). Sir George's article proposing hybrid ships for South American navies, 'Battleship or Aircraft Carrier?', appeared in the 1926 edition of *Brassey's*, pp79-93. In this article, Sir George mentioned that his hybrid battleship had been favourably noted in a paper by Vice-Admiral Amet of the French Navy; Amet's brief comments appeared in '*Le Navire de Guerre Maximum*', *Bulletin de L'Association Technique Maritime et Aéronautique*, no 28 (1924) pp19-45. A discussion of Sir George's article appeared in the October 1926 *USNIP* (vol 52, no 284), pp2078-2079), which mentioned the hybrid scheme of the 'student of naval design'.

Chapter 3: 'This Idiotic Canard'
Without question the best work available on the *Nelson* design, and the preceding G3 battlecruiser design, is Alan Raven and John Roberts, *British Battleships of World War Two* (Annapolis: Naval Institute Press, 1976), pp90-127. Also valuable on the G3 design in N J M Campbell's four-part series 'Washington's Cherrytrees' in *Warship*, no 1, pp2-11; no 2, pp12-19; no 3, pp38-45; and no 4, pp37-41. Valuable background on Anglo-American naval relations can be found in the Roskill work cited in Chapter 2, above. Newspaper articles on this strange affair include:
'Warship of Future a Contest of Wits', *NYT*, 8 January 1923, p21.
'The New British Warships', *NYT*, 9 January 1923, p3.
'Two New Warships of Britain Described', *NYT*, 16 December 1924, p15.
'New British Sea Giants Make Old Navies Obsolete', *Chicago Tribune*, 11 January 1925, part 1, p12. (Reprinted in *NYT*, 11 January 1925, p2.)
'The New Fighting Ship', *Washington Post*, 15 January 1925 (reprinted in *USNIP*, vol 51, no 3 [March 1925], pp483-484).
'Senate Approves Arms Parley', *NYT*, 22 January 1925, p1.
'A Mystery Battleship', *NYT*, 13 October 1925, p22.

Quotations from the *New York American* of 22 January 1925 and the *World* of New York of 26 January 1925 are taken from Sir George Thurston's 'Battleship or Aircraft Carrier?' article in the 1926 edition of *Brassey's*, cited in Chapter 2; his 'experimental battleship', which undoubtedly contributed to the fuss, appeared in the 1923 edition of that same annual, also cited in Chapter 2. This last article also has Sir George's capital ship 'where gun power predominates'.

The description of Colonel Robert R McCormick is taken from the *New Columbia Encyclopedia* (New York: Columbia University Press, 1975), p1643.

Captain Henry H Hough's testimony on the *Nelson* and *Rodney* before the House Subcommittee on Navy Department Appropriations was part of the testimony on the Navy Department Appropriation Bill, 1926 (HR 10724, 68th Congress, 2nd Session). This testimony formed the basis of an article in the *Engineer* (vol CXXXIX, no 3602, 9 January 1925), pp49-50, describing the new battleships. The volume containing the *Annual Reports of the Navy Department* for the Fiscal Year 1923, which were submitted on 15 November 1923, was published in 1924 by the Government Printing Office; material on the gun elevation controversy can be found on pp75-76, 114-17.

The Senate and House had many debates over the gun elevation issue; anyone wishing to read through these long and repetitive arguments can find them in the *Congressional Record* for the years 1923-25 by using the indices. Senator Gerry's remarks on *Nelson* and *Rodney* are in the *Congressional Record*, Vol 66, part 2 (68th Congress, 2nd Session, 1925), pp1969-1970, while Senator McKellar's first resolution can also be found in the *Congressional Record*, vol 66, part 3 (68th Congress, 2nd Session, 1925), p2188; his second submission of the same resolution can be found in Vol 67, part 1, p494 (69th Congress, Special Session/1st Session).

Revue Maritime published '*Les bâtiments*

«*Hush, Hush*»' in its February 1925 (No 62) issue, pp261-4; the sketch appeared on p267. The improbable hybrid illustration appeared in *Popular Mechanics*, vol 43, no 4 (April 1925), pp542-543. Diplomatic correspondence between Britain and the United States on the gun elevation controversy can be found in *Foreign Relations of the United States*, 1923, Vol I, pp24-34, and 1924, vol I, pp6-17 (Washington: State Department, 1938-9).

Material on the Bureau of Construction and Repair's attempts to divine what the *Nelson* would look like can be found in Norman Friedman's *U.S. Battleships: An Illustrated Design History* (Annapolis: Naval Institute Press, 1985), and in an article by Alan D Zimm, 'The USN's Flight Deck Cruiser', in *WI*, vol XVI, no 3 (1979), pp216-45. This article contains Rear Admiral Beuret's hybrid *Nelson* sketch. The wind tunnel experiments with the model of the *Pennsylvania* were reported in the *Journal of the Franklin Institute*, vol 188, no 3 (September 1919), pp389-97.

Hector C Bywater's article on the *Nelson*, and the editor's devastating attack on the whole hybrid theory, can be found in *Scientific American*, vol 133, no 4 (October 1925), pp250-51.

Chapter 4: 'An Exceedingly Useful Type of Warship'

Early Royal Navy attempts to develop carrier doctrine, including carriers of differing functions and characteristics for different roles, are discussed in Norman Friedman, *British Carrier Aviation: The Evolution of the Ships and Their Aircraft* (Annapolis: Naval Institute Press, 1988), pp100-103. American diplomatic manoeuvrings that led to Article IX of the Washington Treaty are analysed in Paul M Craig's '*Lexington* and *Saratoga*, the New Beginning', *USNIP* vol 95, no 12 (December 1969), pp85-92.

The *Progetto Rota* is noted in Giorgio Giorgerini and Augusto Nani, *Le Navi di Linea Italiane 1861-1969*, third edition (Rome: Ufficio Storico Della Marina Militare, 1973), pp59-60. Erminio Bagnasco, *La Portaerei Nella Marina Italiana: Idee, Progetti e Realizzazioni dalle Origini ad Oggi* (Rome: Rivista Marittima, 1989), pp46-8, provides more information, and also describes the *incrociatore antiaereo* of Fioranvanzo (p36). Other Italian carrier projects are described in this volume and by James J Sadkovich in 'Aircraft Carriers and the Mediterranean, 1940-1943: Rethinking the Obvious', *Aerospace Historian*, vol 34, no 4 (winter/December 1987), pp263-71. Sadkovich advances the revisionist view that the lack of carriers was not particularly damaging to Italy during the Second World War. Mussolini's role in blocking carrier construction is discussed by Admiral Romero Bernotti in 'Italian Naval Policy Under Fascism', *USNIP* vol 82, no 7 (July 1950), pp722-31. Bernotti's prewar opposition to Douhet's views are noted in Louis A Signaud, *Douhet and Aerial Warfare* (New York: G P Putnam's Sons, 1941), p55. The consequences of the Italian Navy's lack of an adequate air arm are described in Marc' Antonio Bragadin, *The Italian Navy in World War II* (Annapolis: Naval Institute Press, 1957), pp9-11 and pp21-23. Biographical information on Giuseppe Rota is taken from his obituary in *Engineering*, vol 177, no 4591 (22

January 1954), p99. He is noted as the designer of only the *Campania* and *Bixio* classes in *Conway's, 1906-1921*; the section on Italian ships, written by Aldo Fraccaroli, lists the designers of virtually every class of vessel constructed during this period.

What sparse information there is on the *croiseur de combat* can be found in William H Garzke Jr and Robert O Dulin Jr, *Battleships: Allied Battleships in World War II* (Annapolis: Naval Institute Press, 1980), pp33-35. There is additional information, derived from unnamed French naval journals, in the article by Bywater and Prendergast, 'Post-Treaty Naval Design', *USNIP* vol 51, no 11 (November 1925), pp2125-37. The article prompted considerable correspondence in that periodical's 'Discussion' section from February to September 1926.

The proposed *Duquesne-Tourville* conversions are described in Francis Dousset, *Les porte-avions français: dès origines (1911) à nos jours* (Brest: Éditions de la Cité, 1978), pp 52-53, and in Henri le Masson, *Navies of the Second World War: The French Navy*, vol 1 (Garden City, NY: Doubleday, 1969), pp30-31. Dousset's same work also mentions the *croiseurs porte-avion* of 1922 (p21).

A detailed and well illustrated description and history of *Gotland* is contained in Edward C Fisher Jr and Bertil Gard, 'The Three Faces of *Gotland*', *WI* vol XIII, no 3 (1976), pp193-208. Supplemental information and a profile of the original design with three twin turrets accompanied a letter from Curt Borgenstam in the same journal, vol XIV, no 3 (1977), pp185-6. Another sketch of the three-turret design appeared in the 1929 edition of *Jane's*, p410; issues of that yearbook during 1930-1960 provide further details on the ship. See also R D Layman, 'Sparrows Among the Hawks: Shipboard Aviation in the Smaller Navies, 1919-1939', in *WI*, vol XXI, no 2 (1984), pp138-57 (reprinted in revised form in *Small Air Forces Observer*, vol 9, no 3 [April 1985], pp65-71). Correspondence on the Swedish request to obtain American catapults is contained in General Board file 428, serial 1469, 23 January 1930; these files are in the US National Archives. Details of Swedish acquisition of Hawker Ospreys are given in J Gordon Holmes, 'Harts and Ospreys in Sweden', *Air Pictorial*, vol 47, no 3 (March 1985), pp100-102. Particulars of the Osprey are in Owen Thetford's *British Naval Aircraft 1912-58* (London: Putnam, 1958), pp212-3. *Gotland's* sighting of *Bismarck* and *Prinz Eugen* and how that information came into British hands is described in Henry Denham's autobiography *Inside the Nazi Ring: A Naval Attaché in Sweden 1940-1945* (New York: Holmes & Meier, 1985), pp84-86, and in Ludovic Kennedy's *Pursuit: The Chase and Sinking of the Bismarck* (New York: Viking Press, 1974), pp18-19.

Chapter 5: Carriers, Cruisers and Treaties

The pre-World War origins of War Plan Orange are discussed by Richard W Turk, 'Defending the New Empire, 1900-1914', in *In Peace and War: Interpretations of American Naval History, 1775-1984*, 2nd ed, edited by Kenneth J Hagan (Westport, Conn: Greenwood Press, 1984), pp186-204; its development between the wars is discussed at great length in Admiral James O Richardson's

ghost-written memoirs *On the Treadmill to Pearl Harbor* (Washington: Naval History Division, Department of the Navy, 1973), p176 *passim*. The quotation, which was termed 'The Primary Naval Mission for the United States Fleet', is found on p272. See also William R Braisted's 'On the American Red and Red-Orange Plans, 1919-1939', in *Naval Warfare in the Twentieth Century: Essays in Honour of Arthur Marder*, edited by Gerald Jordan (London: Croom Helm, 1977), pp167-85, and 'War Plan Orange: Evolution of a Strategy' by Louis Morton in *World Politics: A Quarterly Journal of International Relations*, vol XI, no 2 (January 1959), pp221-250.

The various plans for arming American carriers, including particulars of the schemes mentioned in the text, are described by Norman Friedman in *U.S. Aircraft Carriers: An Illustrated Design History* (Annapolis: Naval Institute Press, 1983), pp57-62. Other aspects of the 'battle of the guns' are noted in Scot MacDonald's *Evolution of Aircraft Carriers* (Washington: Government Printing Office, 1964), a compilation of articles originally appearing in *Naval Aviation News*.

Information on *Akagi* and *Kaga* is available in Anthony J Watts and Brian G Gordon, *The Imperial Japanese Navy* (Garden City, New York: Doubleday, 1971), pp171-7; in Hansgeorg Jentschura, Dieter Jung and Peter Mickel, *Warships of the Imperial Japanese Navy, 1869-1945* (Annapolis: US Naval Institute, 1977), pp42-45; and in Hans Lenger-er's three-part article, 'Akagi and Kaga' in *Warship*, no 22, pp127-39; no 23, pp170-7; and no 24, pp305-10. Captain Anderson's article, 'Guns Allowed Aircraft Carriers — A Paradox', appeared in *USNIP*, vol 53, no 5 (May 1927), pp539-43.

MacDonald's *Evolution of Aircraft Carriers, op cit* describes the fleet manoeuvres that led to the development of the task force concept (pp28-38). A dramatic account of *Saratoga's* attack on the Panama Canal is contained in Eugene E Wilson's *Slipstream: The Autobiography of an Air Craftsman* (New York: Whittlesey House, 1950), pp135-48. The origins and development of dive bombing in the US Navy are well described in Peter C Smith's *Dive Bomber: An Illustrated History* (Annapolis: Naval Institute Press, 1982); other sources include Archibald D Turnbull and Clifford L Lord, *History of United States Naval Aviation* (New Haven: Yale University Press, 1949), and David R Mets, 'Dive-Bombing Between the Wars', *The Airpower Historian* vol 12, no 3 (July 1965), pp85-89.

Plans to convert an *Omaha* class 6in cruiser into an aircraft carrier are described in Norman Friedman's *U.S. Aircraft Carriers, op cit*, p37. The Bates proposal for a hybrid cruiser-carrier is described by the same author in *U.S. Cruisers: An Illustrated Design History* (Annapolis: Naval Institute, 1984), p121. Friedman also mentions the Construction and Repair hybrid cruisers sketched during the preliminary design of the *Pensacola* class in 'U.S. Flight-Deck Cruiser Designs', *Warship*, no 13, pp24-37. The General Board's recommendation against cruiser conversions to carriers and hybrid ships can be found in a memo to the Secretary of the Navy dated 16 January 1926, in the General Board files at the National Archives in Washington (series 420-7, serial no 1270).

Representative James V McClintic's bizarre hybrid battleship proposals are described in McClintic's 'Minority Views' to the bill for 'Construction of Certain Naval Vessels' (Report 834, Part 2, on HR 11526, 70th Congress, 1st Session, dated 6 March 1928), most easily available in the *U.S. Serials Set*, vol 8836. He further described his ideas on the floor of the House of Representatives as reported in the *Congressional Record*, 70th Congress, 1st Session (vol 69, part 4), pp4654–4655. Representative Britten's sarcastic attack on the whole idea can also be found in the *Congressional Record*, 70th Congress, 1st Session (vol 69, part 5), pp4845–4846, while McClintic's arguments in support of his measure are from the same volume, pp4850–4851, 4906–4908.

The double-ended cruiser recommended by Taussig can be found in a memo from Taussig to the Secretary of the Navy dated 6 January 1930 in General Board file 420-8 (cruisers); the Bureau of Aeronautics scheme for increased seaplane facilities on cruisers can be found in the same General Board file in a memo dated 11 December 1929.

A good general introduction to the London Naval Conference (although lacking information on the flying-deck cruiser issue) is Raymond G O'Connor's *Perilous Equilibrium: The United States and the London Naval Conference of 1930* (Lawrence, Kansas: University of Kansas, 1962). The roles of Moffett and Pratt are discussed in their respective biographies, Edward Arpee's *From Frigates to Flat-Tops* (Chicago: Lakeside Press, 1953) and Gerald E Wheeler's *Admiral William Veazie Pratt, U.S. Navy: A Sailor's Life* (Washington: Naval History Division, 1974). The presence of van Keuren and Bates at London is revealed by the roster of the American delegation published in *NYT*, 18 December 1930, p2. The hybrid cruiser and battlecruiser designs sketched during the conference are mentioned by Friedman, *U.S. Cruisers, op cit*, p168. The characteristics of the battlecruiser sketch were outlined by Pratt during a General Board hearing held aboard his flagship, USS *Texas*, on 27 May 1930, contained in the General Board Hearings for that year. Moffett's testimony on the ratification of the London Naval Treaty can be found in the Hearings Before the Senate Committee on Naval Affairs on the London Naval Treaty of 1930, pp269–287.

Procter's diesel-engined hybrid cruiser appeared in *USNIP* vol 56, no 6 (June 1930), pp997–1002. Biographical information on him is taken from an obituary in *NYT*, 26 March 1938, p15. His earlier articles on diesel engines for warships can be found in the following issues of *USNIP*:
'Diesel Engines for Capital Ships — A Military Necessity', July 1925 (vol 51, no 7), pp1217–24. (Correspondence regarding this article appeared in the 'Discussion' section of the *Proceedings* in the July, August, September, and November 1925 issues, as well as May 1928.)
'The Present Situation in Regard to Diesel Engines for Capital Ships', July 1929 (vol 55, no 7), pp604–20.

It was the first of these articles that Edward C Magdeburger cited in his 'Diesel Engines for the Navy', published in the *Transactions of the Society of Naval Architects and Marine Engineers* in 1927 (vol 35, pp197–234). The

presence of both James L Bates and Procter at the reading of this paper is shown by the discussion that followed the presentation.

Chapter 6: 'The Forerunner of Future Men-of-War'

The bulk of the material in this chapter is taken from General Board Files 420-2 and 420-8 (cruisers) for the years 1930–31, and the General Board Hearings on the flying-deck cruiser held on 4, 5 and 23 December 1930 and on 16 and 17 July 1931. Secondary sources included Norman Friedman's *U.S. Cruisers, op cit*, Chapter 6; the same author's 'U.S. Flight-Deck Cruiser Designs' in *Warship, op cit*; Alan D Zimm, 'The U.S.N.'s Flight Deck Cruiser' in *WI, op cit*; and 'The Ship That Never Was: The Flying-Deck Cruiser' by Ernest Andrade Jr, in *Military Affairs*, vol 32, no 3 (December 1968), pp132–140. Useful background information can be found in Turnbill and Lord, *History of United States Naval Aviation, op cit*, and Donald W Mitchell, *History of the Modern American Navy* (London: John Murray, 1947).

Moffett's early summing up of the potential roles of the flying-deck cruiser comes from his memo to the Secretary of the Navy, dated 28 May 1930, in General Board file 420-2, Serial 1492. The response of General Board appears in an undated memorandum by Rear Admiral Henry H Hough in the same file. For the role of naval constructors in the Bureau of Aeronautics, see the *History of the Construction Corps of the United States Navy* (Washington: Bureau of Construction and Repair, 1937), pp51–52. Moffett's May 1930 characteristics for a CLV come from Friedman, *U.S. Cruisers, op cit*, p171.

Moffett's request for tests aboard a carrier to determine the minimum flight-deck requirements was submitted in a memo to the CNO dated 26 June 1930 (General Board file 420-2, Serial 1507). The recommendations during the *Saratoga* board were included as an enclosure to a memo from Reeves to the CNO dated 24 September 1930, found in the same General Board file. Likewise, Admiral Schofield's opinion of the hybrid can be found in the same file in a letter to the CNO dated 30 September 1930.

The *USNIP* articles quoted in the chapter are as follows:
Sherman, Forrest, Lt Commander, USN. 'Some Aspects of Carrier and Cruiser Design', vol 56, no 11 (November 1930), pp997–1002. The quote from Corbett comes from *Some Principles of Maritime Strategy* (London: Longmans, Green and Co, 1911). The quote from Sherman's article regarding Coronel, etc, comes from p1002.
Percival, Franklin G, Lieutenant USN (ret), 'Elements Contributing to Aerial Superiority', vol 57, no 4 (April 1931), pp437–47. The quoted passage appears on p439.
Turner, R K, Commander, USN. Letter to the 'Discussions' column, vol 57, no 5 (May 1931), pp673–5.
Kniskern, L A, Lieutenant, (CC), USN. 'A Cruiser Program', vol 57, no 9 (September 1931), pp1229–37.
Kniskern attended several of the General Board hearings as a member of the Bureau of Construction and Repair, as did Turner for the Bureau of Aeronautics.

Another article of background interest is H B Miller's 'The Airplane Carrier: Problems Involved in the Landing and Storing of Naval

Airplanes on the Decks of Their Mother Ships', *Mechanical Engineering* vol 54, no 6 (June 1932), pp389–93.

The General Board tentatively recommended a CLV for the 1932 construction appropriation in a memo to the Secretary of the Navy dated 21 November 1930 (General Board file 420-2, Serial 1507). Moffett's three configurations for the flying-deck cruiser were contained in a memo of 29 October 1930 to the CNO via the chief of Construction and Repair in the same file; he also expressed his belief in this memo that the CLV would have to carry at least eighteen aircraft to be worthwhile. Rock's endorsement of Moffett's memo, dated 3 November 1930, is again in the same file. Early design work on hybrid cruisers, including quadruple-turreted designs, was briefly outlined by Captain van Keuren at the General Board hearing of 4 December 1930.

The General Board's specifications for the CLV can be found in a memo to the Secretary of the Navy dated 26 January 1931 (General Board file 420-8, Serial 1518). Also in this folder is Laning's report on the results of gaming the CLV at the Naval War College (6 December 1930), which refers to the original General Board request for such games of 3 December 1930.

Hearings on HR 14688, and the text of the bill, can be found in 71st Congress, 3rd Session, House, Committee on Naval Affairs, Hearings, 'To Authorize the Construction of Certain Naval Vessels, and for Other Purposes (H.R. 14688)'. Rock's comment on the favourable regard in which the committee held the flying-deck cruiser comes from his testimony at the General Board hearing of 16 July 1931. Zimm, 'The U.S.N.'s Flight Deck Cruiser', *op cit*, characterised Moffett's public support for the CLV as 'little short of sensationalism'. The Naval Affairs Committee's favourable report on the measure was submitted on 17 January 1931 as Report 2291 of the House of Representatives, 71st Congress, 3rd Session; it is most easily found in the Serials Set, vol 9326. The corresponding Senate Naval Affairs Committee report (which is very similar to the House report), was Senate Report No 1322 of the 71st Congress, 3rd Session, submitted on 5 January (calendar day, 19 January) 1931, and accompanied S (Senate Bill) 5288.

McClintic's resurrection of his hybrid battleship idea can be found in the *Congressional Record*, 71st Congress, 3rd Session (vol 74, part 6), pp6173–4; the press release quoting Pratt on flying-deck cruisers appears on p6173.

For the sequence of Construction and Repair schemes, the drawings preserved in the General Board files and the board's hearings on the topic were the main sources. The first hearings were held on 4, 5 and 23 December 1930. Sir George Thurston's views on aircraft aboard cruisers come from his article 'Light Cruisers' in the 1925 edition of *Brassey's Naval and Shipping Annual*, pp58–73. The use of fighters as dive bombers before the advent of specialisation is discussed by J V Mizrahi in 'Carrier Fighter: Curtiss and Its Sea-Going Hawks', *Airpower*, vol 2, no 5 (September 1972), pp18–29, 58–60.

Rock outlined the features of A-2, H-1 and H-2 in a memo to the General Board on 16 January 1931 (General Board file 420-8, Serial 1518). The CNO reported on the 19 January 1931 conference in a memo dated 22 January 1931 to the Secretary of the Navy, in the same file. Moffett's diesel proposal appears in a memo to the Secretary of the Navy routed through the Bureau of Engineering, dated 23 June 1931 (General Board file 420-8, Serial 1545); it was withdrawn on 1 July by a note found in the same file. The final preliminary design is described in Rock's memo to the Secretary of the Navy, dated 2 July 1931, and the General Board hearings of 16 and 17 July 1931 were devoted to this design. Captain Cook's *cri du coeur* came in a memo to the Secretary of the Navy dated 15 July 1931 (General Board file 420-8, Serial 1518), while the Secretary's response of 27 July 1931 is in General Board file 420-8, Serial 1545.

The features of the contract design are taken from drawings of the design in Friedman, *U.S. Cruisers, op cit*, p170 and the same author's article in *Warship*, 'U.S. Flight-Deck Cruiser Designs', *op cit*, pp26-27, 36-37.

The 1931 carrier designs with 8in and 6in guns are also described by Friedman in his *U.S. Carriers, op cit*, pp85, 88-90.

The hearing's on Vinson's bill, HR 6661 of the 72nd Congress, 1st Session, can be found in House, Committee on Naval Affairs, Hearings, 72nd Congress, 1st Session, on HR 6661, 'To Authorize the Construction of Certain Naval Vessels for Replacement and Additions, and for Other Purposes (H.R. 6661) and (H.R. 8230)'. The bill's progress (or lack of it) was reported by *NYT* in the following articles:
'President Opposes Navy Building Bills', 24 January 1932, p1, 26.
'Navy Bill To Await Results At Geneva', 26 January 1932, p12.
'Vinson Issues Call to Revive Navy Bill', 5 February 1932, p30.

The Moffett quote regarding the need for flying-deck cruisers comes from a letter written by his son that appeared in the *USNIP*'s 'Comment and Discussion' section, vol 105, no 11 (November 1979), pp87-88.

Chapter 7: Across the Pacific

The evolution of Japanese naval strategy and tactics under the influence of the Washington Treaty was described by Minoru Genda, one of the planners of the Pearl Harbor attack, in a lecture entitled 'Tactical Planning in the Imperial Japanese Navy', delivered at the US Naval War College on 7 March 1969. The authors are grateful to David Dickson for a transcript. The same subject is more briefly presented, based largely on the Genda lecture, in Clark G Reynolds, *The Fast Carriers: The Forging of an Air Navy* (New York: McGraw-Hill, 1968), pp4-8. Stephen E Pelz, *Race to Pearl Harbor* (Cambridge, Mass: Harvard University Press, 1974), pp32-39, also outlines the 'diminution operation'. US-Japanese naval relations during the 1920s and '30s are well treated in Stephen Howarth, *Morning Glory: The Drama of the Imperial Japanese Navy* (London: H Hamilton, 1983).

Japanese heavy cruisers up to but not including the *Tone* class are exhaustively described and analysed in a seven-part series by Eric Lacroix under the general title 'The Development of the "A Class" Cruisers in the Imperial Japanese Navy' appearing in *WI* vol XIV, no 4 (1977), pp337-57; vol XVI, no 1 (1979), pp41-62; vol XVI, no 4 (1979), pp329-62; vol XVIII, no 1 (1981), pp41-76; vol XVIII, no 4 (1981), pp323-67; vol XX, no 3 (1983), pp232-82, and vol XXI, no 3 (1984) pp246-305.

The work of the British aeronautical mis-

sion to Japan was best described by its leader, Colonel the Master of Sempill (William Francis Forbes-Sempill, later Lord Sempill), in a paper read at the 12th meeting of the 59th session of the Royal Aeronautical Society in London on 3 April 1924. A printed version titled 'The British Aviation Mission to the Imperial Japanese Navy' appears in the *Journal of the Royal Aeronautical Society*, vol XXVIII no 165, September 1924, pp553-84. The further development of Japanese naval aviation is described in Masatake Okumiya and Jiro Horikoshi with Martin Caidin, *The Zero Fighter* (London: Cassell, 1958). The same authors' earlier *Zero!* (New York: E P Dutton, 1956) notes the increase in carrier fighter complements as the result of losses in China, pp24-5. Other useful sources are Katsu Kohri, Ikuo Komori and Ichiro Naito, *The Fifty Years of Japanese Aviation 1910-1960* (Tokyo: Kantosha Co, 1960); Eiichiro Sekigawa, *Pictorial History of Japanese Military Aviation* (London: Ian Allan, 1974), and Toshikazu Ohmae and Roger Pineau, 'Japanese Naval Aviation', *USNIP* vol 98, no 12 (December 1972), pp68-77. Yamamoto's signal contributions to the advancement of naval aviation, and his own association with it, are told in his two English-language biographies: John Deane Potter, *Admiral of the Pacific: The Life of Yamamoto* (London: Heinemann, 1963), and Hiroysuki Agawa, *The Reluctant Admiral: Yamamoto and the Imperial Navy* (Tokyo: Kodansha International, Naval Institute Press edition, 1979). The latter work is superior. The interested reader is also referred to Roger Pineau's essay 'Admiral Isoroku Yamamoto' in Sir Michael Carver, ed, *The War Lords: Military Commanders of the Twentieth Century* (Boston and Toronto: Little, Brown, 1976), pp390-403. The lack of air bases in the Japanese-mandated islands is attested to by Masatake Okumiya in ' "For Sugar Boats or Submarines?" ', *USNIP* vol 94, no 8 (August 1968), pp66-73.

What sparse details remain of the G.6 and G.8 designs can be found in Jentschura, Jung and Mickel, *Warships of the Imperial Japanese Navy, op cit*, p46. These designs are also mentioned in Roger Chesneau, *Aircraft Carriers of the World, 1914 to the Present: An Illustrated Encyclopedia* (Annapolis: Naval Institute Press, 1984), pp165-6.

By far the most detailed and authoritative discussion of the *Tone* class is a four-part article by Hans Lengerer, Sumie Kobler-Edamatsu and Tomoko Rehm Takahara in *Warship* no 41, pp35-42; no 42, pp109-17; no 43, pp139-49, and no 44, pp223-31. This series refutes the assertion that the placement of the main battery was solely for the sake of aircraft arrangements and sheds additional light on the proposed role of the heavy cruiser in prewar IJN strategic and tactical doctrine. The failure of Japanese air reconnaissance at Midway is outlined and criticised in Mitsuo Fuchida and Masatake Okumiya, *Midway: The Battle That Doomed Japan* (Annapolis: US Naval Institute, 1955), pp146-50.

Oyodo's rationale is discussed and her varying particulars are given in Watts and Gordon, *The Imperial Japanese Navy, op cit*, pp163-4; Jentschura, Jung and Mickel, *Warships of the Imperial Japanese Navy, op cit*, p112, and *Maru Special 123, Japanese Naval Vessels* (Tokyo: Maruzen, 1987). Details of the Kawanishi E15K1 can be found in William

Green's *War Planes of the Second World War*, vol 6, *Floatplanes* (Garden City, NY: Doubleday, 1963), pp126-8, and R J Francillon's *Japanese Aircraft of the Pacific War* (London: Putnam, 1970), pp314-6. Masanori Ito notes *Oyodo*'s inadequacy as a flagship in *The End of the Imperial Japanese Navy (1941-1945)* (New York: W W Norton, 1962), p209. Her part in the Mindoro raid is told in Paul S Dull, *A Battle History of the Imperial Japanese Navy (1941-1945)* (Annapolis: Naval Institute Press, 1978), p332, from which the quotation is taken. Oscar Parkes' assessment of *Oyodo* is from his brief article 'The Japanese Cruisers "Agano" and "Oyodo" ', *World Ship Society Warships Supplement* no 3, June 1966, pp11-12.

Chapter 8: On the Trade Routes

Friedman's *British Carrier Aviation, op cit*, pp100-3 describes British 1923 sketch designs for carriers with 8in guns. Information on Prendergast's *Boscowen* comes from 'Centaur-Ships. An Explanation of the "Boscowen" Model', in the October 1926 issue of *The Navy*, pp276-9; the 'super-cruiser' was described in a column headed 'After a Few Years' in the *Naval and Military Record*, 8 September 1926, p502. Both these designs were also described in 'Le bâtiment centaure' in *Revue Maritime*, November 1926 (no 83), pp653-6. The latter journal also published a summary of Prendergast's criticisms of various convoy protection vessels, including *Tishy's Ghost*, in 'Nouveaux types de convoyeurs' in its September 1926 issue (no 81), pp362-6. A good general survey of the genesis and history of the British non-rigid airship during the First World War is given in Robin Higham, *The British Rigid Airship, 1908-1931: A Study in Weapons Policy* (London: G T Foulis, 1961), pp109-123. Particulars of British non-rigids may be found in Owen Thetford, *British Naval Aircraft 1912-58* (London: Putnam, 1958), pp406-9.

Similar details of French and American non-rigids are contained in Thomas G Miller Jr and Douglas H Robinson, 'Nonrigid Airships in World War I', *Cross & Cockade Journal*, vol 5, no 2 (summer 1964), pp97-115. An extensive survey of the history of operation of airships from naval vessels, 1911-61, by R D Layman appears in *WI*, vol XVI, no 4 (1979), pp379-83; a bibliography is included. *Dédalo* is described and illustrated in the same author's *Before the Aircraft Carrier, op cit*, pp103-5. The US Navy was the only service of any nation to operate airships during the Second World War. These operations are described in 'They Were Dependable' — *Airship Operation in World War II*, 2nd ed (Lakehurst, NJ: Naval Airship Training and Experimental Command, 1946), and *Kite Balloons to Airships . . . The Navy's Lighter-than-Air Experience* (Washington: Deputy Chief of Naval Operation [Air Warfare] and Commander, Naval Air Systems Command, 1987). The latter volume also covers First World War lighter-than-air activity.

The main source for the British discussion of the hybrid cruiser is a section of Adm 116/2792, 'Shipboard Aircraft 1931-32', Public Record Office, London, and all quotations are taken from it. Arthur J Marder discusses the exaggerated faith the Royal Navy had in asdic in *From the Dardanelles to Oran: Studies of the Royal Navy in War and Peace 1915-1940*

(London: Oxford University Press, 1974), pp40–41. Jellicoe's appraisal of the German airships appears in his *The Grand Fleet 1914–1916: Its Creation, Development and Work* (New York: George H Doran, 1919), p32. The flying-deck cruiser design of 1933 is mentioned in Friedman's *British Carrier Aviation, op cit*, p218; the 1936 hybrid battlecruiser and the student hybrid designs are mentioned by the same source. J D Lyon of the National Maritime Museum reported finding no trace of these other British flying-deck cruiser designs in a letter to R D Layman dated 11 November 1988. The new 12in gun and mounting are briefly described in N J M Campbell's 'British Naval Guns 1880–1945', part 4, in *Warship* no 20, pp254–5. Chatfield's verdict on hybrids is quoted in G A H Gordon's *British Seapower and Procurement Between the Wars: A Reappraisal of Rearmament* (Annapolis: Naval Institute Press, 1988), p173.

Chapter 9: 'Neither Fish Nor Fowl'
Information on Claude Swanson, including the Roosevelt quote, can be found in the entry on Swanson by Allison Saville in volume 2 of *American Secretaries of the Navy*, edited by Paolo E Coletta (Annapolis: Naval Institute Press, 1980), pp654–67.

All the General Board material on the first round of 1934 flying-deck cruiser studies is concentrated in one file, 420–8, Serial No 1642. There were also two General Board hearings on the CLV/CF, on 31 January and 15 February 1934. The May design is outlined and illustrated by Norman Friedman in his *U.S. Cruisers, op cit*, p172. Swanson's decision regarding the flying-deck cruiser was reported in *NYT*, 14 June 1934, p6: 'Bars Flying Deck on New Cruisers'. That work continued after Swanson's decision, and King's conversion to the cause of the CLV/CF, are shown in a series of memos in General Board file 420–8: King to CNO, 19 September 1934; Reeves (CINCUS) to King, 8 October 1934; Land (Construction and Repair) to King, 8 October 1934; King to CNO, 30 October 1934. Collett's article, 'The Flying Deck Cruiser', was in *USNIP*, vol 60, no 11 (November 1934), p1545.

Construction's 1933 hybrid battleships are described by Norman Friedman in his *U.S. Battleships, op cit*, p231. Friedman also discusses Scheme F and the background leading up to it in the same work, pp 244–50. The quotation is taken from General Board file 420–6 (Battleships).

Procter's bizarre diesel battleship appeared in *Scientific American*, January 1936 (vol 154, no 1), pp18–20, 53. His views on battleship protection are outlined in 'Protection of the Modern Battleship', *USNIP*, vol 62, no 2 (February 1936), pp187–188. The battleship designs he submitted to the General Board can be found in General Board papers, File 420–6, for the year 1934. It should be noted that only the *Scientific American* scheme is in any sense a hybrid.

Roosevelt's described his idea for an aircraft-carrying auxiliary cruiser in a letter to Admiral William Leahy dated 10 November 1937, held in the President's Secretary's File (unindexed) at the Roosevelt Library, Hyde Park, NY.

That the General Board recommended including flying-deck cruisers in the building programme for the coming fiscal year is mentioned in John Major, 'The Navy Plans for

War, 1937–1941' in *In Peace and War, op cit*, pp237–62. General Board papers on the 1939–40 CF proposals are once again concentrated in a single file, 420–8, Serial No 1913. This includes a copy of Ghormley's November 1938 analysis of the need for 'scout carriers'. The small carrier design is described by Norman Friedman in *U.S. Carriers, op cit*, pp116–17, and is illustrated on p107 of the same work. The article by Admiral Moffett's son, then Lt William A Moffett, Jr, entitled 'Airmada', appeared in *USNIP*, vol 67, no 1 (January 1941), pp73–74.

The assessment of Moffett's aims by Rear Admiral William A Moffett, Jr, appeared in the *USNIP*'s 'Comment and Discussion' section, vol 105, no 11 (November 1979), p87. Zimm, *op cit*, was the writer who blamed the flying-deck cruiser's demise on the 'Gun Club'. Ingram's assessment of the air-mindedness of US Navy line officers was given in a side-bar to his article 'An Air-Minded First Line of Defense', *Scientific American*, vol 159, no 1 (July 1938), pp9–11, while the quote from Andrade comes from 'The Ship That Never Was: The Flying-Deck Cruiser', *op cit*.

Chapter 10: 'A Ship of Large Size and Unique Characteristics'
The best treatment of Soviet naval thinking in the years after the Civil War and under Stalin remains Robert Waring Herrick's *Soviet Naval Strategy: Fifty Years of Theory and Practice* (Annapolis: United States Naval Institute, 1968). Herrick's book, based on extensive use of Soviet professional naval journals of the era, discusses the rise of the 'young school' and Stalin's attempts to build an 'oceanic' navy in some detail.

The single best article on the diplomatic manoeuvrings behind the Soviet attempt to obtain a battleship with US help is Malcolm Muir Jr, 'American Warship Construction for Stalin's Navy Prior to World War II: A Study in Paralysis of Policy', *Diplomatic History*, vol 5, no 4 (autumn 1981), pp337–51. The role of navy officers in blocking the Soviet moves is well described in Thomas R Maddux's 'United States-Soviet Naval Relations in the 1930's: The Soviet Union's Efforts to Purchase Naval Vessels', *Naval War College Review*, vol XXIX, no 2 (autumn 1976), pp28–37. Both these articles have excellent footnotes on the source documentation, much of which has been printed in *Foreign Relations of the United States: Diplomatic Papers — The Soviet Union, 1933–1939* (Washington: Department of State, 1952); the relevant documents appear on pp457–491, 670–708, and 869–903. These sections also include material on other Soviet efforts to buy arms, aircraft, etc, in the United States.

On the technical features of the various Gibbs and Cox designs (as well as on Ansaldo's 'U.P. 41' and the later *Sovetskii Soyuz* design), the most complete source is Garzke and Dulin, *Battleships: Allied Battleships in World War II, op cit*, pp306–30. The authors are indebted to Mr Garzke for providing unpublished material on the Gibbs and Cox designs and for discussing them at length with Stephen McLaughlin during a visit to Washington, DC, on 30 April 1989. Also of value is Rolf Erikson's 'Soviet Battleships, Part II' in *WI*, vol XI, no 2 (1974), pp115–133. The landing-only flight-deck theory is given in Jürg Meister, *The Soviet Navy*, vol 1 (Garden

City, NY: Doubleday, 1972), p35, and in Siegfried Breyer, *Battleships of the World, 1905–1970* (London: Conway Maritime Press, 1980), Appendix 4: 'Capital Shipbuilding in the Soviet Union, 1938–1950'. This idea is refuted by a memorandum accompanying a letter from Gibbs and Cox to the Secretary of State, dated 22 April 1938, provided by Mr Garzke. All quotes from William F Gibbs, including those regarding the catapults at the stern, come from his testimony before the General Board in a hearing held on 5 December 1939.

Biographical information on William Francis Gibbs is available in *By Their Works Ye Shall Know Them: The Life and Ships of William Francis Gibbs, 1886–1967* by Frank O Braynard (New York: Gibbs and Cox, 1968); see also the entry by Walter C Bachman in the *Biographical Memoirs* of the National Academy of Sciences of the United States of America, vol XLII (New York: Columbia University Press, 1971), pp46–64; *The National Cyclopedia of American Biography*, vol 53 (New York: James T White, 1971), pp470–471; and Richard Austin Smith, 'The Love Affair of William Francis Gibbs', *Fortune*, vol LVI, no 2 (August 1957), p136ff. Perhaps most insightful of all is a profile in *The New Yorker* by Winthrop Sargeant, 'The Best I Know How', vol XL, no 16 (6 June 1964), p49ff. Sam Carp's comments on Gibbs and the precautions taken with the plans of design B while it was in Moscow are taken from Carp's testimony before the Special Committee on Un-American Propaganda Activities, House of Representatives, *Investigation of Un-American Propaganda Activities in the United States* (76th Congress, First Session; H Res 282) (Washington: Government Printing Office, 1939), pp4941–4977. This document contains much fascinating information, as well as a great deal of repetition and a few moments of unintentional humour. It also illustrates how petty the concerns of the committee could be.

Information on Charles Edison can be found in *American Secretaries of the Navy, op cit*, vol 2, pp668–74. The US navy evaluation of the Gibbs and Cox design comes from the General Board papers, File 420–6 (Battleships): Admiral Sexton's memorandum of 24 October 1939, and Serial No 1911, an analysis of the design sent to the Acting Secretary of the Navy (Edison), which includes a copy of Edison's letter to the President of the General Board of 20 November 1939.

The interesting imaginary designs appeared in 'The Russian Navy Is Reborn', *Life*, vol 19, no 25 (17 December 1945), pp91–94. The prospective size of the Gibbs design was reported in *NYT*, 29 April 1938, p5, 'Largest Warship Planned by Soviet'. The exaggerated description of the design can be found in 'Technological Revolutionist', *Time*, vol XL, no 13 (28 September 1942), pp20–22.

Chapter 11: 'The Results of a Psychological Maladjustment'
The major documents on British hybrid schemes are Adm1/11324 (for Slattery's idea and subsequent discussions) and Adm1/11950 for Boyd's proposal and the Admiralty's response. Secondary sources include Raven and Robert's *British Battleships of World War Two, op cit*, pp402–4; the same authors' *British Cruisers of World War Two, op cit*, p273, and Friedman's *British Carrier Aviation, op cit*, pp218–21. The hybrid *Lion* sketch appeared in

Antony Preston, *Battleships 1856-1977* (London: Phoebus/BBC, 1977), p125.

History and data on the Fairey Flycatcher can be found in Owen Thetford's *The Fairey Flycatcher*, Profile Publication No 56 (Leatherhead, Surrey: 1965). Photos of *Hood* with a Flycatcher aboard appear in D G Weldon, 'H.M.S. Hood', *WI*, vol IX, no 2 (1972), p131, and Maurice Northcott, *Hood: Design and Construction* (London: Bivouac Books, 1975), p22. The plan to replace floats with wheels in wartime is mentioned by Norman Friedman in *British Carrier Aviation, op cit*, but no confirming documentation is cited. The description of the *Ark Royal*'s reliance on AA guns during her first air attack is from William Jameson, *Ark Royal 1939-1941* (London: Rupert Hart-Davis, 1957), p29.

Tom Phillip's dawning appreciation of aircraft is discussed in Arthur J Marder's *Old Friends, New Enemies: The Royal Navy and the Imperial Japanese Navy: Strategic Illusions, 1936-1941* (Oxford: Oxford University Press, 1981), pp385-8. The quotation is taken from Phillip's minute of 20 April 1941 in Adm1/11324.

The BAC Ship appeared in the *Illustrated London News*, vol 200, no 5383 (20 June 1942), pp714-5, and vol 200, no 5384 (27 June 1942), p738. 'The Fusion of Warship Types' was published in the *Engineer*, vol CLXXV, no 4548 (12 March 1943), p212, while Reavis' carrier-cruiser appeared in 'The Shape of Ships to Come', *Collier's*, vol 111, no 11 (13 March 1943), pp12-16.

Ewen Montagu described the hybrid deception scheme in his *Beyond Top Secret U* (London: P Davies, 1977), pp169-71. The authors are indebted to Charles Schedel for bringing this reference to their attention.

The French wartime hybrid schemes are described in Dousset, *Les Porte-Avions Français, op cit*, pp66, 68 and 118.

The complicated story of *Graf Zeppelin*'s genesis and design is told by her chief designer, Wilhelm Hadeler, in *Der Flugzeuträger: Sein Wesen und sein Werden von 1911 bis zur Gegenwart* (Munich: J F Lehmanns Verlag, 1968) and in Hadeler's 'The Aircraft Carrier in the German Navy 1934-1945', *American Society of Naval Engineers Journal*, vol 68, no 3 (August 1956), pp431-440. Various interpretations and criticisms of the design appeared in an article in *USNIP* and the correspondence that followed: Clark G Reynolds, 'Hitler's Flattop — The End of the Beginning', vol 93, no 1 (January 1967), pp41-49; no 5 (May 1967), pp126-127; no 10 (October 1967), pp101-102; no 12 (December 1967), pp112-114; and vol 94, no 2 (February 1968), pp102-103.

Early design features of the carrier can also be found in M J Whitley's two-part article 'Graf Zeppelin' in *Warship* no 31, pp153-164, and no 33, pp29-37. Part 2 of this article includes information on the small flight-deck cruiser designs, while information on the larger series comes from an article by Wilhelm Hadeler, 'Projektskizzen von Flugzeugschiffen der Kriegsmarine aus dem zweiten Weltkriege' in *Marine Rundschau*, vol 69, nos 1/2 (January-February 1972), pp1-40. An English translation of this article was published in *F.P.D.S. Newsletter*: part 1 appeared in vol I, no 3; part 2: vol I, no 4; part 3: vol II, no 3; part 4: vol III, no 1 (this is the section directly concerned with the hybrid designs); part 5: vol III, no 5.

Chapter 12: Phantoms of the Pacific

The Japanese conversion programme is outlined by Hajime Fukaya in 'Japan's Wartime Carrier Construction', *USNIP* vol 81, no 9 (September 1955), pp1031-37. By far the most complete description of *Mogami*, including her reconstruction as a hybrid and her loss, is contained in Lacroix, *WI*, vol XXI, no 3 (1984), *op cit*. Ito quotes the *Mogami* seaplane's Leyte Gulf reconnaissance report in *The End of the Imperial Japanese Navy, op cit*, p135.

The various conversion schemes considered for the battleships following Midway are outlined in 'Senkan no kubo kaizo e no kento' ('Investigations into aircraft carrier conversions of battleships') by Yasuo Abe in *Maru Special 116, Japanese Naval Vessels* (Tokyo: Maruzen, 1986). The authors are grateful to Ray Casanas for his fluid translation of this article. Details of the conversions as carried out can be found in Jentschura, Jung and Mickel, *Warships of the Imperial Japanese Navy, op cit*, pp26-8, in Watts and Gordon, *The Imperial Japanese Navy, op cit*, pp52-56, in Watt's earlier book *Japanese Warships of World War II* (London: Ian Allan, 1966), pp13-16, and in Seigfried Breyer, *Battleships and Battle Cruisers, 1905-1970* (Garden City, NY: Doubleday, 1973), pp343-6. The concern over stability which led to the use of an 8in layer of concrete is described in Norman Friedman, *Modern Battleship Design and Development 1905-1945* (London: Conway Maritime Press, 1978), p51; the deficiency in the after 14in gun turrets' elevation is mentioned in the same book on p105 and in John Campbell, *Naval Weapons of World War Two* (London: Conway Maritime Press, 1985), pp183-4. The operations of *Ise* and *Hyuga* while under the command of Admiral Matsuda were told by him during interrogation in Tokyo on 12 November 1945 and appear in *United States Strategic Bombing Survey (Pacific): Interrogations of Japanese Officials*, vol 1 (Washington: Government Printing Office, 1947), pp277-83. Full particulars of their aircraft, the *Zuiun* and the *Suisei*, are in Francillon, *Japanese Aircraft, op cit*, pp284-7 and pp454-61, respectively. The rocket launchers are described by Hans Lengerer and Tomoko Rehm-Takahara in 'The 12cm Multiple Rocket Launcher of the Imperial Japanese Navy', in *Warship* no 34, pp125-33. The American pilots' comment on their heavy AA fire can be found in Samuel Eliot Morison, *United States Naval Operations in World War II*, vol XII: *Leyte* (Boston: Little, Brown, 1958), p327.

The imaginary Japanese hybrid cruisers appear in Critchell Remington, ed, *Fighting Fleets: A Survey of the Navies of the World* (New York: Dodd, Mead, 1944), p45 and p149, and in Jay Launer's *The Enemies' Fighting Ships* (New York: Sheridan House, 1944), p48 and pp99-100. Admiral Pratt's article appeared in the 4 December 1944 issue of *Newsweek* (vol XXIV, no 23), p31. ONI's view of the *Tones* can be found in *Japanese Naval Vessels of World War Two as Seen by U.S. Naval Intelligence* (Annapolis: Naval Institute Press, 1987), a reprint of several wartime recognition manuals. Speculation on how the names of the phantom ships were arrived at is contained in David Dickson's article 'Japan's Hybrid Battleships and Cruisers . . . Fact and Fancy', *WI*, vol VII, no 4 (December 1970), pp356-75 (this article, incidentally, uncritically accepts the *Tones* as hybrids). The author speculated about the subject earlier in a letter to R D Layman dated 5 March 1969. Bruno Gruenwald's description of how Launer arrived at the names was given in a letter to R D Layman dated 28 July 1990.

Chapter 13: Extinction?

Various aspects of postwar naval developments are dealt with in Norman Friedman's *The Post-war Naval Revolution* (Annapolis: Naval Institute Press, 1986). Information on the FX-1400 can be found in Campbell's *Naval Weapons of World War Two, op cit*, p276; the spur this weapon provided to guided-missile countermeasures is described in Norman Friedman's *U.S. Naval Weapons* (Annapolis: Naval Institute Press, nd), pp149-150.

Information on aircraft characteristics is taken from Lloyd S Jones, *U.S. Naval Fighters* (Fallbrook, California: Aero Publishers, 1977) and a table in Norman Friedman's *Carrier Air Power* (London: Conway Maritime Press, 1981), pp172-189. Also useful was Kenneth Munson, *Fighters In Service: Attack and Training Aircraft Since 1960* (New York: Macmillan, 1971).

The destruction of HMS *Glorious* is described in Donald Macintyre's *Narvik* (London: Pan Books, 1962), pp220-223 and in *Battleship Scharnhorst* by Albert Vulliez and Jâcques Mordal (Fair Lawn, NJ, Essential Books, 1958), pp72-75. The best description of the action off Samar and the destruction of the *Gambier Bay* is still Morison's *United States Naval Operations in World War II*, vol XII, *op cit*, pp242-316. The incident involving *Formidable* at Matapan was revealed for probably the first time by T H R Campling, her gunnery control officer that night, in 'Another Night to Remember', *Jabberwock* (journal of the Society of Friends of the Fleet Air Arm Museum), no 21 (January 1989), pp29-31.

Lee J Levert's 'battle-carrier' can be found in his *Fundamentals of Naval Warfare* (New York: Macmillan,, 1947), pp436-448. The quoted passage regarding *South Dakota*'s radar-controlled AA gunfire effectiveness appears on p52. The official version can be found in *Dictionary of American Naval Fighting Ships*, vol VI, p561. Questions about *South Dakota*'s actual score are raised in Ivan Musicant's *Battleship at War: The Epic Story of the USS Washington* (Orlando, Florida: Harcourt Brace Jovanovich, 1986), pp101-102, from which the quote is taken. The relative effectiveness of variable time (VT) fuses and conventional AA fuses comes from Friedman, *U.S. Naval Weapons, op cit*, p88.

The 1947 US Navy study that mentions supporting a strategic bombing campaign by destroying enemy fighters is briefly described in Michael A Palmer's *Origins of the Maritime Strategy: American Naval Strategy in the First Postwar Decade* (Contributions to Naval History No 1) (Washington: Naval Historical Center, 1988), p28.

The hangar size of the *Midway* class carriers and details of their air group come from Friedman's *U.S. Aircraft Carriers, op cit*, p395.

Friedman has described the 'self-protecting CVAN' twice: in a letter to *USNIP*, vol 105, no 4 (April 1979), pp87-89, and in his *U.S.*

Aircraft Carriers, op cit, p376. The Bell XF-109 is described and illustrated in Lloyd S Jones' *U.S. Fighters* (Fallbrook, California: Aero Publishers, 1975), pp293-295.

Chapter 14: Vertical Monopoly

The decline of the shipboard seaplane and the reasons for it are discussed in R D Layman's 'The Shipboard Catapult: Its History and Development', *WI*, vol VII, no 3 (1970), pp249-72. General histories of the development and military application of the Autogiro and helicopter can be found in Kenneth Munson, *Helicopters and Other Rotorcraft Since 1907* (London: Blandford Press, 1968); Bill Gunston and John Batchelor, *Helicopters 1900-1960* (London: Phoebus, 1977); Norman Polmar and Floyd D Kennedy Jr, *Military Helicopters of the World: Military Rotary-Wing Aircraft Since 1917*, and Robert A Hasskarl Jr, 'Early Military Use of Rotary-Wing Aircraft', *The Airpower Historian*, vol 12, no 3 (July 1965), pp75-77, from which the quotation regarding the limitations of the Autogiro is taken. The engineering and aerodynamics of the helicopter are well described in Alfred Gessow's 'The Changing Helicopter', *Scientific American*, vol 210, no 4 (April 1967), pp38-46. The joint American-British shipboard trials are described in J M Waters Jr, 'Little Ships With Long Arms', *USNIP*, vol 91, no 8 (August 1965), pp74-81, and Robert L Scheina, 'The Helicopter Goes to War', *Warship* no 11 (July 1979), pp168-73. The conflicting demands of strike aircraft and ASW aircraft are described in Friedman, *Carrier Air Power, op cit,* pp122-129.

For *Jeanne d'Arc*, the standard source is Dousset, *Les Porte-Avions Français, op cit,* pp92-95, 134-6. Another useful source is *Conway's, 1947-1982*, part 1: *The Western Powers*, pp29-30. Supplementing these are 'The New *Jeanne d'Arc*' by Pierre Clement in *USNIP*, vol 90, no 10 (October 1964), pp123-5; various editions of *Jane's* during the 1960s (especially the 1961-62 edition); and '*Jeanne d'Arc*, the French Cruiser Helicopter Carrier', in *Military Modelling*, vol 1, no 9 (September 1971), pp456-60, which has photos of a model and drawings of the ship as she would have appeared had the Masurca launcher been fitted. The ship's latest characteristics are taken from the 1988-89 edition of *Jane's*, p170, and the 1988-89 edition of *Combat Fleets*, p130. Information on the development of the Mascura missile system is taken from Bill Gunston's *Illustrated Encyclopedia of the World's Rockets and Missiles* (London: Salamander Books, 1979), p182.

Andrea Doria, Caio Duilio and *Vittorio Veneto* are described in Giorgio Giorgerini and Augusto Nani, *Gli Incrociatori Italiani 1861-1964* (Rome: Ufficio Storico della Marina Militare, 1964), pp687-96, and *Conway's, 1947-1982*, part I, *op cit*, pp67-8. Also helpful was '*Andrea Doria, Caio Duilio* and *Vittorio Veneto* — Cruisers of the Italian Navy' by Ubaldo Garagnani in *USNIP*, vol 94, no 10 (October 1968), pp138-41. Their latest characteristics are taken from the 1988-89 edition of *Jane's*, pp287-8, and *Combat Fleets* for the same year, pp303-4.

The literature on *Moskva* is extensive. John Jordan, *Soviet Warships: The Soviet Surface Fleet, 1960 to the Present* (London: Arms and Armour Press, 1983), pp43-55, is very thorough, and there is an interesting entry on her in *Conway's, 1947-1982*, part II:

The Warsaw Pact and Non-Aligned Nations, p480. Norman Polmar calls her a hybrid in his *Guide to the Soviet Navy*, 3rd edition (Annapolis: Naval Institute Press, 1983), p130, as well as providing useful background information on Soviet naval developments. Her current characteristics are taken from the 1988-89 editions of *Combat Fleets* (p576) and *Jane's* (p570).

Most of the information on the conversion of *Blake* and *Tiger* came from *Conway's, 1947-1982*, part I:, *op cit*, p151 and Leo Marriott, *Royal Navy Aircraft Carriers 1945-1990* (London: Ian Allan, 1985), pp109-12. The original idea of converting these ships for assault rather than ASW work is mentioned in Eric J Grove, *Vanguard to Trident: British Naval Policy Since World War Two* (Annapolis: US Naval Institute, 1987), p252. Their characteristics as converted were taken from *Combat Fleets, 1978/79*, p188; an article by Bob Sweet, 'H.M.S. Blake: Command Helicopter Cruiser' in *Military Modelling*, vol 1, no 12 (December 1971) was also useful. Finally, the fate of HMS *Blake* was found in J J Colledge's *Ships of the Royal Navy* (Annapolis: Naval Institute Press, 1987), p55.

The career of *De Zeven Provinciën* in the Royal Netherlands Navy was described by L L von Münching in 'H.NL.M.S. De Zeven Provinciën C-802', *WI*, vol XIII, no 4 (1976), pp251-69. Her conversion to the Peruvian helicopter cruiser *Aguirre* is outlined in *Combat Fleets, 1988/89*, p440, and in *Conway's, 1947-1982*, part I, *op cit*, p422.

Useful throughout this section has been Norman Friedman's *Naval Radar* (Annapolis: Naval Institute Press, 1981) and his *Modern Warship Design and Development* (Greenwich: Conway Maritime Press, 1979).

The development of the Harrier and Sea Harrier is taken chiefly from Francis K Mason, *Harrier*, 2nd ed (Annapolis: Naval Institute Press, 1983) and Bill Gunston, *Modern Fighting Aircraft*, vol 5: *Harrier* (London: Salamander Books, 1984); the quote about the Harrier operating from more types of ship than any other aircraft is on p32 of the latter. Also useful was Gunston's earlier *Harrier* (Osceola, Wisconsin: Specialty Press, 1981), particularly for the early development of the aircraft. Another brief but helpful publication is *Harrier in Action*, by Don Linn (Carrollton, Texas: Squadron/Signal Publications, 1982). Other STOVL projects of recent years are described in Bill Gunston's *An Illustrated Guide to Future Fighters and Combat Aircraft* (New York: Prentice-Hall, 1987).

The Grumman 'Nutcracker' scheme was described and illustrated in *Air Pictorial*'s 'World Air News' column, vol 38, no 12 (December 1976), p468. SkyHook has been described in a number of articles and books; among the most complete treatments are 'SkyHook: Tactical Air for Smaller Ships' by Dr John Fozard, Heinz Frick and Denis J Mottram in *USNIP* vol 112, no 11 (November 1986), pp60-3 (whence comes the rather Byzantine quote), and Bill Gunston, *Modern Fighting Aircraft*, vol 5: *Harrier, op cit*, pp60-1.

Chapter 15: Variations on a Theme

Various types of landing craft through the centuries are noted in Alfred Vagts, *Landing*

Operations: Strategy, Psychology, Tactics, Politics, From Antiquity to 1945 (Harrisburg, Pa: Military Service Publishing, 1946). A brief survey is given in Brian Friend's 'Landing Craft Through the Ages'; pt 1, *Warship*, no 45. Horse transports of the ancient world are discussed by Lionel Casson in his *Ships and Seamanship in the Ancient World* (Princeton, NJ: Princeton University Press, 1971), pp 93-4, and J S Morrison and R T Williams, *Greek Oared Ships 900-322 B.C.* (Cambridge: Cambridge University Press, 1968), pp248-9. Elephant transport vessels are mentioned repeatedly in H H Scullard's *The Elephant in the Greek and Roman World* (Cambridge: Thames and Hudson, 1974).

Details of *Akitsu Maru, Nigitsu Maru* and *Kumano Maru* are mainly from Jentschura, Jung and Mickel, *Warships of the Imperial Japanese Navy, op cit*, p61, and Watts and Gordon, *The Imperial Japanese Navy, op cit*, pp207-9. The Kokusai Ki-76 is described in Francillon, *Japanese Aircraft of the Pacific War, op cit*, pp147-9. The Kayaba Ka-1s is described in Francillon, *op cit*, pp143-5; Polmar and Kennedy, *Military Helicopters of the World, op cit*, pp103-4, and M W Williams, 'The Autogyro at Sea: Japan's Kayaba Ka-1s of 1944', *Aircraft Modelworld*, vol 5, no 8 (November 1988), pp240-1, 248, which also adds some details about *Akitsu Maru* (autogyro is a popular generic word for the specific trademark name Autogiro).

The postwar careers of the *Iowas* and the various conversion schemes are described in Robert O Dulin Jr and William H Garze Jr, *Battleships: United States Battleships in World War II*, (4th printing with corrections) (Annapolis: Naval Institute Press, 1985), pp277-91; Norman Friedman, *U.S. Battleships, op cit*, pp397-402 and Malcolm Muir, *Iowa Class Battleships: Iowa, New Jersey, Missouri and Wisconsin* (Poole, Dorset: Blandford Press, 1987), pp72-137. Rear Admiral John McCain discussed his 'Commando Ship' conversion plan in 'Amphibious Warfare During the Next Decade', *USNIP*, vol 89, no 1 (January 1963), pp104-11; the idea was also noted in the 13 October 1962 issue of *Navy Times*; this article was reprinted in *USNIP*, vol 89, no 2 (February 1963), p152; General Burger's quote is taken from this source. The same issue of *USNIP* had an illustration of a model of the commando ship conversion on p113.

Colonel Robert D Heinl discussed his 'Sea Control Ship' conversion idea for the *Iowas* in a letter to the *USNIP*, vol 98, no 9 (September 1972), pp88-90. Charles E Myers described his 'interdiction/assault ship' proposal in 'A Sea-Based Interdiction System for Power Projection', *USNIP*, vol 105, no 11 (November 1979), pp103-6; Hayward's V/STOL reactivation idea is mentioned in Muir, *Iowa Class Battleships, op cit*, p120. The latter work discusses the various Phase II proposals on p130, as does Howard W Serig, Jr in 'The Iowa Class: Needed Once Again', *USNIP*, vol 108, no 5 (May 1982), pp134-49. The navy's sketch of a Phase II *Iowa* with flight deck aft was published in *WI*, vol XVIII, no 2 (1981), p162; the Martin Marietta scheme was described by Ronald T Pretty, 'US Battleship Reactivation Progress', *Jane's Defence Review*, vol 3, no 4 (1982), pp403-5; a model with the same basic configuration accompanied a letter by Commander Jake Stewart, USN, to *USNIP*, vol

106, no 11 (November 1980), pp131-2. The same model seems to have been used to illustrate 'The BB(V)' by Joseph C Antoniotti, *USNIP*, vol 108, no 2 (February 1982), pp99-100. The 'New FMC Vertical Load Naval Gun Mount' was described in *Jane's Defence Review*, vol 2, no 4 (1981), pp366-7.

Pulver's *Iowa* conversion was published in the July 1980 *USNIP* (vol 106, no 7), pp86-7; Anderson's scheme appeared in the July 1981 (vol 107, no 7) issue of the same publication, pp21-2.

Rear Admiral Piotti's comment on Phase II was part of his testimony on *Reactivation of Battleships* (Hearing before the Seapower and Strategic and Critical Materials Subcommittee of the Committee on Armed Services, House of Representatives, 97th Congress, 2nd Session, December 15, 1982) (Washington: US Government Printing Office, 1983), p9. Vice Admiral Walters' comment was noted in 'Navy Faces Trouble Over Battleship Plans' by Hugh Lucas, in *Jane's Defence Weekly*, vol 1, no 14 (14 April 1984), p552.

Chapter 16: Through-Deck Cruisers

The background to modern Soviet naval policy is covered in Herrick, *Soviet Naval Strategy, op cit*; Norman Polmar, *Guide to the Soviet Navy*, 4th edition (Annapolis: Naval Institute Press, 1986); Floyd D Kennedy, Jr, 'Soviet Doctrine on the Role of the Aircraft Carrier', *Naval War College Review*, vol XXXII, no 1 (February 1979), pp48-58; Charles C Petersen, 'Aircraft Carrier Development in Soviet Naval Theory', *Naval War College Review*, vol XXXVII, no 1 (January-February 1984); and Jürgen Rohwer, 'The Kiev: A Turning Point in Soviet Strategy?', *Aerospace Historian*, Vol 24, No 2 (summer, June 1977), pp78-81. Polmar's book provided both Khruschev's quote on aircraft carriers (p22) and the late-1971 date for the discovery of *Kiev*'s construction (p76); disparaging Soviet evaluations of aircraft carriers are quoted in 'Their Sea-Based Aviation' by Kevin Lynch, *USNIP*, vol 108, no 10 (October 1982), pp46-52.

Early reports on *Kiev* can be found in the following newspaper articles:
Getler, Michael, 'Huge New Soviet Ship is Under Construction', *Washington Post*, 8 January 1972, pA10. This seems to be the first published mention of the new Soviet construction.
Shabad, Theodore, 'Russians May be Building a Carrier', *NYT*, 18 January 1972, p9. This article includes the mention of elevator wells and aviation fuel tanks.
Beecher, William, 'A Soviet Carrier in '73 is Indicated', *NYT*, 17 October 1972, p15.
'Laird Urges Pact on Vietnam Arms', *NYT*, 20 January 1973, p7. This article mentions the release of the US Navy artist's impression of *Kiev*.
Beecher, William, 'Soviet Said to Be Building Second Carrier', *NYT*, 27 February 1973, p2.
Admiral Zumwalt's quote regarding the new Soviet ship comes from his testimony in *Political and Strategic Implications of Homeporting in Greece*, Joint Hearings Before the Subcommittee on Europe and the Subcommittee on the Near East of the Committee on Foreign Affairs, House of Representatives, 92nd Congress, 2nd Session (Washington: US Government Printing Office, 1972), p24.

T G Martin's prescient article, 'A Soviet Carrier on the Horizon?' appeared in *USNIP*, vol 96, no 12 (December 1970), pp46-51. A line drawing based on the US Navy artist's impression of *Kiev* can be found in *Jane's*, 1974-75 edition, p532; the early estimates for *Kiev*'s characteristics are taken from the same source. A sketch by Siegfried Breyer based on the DoD rendering appeared in 'Neue sowjetische Kriegsshifttypen', *Marine Rundschau*, vol 70, no 7 (July 1973), pp398-401; this sketch was reproduced on p159 of Norman Polmar's 'The Soviet "Aircraft Carrier" ', *USNIP*, vol 100, no 5 (May 1974), pp144-161; Polmar's article also includes speculation on the evolution of Soviet thought, potential roles of the ship and the composition of her air squadron.

For various interpretations of *Kiev*'s roles, see William R Hynes, 'The Role of the *Kiev* in Soviet Naval Operations', *Naval War College Review*, vol XXIX, no 2 (autumn 1976), pp38-46; 'Soviet Carrier Strategy' by John T Funkhouser, *USNIP*, vol 99, no 12 (December 1973), pp27-37; Norman Polmar, 'The Soviet Aircraft Carrier', *USNIP*, vol 102, no 10 (October 1976), pp138-141; and Harlan B Miller, 'Seeing Others as We See Ourselves: Missions for the *Kiev*', *Naval War College Review*, vol XXXII, no 2 (March-April 1979), pp105-108.

The characteristics of *Kiev* are taken from *Jane's*, 1989-90, p579, and *Combat Fleets*, 1988/89, pp572-573. See also Jordan's *Soviet Warships, op cit*, pp77-99. Two useful analyses were published in *USNIP*, vol 103, no 7 (July 1977): 'U.S. Observations of the *Kiev*' by J W Kehoe *et al* (pp105-111) and 'The *Kiev*: A German View' by Ulrich Schulz-Torge (pp111-115). The double-deck hangar possibility is mentioned by the second of these articles, on p112. The information on the 'Freehand' comes from *Jane's All the World's Aircraft*, 1968-69, (London: BPC, 1968), pp438-9. Information on the Yak 38 'Forger' is taken from the same annual's 1988-89 edition, pp273-274, and 'Russia's Forger VTOL Aircraft — a More Detailed Analysis' in *International Defense Review*, vol 9, no 6 (1978), pp909-912. Jordan called *Kiev* a hybrid in 'The Kiev — Cruiser or Carrier?' in *Warship*, no 3, pp32-37.

Friedman's *British Carrier Aviation, op cit*, was the principal source for information on the early escort cruiser designs. The political debate over CVA-01 is well covered in William S Johnson, 'Defense Budgetary Constraints and the Fate of the Carrier in the Royal Navy', *Naval War College Review*, vol XXV, no 5 (May-June 1973), pp12-30. An excellent technical description of *Invincible*, including sketches of Study 21 and Study 22, can be found in a paper by A F Honnor, RCNC and D J Andrews, RCNC, 'HMS Invincible: The First of a New Genus of Aircraft Carrying Ships', *Transactions of the Royal Institution of Naval Architects*, vol 124 (1982), pp1-13. The comments of *Invincible*'s first captain on her handling come from the discussion that followed the presentation of this paper, pp13-23. For the political and economic background to the design, see Eric J Grove, *Vanguard to Trident, op cit*, especially Chapter 9. Another angle on the design is provided by D K Brown's *A Century of Naval Construction: The History*

of the Royal Corps of Naval Constructors (London: Conway Maritime Press, 1983), pp254-257. Also helpful were two articles from *International Defense Review*: Derek Wood's 'The Through Deck Cruiser Concept', vol 7, no 6 (1973), pp747-749, and R B Pengelley's 'The Royal Navy's Invincible-class Cruisers', vol 12, no 8 (1978), pp1335-1340. The latter includes the quote about the location of the admiral's bridge.

Early artists' impressions and models showing *Invincible* can be found in *Jane's*, 1972-73, p349 (incidentally, the 1971-72 edition was the first to include an artist's impression of the ship [pp342-43], but it was reversed, so that the island appeared on the port side). These drawings and models show the Exocet launchers, as do the more refined sketches in the 1973-74 edition of the same yearbook on p318; the 1974-75 edition, p333, has the same illustration with the Exocets airbrushed out. Characteristics for the ships and present modification programmes were found in *Jane's* for 1988-89, p653, and *Combat Fleets*, 1988/89, p204. The latter book makes the comment about the 'awkward' location of the Sea Dart launcher. *Jane's* gives the thirty-six-missile capacity figure, while *Combat Fleets* says twenty-two missiles. *Conway's, 1947-1982*, part I, pp148-149, has some interesting comments on the design.

The operations of *Invincible* during the Falklands conflict were based on David Brown's *The Royal Navy and the Falklands War* (London: Leo Cooper, 1987), and also on Grove, *Vanguard to Trident, op cit*, pp361-382. Notes on the performance of all the carriers involved in the conflict can be found in an article by A D Baker III, 'Aircraft Carriers in the Falklands', *USNIP*, vol 110, no 2 (February 1984), pp102-105. Gunston's *Modern Fighting Aircraft*, vol 5: *Harrier, op cit* includes several useful tables on Harrier and Sea Harrier operations during the conflict on p46.

F P U Croker's attempt to determine what a 'through-deck cruiser' was can be found in 'S/VTOL Afloat', *Marine News*, vol XXIV, no 1 (January 1970), pp12-14.

Characteristics of *Giuseppe Garibaldi* are taken from *Jane's*, 1989-90, p294 and *Combat Fleets*, 1988/89, p300-2. Also helpful was *Modern Carriers*, edited by Ray Bonds (London: Salamander Books, 1988), pp28-31.

Chapter 17: Sub Aquae Ad Astra

Details of all Japanese aircraft-carrying submarines can be found in Dorr Carpenter and Norman Polmar, *Submarines of the Imperial Japanese Navy* (Annapolis: Naval Institute Press, 1986); Watts and Gordon, *Imperial Japanese Navy, op cit*, and Jentschura, Jung and Mickel, *Warships of the Imperial Japanese Navy, op cit*. Richard Compton-Hall, *Submarine Warfare: Monsters & Midgets* (Poole, Dorset: Blandford Press, 1985), pp65-79, focuses mainly on the *I-400* class, as does Terry C Treadwell, *Submarines With Wings: The Past, Present and Future of Aircraft-Carrying Submarines* (London: Conway Maritime Press, 1985), pp65-74. The latter also describes the *Seiran*, although the aircraft is covered in more detail in Green, *Floatplanes, op cit*, pp118-20, and Francillon, *Japanese Aircraft, op cit*, pp291-4, from which the quotation is taken.

The proposed operations of the *I-13* and

I-400 classes, their training and the preliminaries to the Ulithi strike are given in the works by Carpenter and Polmar, Compton-Hall and Treadwell cited above, and in Mochitsura Hashimoto, *Sunk! The Story of the Japanese Submarine Fleet, 1941-45* (New York: Henry Holt, 1954), pp211-13, and Zenji Orita, *I-Boat Captain* (Canoga Park, California: Major Books, 1976), pp317-30. There are many discrepancies among these sources as to the submarines' sailing and arrival dates for the Ulithi operation, and the routes taken. Orita may be the most reliable. It is he who doubts the official version of *I-13*'s loss; he is also the only source to tell exactly how the two *Seirans* were lost during training.

The story of the submarines' surrender at sea is told by E John Long in 'Japan's "Underseas Carriers"', *USNIP*, vol 76, no 6 (June 1950), pp607-13. Their voyage to Pearl Harbor is described by Thomas O Paine in 'I Was a Yank on a Japanese Sub', *USNIP*, vol 112, no 9 (September 1986), pp73-78, from which the quoted assessment is taken. The final quotation is from Hajime Fukaya, 'Three Japanese Submarine Developments', *USNIP*, vol 78, no 8 (August 1952), pp863-7.

The Douglas Attack Aircraft Model 640 is described in Treadwell, *Submarines With Wings, op cit*, pp89-9. The General Dynamics submarine aircraft is mentioned in the 'Military Report' column of *Air Progess* vol 17, no 4, July 1965, p58, and a note on the Reids' claim appears in the same publication, p12. C C Abt's article 'The Submarine-Aircraft Carrier', from which the quotation is taken, is in *USNIP*, vol 89, no 10 (October 1963), pp149-53. D K Brown's evaluation and criticism of the Abt design is contained in a letter to R D Layman dated 13 March 1989, from which the chapter's concluding quotation is taken. Anthony Mammola's assessment of the design is from a letter to R D Layman dated 17 April 1989. Treadwell's suggestions for a SkyHook-equipped submarine appear in his *Submarines With Wings, op cit*, pp1-4 and pp85-90. The quotation is on p1. An early suggestion for elimination of landing gear on shipboard aircraft can be found in Charles C Turner's *Aircraft of To-day: A Popular Account of the Conquest of the Air* (London: Seeley, Service, 1918), pp284-5.

Chapter 18: The 'New Capital Ship'?

Michael A Cairl's article 'Through-Deck Cruiser: The New Capital Ship' appeared in *USNIP*, vol 104, no 12 (December 1978), pp34-42; Friedman's critique was published in vol 105, no 4 (April 1979), pp87-89.

The possibility of a Soviet 'air-capable battleship' was discussed by Scott C Truver in 'Admiral Gorshkov's BBVN?' in *USNIP*, vol 111, no 1 (January 1985), pp118-120; the same article provides the quote by Norman Polmar. Siegfried Breyer, 'The Construction of Large Surface Ships for the Soviet Navy', *Naval Forces*, vol V, no II (1984), pp46-54, cites the 'Japanese study' of the new Soviet carrier; 'The Aircraft Carrier Kreml' appeared in *Strategy and Defense*, October 1984, pp28-29. The description of the 'universal ship' comes from an article by Michael MccGwire, 'Gorshkov's Navy', part I, *USNIP*, vol 115, no 8 (August 1989), pp44-51. Gorshkov dismissed such vessels in an article originally published

in the Soviet naval journal *Morskoi Sbornik*; it was published in translation in *Red Star Rising at Sea* (Annapolis: Naval Institute Press, 1974), pp123-35.

Information on and an assessment of *Baku* is given in Norman Friedman's 'World Naval Developments' column in *USNIP*, vol 114, no 10 (October 1988), p197. A good series of photographs of this ship (including shots with Soviet sailors skateboarding on the flight deck) can be found in *WI*, vol XXV, no 3 (1988), on the cover and on pp302-303. Information on *Tbilisi* comes from a series of short articles in *Jane's Defence Weekly*: 'More Details of New Soviet Carrier', vol 11, no 24 (17 June 1989); Simon Elliott and Nick Cook, '2nd Soviet Carrier Fitting Out, Tbilisi Delays Trials', vol 12, no 19 (11 November 1989); and 'Tbilisi Raises New Montreux Debate', vol 12, no 20 (18 November 1989). See also Norman Polmar, 'Continuing Warship Construction' in 'The Soviet Navy' column of *USNIP*, vol 116, no 1 (January 1990), pp132-4. That she in fact has no anti-ship battery was confirmed by Guy de Bakker in 'Tbilisi's Punch', *International Defense Review*, vol 23, no 1 (1990), pp19-20.

Rains and Adams' *Spruance* scheme is described by the designers in 'The Fight Deck DD 963)' in *Naval Engineers Journal*, vol 90, no 2 (April 1978), pp149-156. The Gruman-Santa Fe conversion scheme is described and illustrated by Norman Polmar in a letter in *USNIP* vol 104, no 6 (June 1978), pp93-4 (this letter also features an illustration of the original US air-capable *Spruance* proposal), and in another letter by the same author to *WI*, vol XV, no 3 (1978), pp106-7. Commander Ghiradella's version of an air-capable *Spruance* was described and illustrated in his letter in *USNIP* vol 104, no 7 (July 1978), pp88-9.

The deep vee hulled frigate proposed by Hydro Research Systems appeared in *International Defense Review* vol 17, no 8 (1984), pp1114-5. The Vosper Thornycroft design was illustrated in 'SkyHook: Tactical Air for Smaller Ships' by Fozard, Frick and Mottram, *op cit*, p61, and *Modern Carriers, op cit*, p7; further information on the design was supplied to the authors by British Aerospace.

The Hawker Siddeley hybrid cruiser was illustrated in an article by John Fozard, 'Wind, Seapower and Jet V/STOL' in *USNIP*, vol 103, no 9 (September 1977), pp109-114. The strike cruiser programme is described by Norman Friedman in his *U.S. Cruisers, op cit*, pp419-422, in which Leopold's Concept L is illustrated. A model of Concept M is illustrated in James L George, ed, *The U.S. Navy: The View From the Mid-1980s* (Boulder, Colorado: Westview Press, 1985), p176. The 'under 10,000-ton warship of the early 21st century' appeared in Reuven Leopold, 'Technology and Warship Design', *USNIP*, vol 104, no 3 (March 1978), pp36-47, whence comes the first of the Leopold quotes. The other quotes come from *The U.S. Navy: The View From the Mid-1980s, op cit*, p174.

Appendix A: What's Wrong With This Picture?

Don Carey described his *Tosa* and other 'Japanese' hybrids in 'Raider X and Company', *Alnavco Log*, vol 8, no 1 (June 1974), pp6-7. Information on the projected battlecruisers of the B-64/B-65 class can be found in Jentschura, Jung and Mickel, *Warships of the*

Imperial Japanese Navy, op cit, p40.

Appendix B: Merchant Hybrids

Information on John L Bogert's career is taken from his obituary in the *NYT*, 12 August 1956, p84. The description of *Democracy* comes from his article 'The Submarine Problem — XV: The Merchantman as a Submarine Destroyer', *Scientific American*, vol 117, no 12 (22 September 1917), pp208, 219-220. The description of the 'accelerating belts' is from his article 'Flight Acceleration and Retardation', *Marine Journal*, 15 July 1941. The account of his quarrel with the US Navy, and the quotations, are drawn from his article 'Convoy Protection by Plane Carriers the Lesson of Both Wars', *Marine Journal*, September 1945, and his lengthy letter to Secretary of the Navy James Forrestal dated 15 August 1946. All this material comes from papers held by the New York Public Library.

The Hamburg-Amerika Linie's attempts to fly aircraft from its vessels are described in R D Layman, *To Ascend From a Floating Base: Shipboard Aeronautics and Aviation, 1783-1914* (Cranbury, NJ: Fairleigh Dickenson University Press, and London: Associated University Presses, 1979), pp113-114. Use of aircraft by *Ile de France* is noted by the same author in 'The Shipboard Catapult: Its History and Evolution', *WI, op cit*. Similar use of aircraft by *Bremen* and *Europa* is discussed by John H Ellingworth in the 'Your Questions Answered. . .' feature of *Air Pictorial*, vol 36, no 9 (September 1974), pp364-65. Norman Bel Geddes' aircraft-equipped liner is described and illustrated in his *Horizons* (Boston: Little, Brown, 1932), pp25-43.

The d'Eyncourt-Narbeth mercantile aircraft carrier design was presented in 'A Proposed Aircraft Carrying Mail Steamer' in *Transactions of the Institution of Naval Architects*, vol 65 (1923), pp6-31. This includes the discussion provoked by the design. N L Allen of Leeds University reappraised the design in 'Why Not a Passenger Aircraft-Carrier?', *Ships Monthly*, vol 6, no 1 (January 1971), pp25-27. Those who may prefer to read about the design in Dutch will find it described and illustrated in L L von Münching, *Vliegkampschepen* (Alkmarr: Alkenreeks, nd), p23. The DH.9c and DH.34 are described in A J Jackson's *de Havilland Aircraft Since 1909*, revised edition (Annapolis: Naval Institute Press, 1987), pp121-35 and pp169-74.

The full story of the Blue Ribbon Line and the *Flying Cloud* is told in David L Williams and Richard P de Kerbrech, *Damned by Destiny* (Brighton, Sussex: Teredo Books, 1982), pp75-87, from which the quote regarding the Shipping Board's rejection of the scheme is taken. This book also describes the 'Yankee Clippers' (pp113-17), the 'Liberty Liners' (pp231-40) and the P-4-P design (pp149-54). A sketch of Construction and Repair's conversion plan for *Flying Cloud* appears in Norman Friedman, *U.S. Aircraft Carriers, op cit*, p126.

Technical aspects of the design and creation of the merchant aircraft carriers are described by J Lenaghan in 'Merchant Aircraft Carrier Ships ("Mac" Ships)', *Transactions of the Institution of Naval Architects*, vol 89, no 2 (April 1947), pp96-111. Particulars and the fates of most are given in H T Lenton and J J Colledge, *Warships of World War II* (London:

Ian Allan, nd), pp255-60. Operational histories are contained in Kenneth Poolman's *The Catafighters and Merchant Aircraft Carriers* (London: William Kimber, 1970).

The ARAPAHO concept and experiments are outlined and described at length by the system's project officer, James J Mulquin, in three articles: 'The ARAPAHO System and Its Implications for Future Ship-Aviation Concept Development', *Naval Engineer's Journal*, vol 85, no 5 (October 1973), pp25-34; 'Project ARAPAHO', *Naval Aviation News*, June 1976, pp30-31; and 'ARAPAHO Goes to Sea', *Naval Aviation News*, February 1983, pp30-33.

The story of the conversion and service of the Falklands aircraft ferries is told in Roger Villar's *Merchant Ships at War: The Falklands Experience* (London: Conway Maritime Press, and Annapolis: Naval Institute Press, 1984), pp75-88 and pp178-79. The SCADS concept is described in 'SCADS — Shipborne Containerised Air and Defense System', *Naval Forces/Special Supplement: British Aerospace*, vol V, no VI (1984), pp32-4, and in 'SCADS: Shipborne Containerised Air Defense System', a brochure provided to the authors by British Aerospace; it was also discussed in Bill Gunston's *Modern Fighting Aircraft*, vol 5: *Harrier, op cit*, pp59-60.

Index